B/4/79.

5.50

PERGAMON INTERNATIONAL LIBRARY
of Science, Technology, Engineering

The 1000-volume original paperback li
industrial training and the enj
Publisher: Robert Max

G000067571

INTRODUCTION TO GENERAL RELATIVITY

THE PERGAMON TEXTBOOK
INSPECTION COPY SERVICE

An inspection copy of any book published in the Pergamon International Library will gladly be sent to academic staff without obligation for their consideration for course adoption or recommendation. Copies may be retained for a period of 60 days from receipt and returned if not suitable. When a particular title is adopted or recommended for adoption for class use and the recommendation results in a sale of 12 or more copies, the inspection copy may be retained with our compliments. The Publishers will be pleased to receive suggestions for revised editions and new titles to be published in this important International Library.

INTERNATIONAL SERIES IN NATURAL PHILOSOPHY
VOLUME 63
GENERAL EDITOR: D. TER HAAR
A List of other Titles on Natural Philosophy follows Index

SOME OTHER TITLES OF INTEREST

BRUCE, J. P. & CLARK, R. H.
Introduction to Hydrometeorology

GRIFFITHS, D. H. & KING, R. F.
Applied Geophysics for Engineers and Geologists

McLELLAN, H. J.
Elements of Physical Oceanography

PATERSON, W. S. B.
The Physics of Glaciers

PICKARD, G. L.
Descriptive Physical Oceanography

SCORER, R. S. & WEXLER, H. A.
A Colour Guide to Clouds

INTRODUCTION TO GENERAL RELATIVITY

by

H. A. ATWATER

Department of Physics
The Pennsylvania State University

PERGAMON PRESS

OXFORD · NEW YORK · TORONTO
SYDNEY · PARIS · FRANKFURT

U.K.	Pergamon Press Ltd., Headington Hill Hall, Oxford OX3 0BW, England
U.S.A.	Pergamon Press Inc., Maxwell House, Fairview Park, Elmsford, New York 10523, U.S.A.
CANADA	Pergamon of Canada, Suite 104, 150 Consumers Road, Willowdale, Ontario M2J 1P9, Canada
AUSTRALIA	Pergamon Press (Aust.) Pty. Ltd., P.O. Box 544, Potts Point, N.S.W. 2011, Australia
FRANCE	Pergamon Press SARL, 24 rue des Ecoles, 75240 Paris, Cedex 05, France
FEDERAL REPUBLIC OF GERMANY	Pergamon Press GmbH, 6242 Kronberg-Taunus, Pferdstrasse 1, Federal Republic of Germany

First edition 1974

Reprinted (with corrections) 1979

Library of Congress Cataloging in Publication Data

Atwater, Harry Albert, 1921-
Introduction to general relativity.
(International series in natural
philosophy, v. 63)
1. General relativity (Physics) I. Title.
QC173.6.A88 1974   530.1'1   73-16251

ISBN 0-08-017692-5 (hardcover)
ISBN 0-08-017718-2 (flexicover)

Printed in Great Britain by A. Wheaton & Co. Ltd., Exeter

Contents

Preface

IN PREPARING this book it has been the writer's aim to make available to the student a realistic working acquaintance with the concepts and modes of calculation used in general relativity, to the extent that he can genuinely understand an appreciable segment of the modern literature on gravitation and cosmology, or so that he will find himself at ease with the fundamental ideas, if he proceeds to a more intensive study of relativity theory.

It is the writer's belief that in too many students' experience the theory of general relativity is an object kept in a limbo of obscurity, from which its principal formulae are periodically trundled out on exhibition, then to be returned to their neglected state. It is with the hope that ritual pageantry of this kind can be replaced by use and understanding that the present book is written. When modern students discover that general relativity theory is neither abstruse nor difficult, and that the time spent in becoming familiar with tensor algebra is more than compensated for by the computational power gained through its use, the study of relativity and gravitation will be well advanced toward that period of expansion which many observers now see beginning. Indications of an increase in the applications of relativity are seen in the growing acceptance of black holes as credible components of the universe, in the increasing number of investigators setting up gravitational wave detectors, and even in occasional evidence of interest in a possible relationship between general relativity and fundamental particle theory.

The preparation which is assumed of readers of the text is: a knowledge of classical mechanics, ideally but not necessarily including the use of the Lagrangian function, some familiarity with matrices and matrix algebra, and an acquaintance with Maxwell's equations of the electromagnetic field. The emphasis throughout the book is upon the actual performance of relativistic calculations, rather than on mathematical rigor or exhaustive completeness. The principal concern of the book is with general relativity rather than with the special theory. There seemed to be little need to add another treatment of special relativity to the large number of good ones that already exist: a recent visit to the science library at the author's university revealed that there were on the shelves no fewer than seventeen books on special relativity at the introductory level which have been published since 1965. By contrast, the general theory of relativity has been severely neglected at the introductory level. Therefore it is felt that the present book can fill a need for a treatment of this subject.

In the writing of the book the author inevitably owes a debt to many teachers and colleagues over many years for their contributions to his interest in and understanding of the fascinating subject of general relativity. These numerous benefactors are thanked collectively here. Finally, he acknow ledges a debt of thanks to his wife Margaret for indispensable help with typing of the manuscript, and to all others who aided in its preparation.

Chapter 1

Introduction

RELATIVITY is that branch of physics which makes a maximum exploitation of the role of the coordinate frameworks used in the expression of the laws of nature. The utilization of coordinate geometry is extended to both the more effective statement of known laws as well as to the deduction of new physical laws. It is the aim of relativity theory to find modes of expression of the laws of physics such that they are not altered or specialized by the coordinates of the frame of reference in which these laws are written. The principle which assumes that such modes of expression are necessary and can be found is called the Principle of Covariance.

In its historical development, the theory of relativity has grown in the two major subdivisions called special relativity and general relativity. These two are not separate theories, but are both parts of the same theory, special relativity being in fact a special case of general relativity. The two branches of relativity differ greatly in the domains and extent of the fields of physics in which they have found application. Special relativity, dealing with the coordinate geometry of inertial frames, has found wide application in mechanics, electromagnetism and quantum theory. General relativity, which includes the study of the coordinates of non-inertial frames and "curved" space–time domains, has been applied largely to the theory of gravitation and the structure of the universe.

The need for a satisfactory theory of relativity became imperative in physics in the late nineteenth century, after the development of classical electromagnetic theory in its present form. It became apparent at that time that experimental observations of the propagation of light presented

I.G.R.—A*

inconsistencies with the then-prevalent notions concerning the effects of motion of the observer with respect to the medium in which the light was assumed to travel. In order to obtain a description of the travel of light that was compatible with observation, it became necessary to adopt the transformation law proposed by Lorentz relating the coordinates of frames in uniform relative motion.

The classical mechanics of Newton provided a correct and internally consistent description of the motions of material particles in nature, as long as its domain of application was restricted to material particles and coordinate frames having relative speeds which were a small fraction of the velocity of light. Its great success in accurately predicting the outcomes of terrestrial events and astronomical motions gave no reason to suspect its validity. The degree and kind of approximation that existed latent in Newton's laws were found only as an outcome of the discovery of the Lorentz transformation, after the latter transformation had been adopted in order to provide a correct description of the propagation of light as seen by a moving observer.

Because of the emphasis placed upon the relationship of the choice of coordinate frame to the form assumed by physical laws, the properties of coordinate systems and their transformations occupy an important position in the study of relativity. Spatial locations in the physical world are specified by three position coordinates such as (x, y, z), (r, θ, z), or (r, θ, ϕ), but it became apparent in the development of relativity theory that time appears naturally as a fourth coordinate of parallel importance in the description of natural events, in a four-dimensional event space: (t, x, y, z), (t, r, θ, z), (t, r, θ, ϕ), or (x^0, x^1, x^2, x^3). The general coordinate in this four-dimensional (or better, one plus three-dimensional) coordinate space will be written with a Greek-letter index, as, for example, x^μ, where $\mu = 0, 1, 2, 3$. Greek-letter indices will run over four values, whereas Roman-letter indices, e.g. x^j, will run over three values, $j = 1, 2, 3$, in the representation of the spatial coordinates only.

Although the time coordinate x^0 is placed on an equal footing with the space coordinates x^1, x^2, x^3, in the one plus three-dimensional notation we have specified, no implication is thereby made that time has the same physical character as the space coordinates in relativity. Time is distinct in character from space, as we know from our experience in non-relativistic physics. Time intervals are measured with a clock and spatial intervals with a meter stick, nor can these functions be interchanged in any generally useful way.† The latter statement remains true even if we define time with different units by setting $x^0 = ct$, where c is the velocity of light ($c = 2\cdot998 \times 10^8$ m/sec). It is possible to make coordinate transformations of the form $\bar{x}^v = \bar{x}^v(x^\mu)$ in which the event-points of the four-dimensional domain x^μ are remapped on a new set of points $\bar{x}^v$ in a definitely specified way, but in which the physical identities of the clock-measured coordinates and the meter-stick-measured coordinates are submerged. We shall attempt to avoid such situations in this book, preferring to work wherever possible with coordinates which have a clear-cut and unambiguous physical meaning, for which measurements could be carried out if wanted.

1.1. Newton's Laws and the Galilean Transformation

It was stated at the outset that the Principle of Covariance, expressing the invariance of physical laws under transformation of coordinates, is taken as a fundamental axiom of the theory of relativity. This is not a new principle, peculiar to relativity theory alone, for Newton's laws of classical mechanics retain their validity under transformation to new coordinate axes. This characteristic is illustrated in the following example.

We may write Newton's laws of motion for a point mass m in the form:

$$F_i = m\ddot{x}_i \quad (i = 1, 2, 3), \tag{1.1a}$$

$$\sum_j F_{ij} = 0 \tag{1.1b}$$

† The significance of the time coordinate in relativity has been somewhat obscured by an often-repeated quotation from H. Minkowski, given in an address on the four-dimensional formulation of special relativity, delivered at the 80th Assembly of German Natural Scientists and Physicians at Köln, Sept. 21, 1908. Minkowski exclaimed in the colorful language of his time, "Henceforth space by itself, and time by itself, are doomed to fade away into mere shadows, and only a kind of union of the two will preserve an independent reality." In a commentary on Minkowski's paper, Prof. Arnold Sommerfeld remarked, "What will be the epistemological attitude towards Minkowski's conception of the time–space problem is another question, but, as it seems to me, a question which does not essentially touch his physics." (Both quoted in *The Principle of Relativity*, A. Einstein *et al.*, Dover Publications, New York, pp. 75, 92.)

where the dots over position coordinates x_i have the conventional significance of time differentiations.† Equation (1.1a) comprises the first and second laws, and may also be considered to provide the definition of a force. If F_i in this equation is assumed to include all of the externally applied forces of the jth kind acting in the ith direction upon the mass m, then the domain of validity of Newton's laws is restricted to the so-called inertial frames of reference. An inertial frame is a coordinate frame with respect to which a mass point undergoes no acceleration when it is subjected to no outside forces. A practical description of an inertial frame is, therefore, a coordinate frame which is at rest or in straight-line motion at constant speed with respect to the center of mass of the aggregate of the distant fixed stars.

Among the "outside", or externally applied, forces acting upon the mass point m in eqns. (1.1), we include magnetic and electrical forces, spring forces and forces of mechanical constraint. If we include "inertial forces" such as, for example, the so-called centrifugal and coriolis forces in our list of "outside" forces, then an accelerated frame could be treated as inertial. However, we do not normally do this, but use the fixed stars as our criterion of non-acceleration, in the relativity of inertial frames.

For an observer at rest in a coordinate frame $\bar{E}$, the coordinates of which are $(\bar{t}, \bar{x}, \bar{y}, \bar{z})$ and which is in uniform rectilinear motion at constant velocity V with respect to frame E, with coordinates (t, x, y, z), the Galilean transformation is

$$
\begin{aligned}
\bar{t} &= t, \\
\bar{x} &= (x - Vt), \\
\bar{y} &= y, \\
\bar{z} &= z
\end{aligned}
\tag{1.2}
$$

where the coordinate axes of the barred and unbarred frames are parallel, and the relative motion is in the direction of the x-axes. The coordinate

---

† It will be recognized that here we treat time as a parameter, upon which the space coordinates depend, rather than as an independent variable of a four-dimensional continuum. Expressions in which the coordinates appear as functions of time may, in fact, be regarded as descriptions of lower-dimensional subsurfaces in the four-dimensional space.

transformation of eqns. (1.2) may be described by the matrix of transformation coefficients:†

$$\frac{\partial \bar{x}^\mu}{\partial x^\nu} = \begin{bmatrix} 1 & 0 & 0 & 0 \\ -V & 1 & 0 & 0 \\ 0 & 0 & 1 & 0 \\ 0 & 0 & 0 & 1 \end{bmatrix}. \tag{1.2a}$$

The Galilean transformation of eqns. (1.2) includes the expression of the Newtonian assumption that the time scale is universal, or that time "flows equally" for all observers.

For a mass point m in coordinate frame $\bar{E}$ which is constrained about the point $\bar{r}_0 = (\bar{x}_0, \bar{y}_0, \bar{z}_0)$ by a spring force with spring constant k the equations of motion [eqns. (1.1)] take the form

$$m\ddot{\bar{x}} = -k(\bar{x} - \bar{x}_0),$$
$$m\ddot{\bar{y}} = -k(\bar{y} - \bar{y}_0), \tag{1.3}$$
$$m\ddot{\bar{z}} = -k(\bar{z} - \bar{z}_0).$$

When the Galilean transformation, eqns. (1.2), is applied to these equations of motion using $\bar{x} = (x - Vt)$, $\bar{x}_0 = (x_0 - Vt)$, $\bar{y}_0 = y_0$, $\bar{z}_0 = z_0$, etc., we find

$$m\ddot{x} = -k(x - x_0),$$
$$m\ddot{y} = -k(y - y_0), \tag{1.4}$$
$$m\ddot{z} = -k(z - z_0).$$

The identity of the character of eqns. (1.4) with eqns. (1.3) is an expression of the covariance of Newton's laws under Galilean transformation.

To the physicists of the nineteenth century the Galilean transformation (1.2) was accepted as being manifestly correct, since it seemed to be an explicit and indisputable statement of what was actually happening, during the relative translation of two coordinate frames. A conflict with experiment appeared, however, when this transformation was applied to problems involving the propagation of light.

† It may be observed that in calculating the matrix element $\partial \bar{x}^\mu/\partial x^\nu$ we associate the numerator of the differential quotient with the rows of the matrix, and the denominator with its columns.

1.2. Electromagnetism and the Galilean Transformation

During the early development of the wave theory of light, the question arose concerning whether electromagnetic waves were propagated in an actual medium, or "ether". If propagation took place in an ether, it was assumed that coordinate axes fixed in that medium must constitute an obvious frame of reference with respect to which all observers were either stationary or in relative motion. As is now well known, all attempts to discover experimentally the existence of a stationary medium in which electromagnetic fields are propagated were met with failure. It became necessary to conclude that light was seen by every inertial observer to propagate isotropically in space at the standard speed c, irrespective of his state of uniform motion with respect to any other inertial coordinate frame. (We have at the present time no data on values of the velocity of light measured by observers in non-uniform, or accelerated, motion of appreciable magnitude.) These observations of the invariance of the velocity of light pointed to the physical requirement that the equations of electromagnetism should be transformable in such a manner that they retain their standard form upon transformation to the coordinates of any reference frame in uniform motion with respect to the original. The Galilean transformation fails to fulfill this requirement, as we may show.

The content of classical electromagnetic theory is summarized by Maxwell's equations:

$$\nabla \cdot \boldsymbol{D} = \varrho,$$

$$\nabla \times \boldsymbol{E} = -\dot{\boldsymbol{B}},$$

$$\nabla \cdot \boldsymbol{B} = 0, \tag{1.5}$$

$$\nabla \times \boldsymbol{H} = \boldsymbol{J} + \dot{\boldsymbol{D}}.$$

By combining the two curl equations, we obtain the equation for wave propagation in free space:

$$\nabla^2 E = \frac{1}{c^2} \ddot{E} \tag{1.6}$$

where we have used the fact that $\mu_0 \varepsilon_0 = 1/c^2$ in the mks system of units.

Equation (1.6) is a vector equation having three space components. The x-component equation in rectangular coordinates (t, x, y, z) is

$$\frac{\partial^2 E_x}{\partial x^2} + \frac{\partial^2 E_x}{\partial y^2} + \frac{\partial^2 E_x}{\partial z^2} = \frac{1}{c^2} \frac{\partial^2 E_x}{\partial t^2}. \tag{1.7}$$

Applying the Galilean transformation, eqns. (1.2), with use of the rule for partial differentiation of a function of coordinates

$$\frac{\partial F(\bar{x}^\mu)}{\partial x^\nu} = \sum_\mu \frac{\partial F(\bar{x}^\mu)}{\partial \bar{x}^\mu} \frac{\partial \bar{x}^\mu}{\partial x^\nu}. \tag{1.8}$$

Equation (1.7) becomes, with use of eqns. (1.2) and (1.8),

$$\frac{\partial^2 \bar{E}_x}{\partial \bar{x}^2} + \frac{\partial^2 \bar{E}_x}{\partial \bar{y}^2} + \frac{\partial^2 \bar{E}_x}{\partial \bar{z}^2} = \frac{1}{c^2} \frac{\partial^2 \bar{E}_x}{\partial \bar{t}^2} + \frac{V^2}{c^2} \frac{\partial^2 \bar{E}_x}{\partial \bar{x}^2} - \frac{2V}{c^2} \frac{\partial^2 \bar{E}_x}{\partial \bar{x}\, \partial \bar{t}}. \tag{1.9}$$

The appearance of the two new terms on the right side of eqn. (1.9) demonstrates that the wave equation does not maintain its form under Galilean transformation. Since we know from experiment that waves do not obey an equation like eqn. (1.9) in inertial coordinate frames, we discard the Galilean transformation and with it the Newtonian assumption of a universal time coordinate valid for all observers.

1.3. The Lorentz Transformation

The task of constructing a coordinate transformation to replace the Galilean transformation for use with the equations of the electromagnetic field demanded the introduction into physics of a previously unrecognized characteristic of the propagation of light—its constancy to all inertial-frame observers—as well as the adoption of the viewpoint that all inertial coordinate frames are equally suitable for the description of natural events. The latter view led to the growth of the concept that the equations of physics should be expressible in a form that is not altered upon transformation to the coordinates of another frame. This characteristic of form invariance is the essence of the Principle of Covariance. The principle is properly applied to the equations of physics when expressed in tensor form. We have not yet explicitly written tensor expressions, but a simple illustration of what is meant by the characteristic of form invariance is obtained by consideration of a typical vector-operator equation, such as the conservation equation for electric charge of density ϱ:

$$\nabla \cdot \varrho v = -\dot{\varrho}. \tag{1.10}$$

Clearly this equation is non-committal as to the system of coordinates in which the divergence statement is made, i.e. it has the same meaning in all coordinate frames. The Cartesian coordinate form of the equation can be made even more compact by defining the four-component vector $U^\mu = (\varrho, \varrho v_x, \varrho v_y, \varrho v_z)$ in the coordinate space $x^\mu = (t, x, y, z)$, whereupon eqn. (1.10) can be written

$$0 = \sum_\mu \frac{\partial U^\mu}{\partial x^\mu} = \sum_\mu \partial_\mu U^\mu = \sum_\mu U^\mu{}_{,\mu} = \sum_\mu U^\mu{}_{|\mu}, \tag{1.11}$$

where various conventionally used notations for the partial derivative are displayed, in eqn. (1.11).

It will be convenient to introduce at this point a notational convention that provides great simplification in the mathematics of relativity. This is the Einstein summation convention, according to which summation is understood to be carried out over an index symbol that appears in an upper and a lower position in any expression. This convention allows the summation signs to be omitted in the expressions of eqn. (1.11). Thus, using the sum convention, eqn. (1.11) becomes

$$0 = \frac{\partial U^\mu}{\partial x^\mu} = \partial_\mu U^\mu = U^\mu{}_{,\mu} = U^\mu{}_{|\mu}. \tag{1.11 a}$$

The expressions of eqn. (1.11) are correct in their explicit form for Cartesian coordinate frames, in which all spatial coordinates have the same dimensions (of length), and the time-like components are as defined. Had we employed coordinates (ct, x, y, z) the vector U^μ would then have been defined: $(c\varrho, \varrho v_x, \varrho v_y, \varrho v_z)$. For curvilinear and more general coordinate frames, we shall introduce the tensor derivative, or absolute derivative, to replace the ordinary differential appearing in eqn. (1.11).

In summary, the relativistically correct coordinate transformation for use among inertial frames will be determined by the two governing principles:

1. Light travels isotropically in all inertial frames with the standard speed c.
2. All inertial reference frames are equally valid for the expression of the laws of physics.

The Lorentz transformation can be derived in an elementary way by the application of these two principles. We consider again the situation in which two rectangular coordinate frames, $\bar{E}$ and E, move at a constant relative velocity V in the direction of their x-axes. The first principle states that a pulse of light from a point source at the origin will be seen to spread out with spherical wavefronts in both frames:

$$\frac{d|\bar{r}|}{d\bar{t}} = c, \quad \frac{d|r|}{dt} = c \tag{1.12}$$

where $\bar{r} = (\bar{x}^2 + \bar{y}^2 + \bar{z}^2)^{1/2}$ and $r = (x^2 + y^2 + z^2)^{1/2}$ are radial distances from the point source as measured in the respective frames and the origins are assumed to coincide at the instant of the emission of the light. It is assumed that distances measured transverse to the direction of relative motion must be unaffected by the motion:

$$\bar{y} = y,$$
$$\bar{z} = z. \tag{1.13}$$

If eqns. (1.13) were not true, a meter stick held transversely in one frame would be seen to exceed in length a transverse meter stick in the second frame at the instant of their passing. The asymmetry between frames implied by this conclusion violates the equivalence of all inertial frames required by the second principle above.

We rewrite eqns. (1.12) in the form

$$0 = c^2 \, d\bar{t}^2 - d\bar{r}^2 = c^2 \, dt^2 - dr^2. \tag{1.14}$$

In rectangular coordinate form, eqn. (1.14) is

$$c^2 \, d\bar{t}^2 - d\bar{x}^2 - d\bar{y}^2 - d\bar{z}^2 = c^2 \, dt^2 - dx^2 - dy^2 - dz^2. \tag{1.15}$$

Due to eqns. (1.13) this becomes

$$c^2 \, d\bar{t}^2 - d\bar{x}^2 = c^2 \, dt^2 - dx^2. \tag{1.16}$$

We assume that coordinates $\bar{x}$ and $\bar{t}$ are linearly related to x and t in the form

$$\bar{t} = at + bx, \tag{1.17a}$$

$$\bar{x} = ft + gx. \tag{1.17b}$$

Substitution from eqns. (1.17) into eqn. (1.16) yields

$$c^2 \, dt^2 - dx^2 = c^2 \, dt^2 \left[a^2 - \frac{f^2}{c^2} \right] + dx^2 (c^2 b^2 - g^2) + 2(c^2 ab - fg) \, dx \, dt. \tag{1.18}$$

The equality in eqn. (1.18) can be satisfied by requiring

$$a^2 - \frac{f^2}{c^2} = 1, \quad (g^2 - c^2 b^2) = 1,$$

$$(c^2 ab - fg) = 0. \tag{1.19}$$

We obtain an additional relation among the coefficients by noting that the origin of $\bar{E}$ is seen from system E to move at velocity $(-V)$. Thus, setting $\bar{x} = 0$ in eqn. (1.17b), we have

$$\frac{dx}{dt} = -\frac{f}{g} = -V. \tag{1.20a}$$

Conversely, the origin of E travels at $+V$ in $\bar{E}$. Setting $x = 0$ in eqns. (1.17a) and (1.17b), we have

$$\frac{d\bar{x}}{d\bar{t}} = \frac{f}{a} = V. \tag{1.20b}$$

Combining eqn. (1.20b) with the first of eqns. (1.19), we find:

$$a^2 = (1 - V^2/c^2)^{-1}.$$

Solving the remainder of eqns. (1.19) to (1.20) yields the Lorentz transformation:

$$\bar{t} = \gamma \left[t + \frac{V}{c^2} x \right],$$

$$\bar{x} = \gamma(Vt + x), \qquad\qquad (1.21)$$

$$\bar{y} = y,$$

$$\bar{z} = z,$$

where we have defined $\gamma = (1 - V^2/c^2)^{-1/2}$. The inverse transformation may be obtained by interchanging the barred and unbarred variables, and replacing V with $-V$:

$$t = \gamma \left(\bar{t} - \frac{V}{c^2} \bar{x} \right),$$

$$x = \gamma(-V\bar{t} + \bar{x}), \qquad\qquad (1.21\,\text{a})$$

$$y = \bar{y},$$

$$z = \bar{z}.$$

The Lorentz transformation supplies the relationship between the position and time coordinates (t, x, y, z) of an event in inertial frame E with the corresponding four coordinates $(\bar{t}, \bar{x}, \bar{y}, \bar{z})$ of the same event as observed in inertial frame $\bar{E}$.

The Lorentz transformation written in the form of eqns. (1.21) is not an orthogonal transformation. A general linear coordinate transformation between the n-dimensional spaces represented by coordinates x^i and $\bar{x}^i$ ($i = 1, 2, ..., n$) may be written

$$x^i = a^i{}_j \bar{x}^j \qquad\qquad (1.22)$$

where the $a^i{}_j$ are constants. In a Euclidean coordinate space the squared length of a vector x^i, the distance from the origin, is given by $\sum_i (x^i)^2$. We say that the transformation [eqn. (1.22)] is length-preserving if

$$\sum_i (x^i)^2 = \sum_j (\bar{x}^j)^2. \qquad\qquad (1.23)$$

In ordinary Cartesian three-space this requirement takes the form

$$x^2 + y^2 + z^2 = \bar{x}^2 + \bar{y}^2 + \bar{z}^2. \tag{1.24}$$

Substitution into eqn. (1.23) from eqn. (1.22) shows that the conditions for preservation of length of a vector are†

$$\sum_j (a^i{}_j)^2 = 1, \tag{1.25}$$

$$\sum_j (a^i{}_j)(a_k{}^j) = 0 \qquad (i \neq k). \tag{1.26}$$

Both eqns. (1.25) and (1.26) can be summarized by

$$\sum_j (a^i{}_j)(a^k{}_j) = \delta_{ik} \tag{1.27}$$

where δ_{ik} is the Kronecker symbol, which has the properties: $\delta_{ik} = 1$, $(i = k)$, and $\delta_{ik} = 0$, $(i \neq k)$. A linear transformation [eqn. (1.22)] which has the properties specified by eqns. (1.27) is an orthogonal transformation, and eqns. (1.27) are the orthogonality conditions.‡

Using the abbreviation $\beta = V/c$, the transformation matrix of the Lorentz transformation [eqns. (1.21)] may be written

$$\frac{\partial \bar{x}^\mu}{\partial x^\nu} = \begin{bmatrix} \gamma & \beta\gamma/c & 0 & 0 \\ c\beta\gamma & \gamma & 0 & 0 \\ 0 & 0 & 1 & 0 \\ 0 & 0 & 0 & 1 \end{bmatrix}. \tag{1.28}$$

This matrix can be given a more symmetrical form by replacing the time variable $x^0 = t$ with the new variable $x^0 = ct$:

$$\frac{d\bar{x}^\mu}{dx^\nu} = \begin{bmatrix} \gamma & \beta\gamma & 0 & 0 \\ \beta\gamma & \gamma & 0 & 0 \\ 0 & 0 & 1 & 0 \\ 0 & 0 & 0 & 1 \end{bmatrix}. \tag{1.29}$$

† The use of the summation convention is temporarily suspended in eqns. (1.25) and (1.26) to avoid the need for the raising and lowering of indices. This procedure is introduced in Chapter 2.

‡ I. S. Sokolnikoff, *Tensor Analysis*, pp. 27 ff. J. Wiley & Sons, New York, 1951.

It can be seen by inspection that the Lorentz transformation matrix of eqn. (1.29) satisfies neither of the orthogonality conditions specified by eqns. (1.25) and (1.26). The magnitude of the quantity

$$\sum (x^i)^2 = c^2t^2 + x^2 + y^2 + z^2$$

is not preserved under Lorentz transformation. The quantity that is preserved, as a consequence of the manner in which the Lorentz transformation was derived [cf. eqns. (1.14) and (1.15)], is

$$s^2 \equiv c^2t^2 - x^2 - y^2 - z^2. \tag{1.30}$$

The quantity s^2 is an invariant in inertial frames: it is found to have the same constant (null) value by observers in all inertial frames, when it corresponds to event-points on the path of a propagating beam of light.

In order to salvage the advantages of orthogonal coordinate systems and their transformation properties for the $3 + 1$-coordinate manifold of events in space and time, Minkowski devised the artifice of using the imaginary time-coordinate definition: $x_0 = ict$. Then, in coordinates $(x^0, x^1, x^2, x^3) \equiv (ict, x, y, z)$, eqn. (1.30) becomes

$$-s^2 = (x^0)^2 + (x^1)^2 + (x^2)^2 + (x^3)^2. \tag{1.31}$$

In Minkowski's coordinates, the Lorentz transformation [eqn. (1.29)] becomes

$$\frac{d\bar{x}^\mu}{dx^\nu} = \begin{bmatrix} \gamma & i\beta\gamma & 0 & 0 \\ -i\beta\gamma & \gamma & 0 & 0 \\ 0 & 0 & 1 & 0 \\ 0 & 0 & 0 & 1 \end{bmatrix}. \tag{1.32}$$

The Minkowski form of the Lorentz transformation [eqn. (1.32)] satisfies the orthogonality conditions of eqns. (1.25) and (1.26) since

$$\gamma^2 - \gamma^2\beta^2 = 1$$

and

$$-i\beta\gamma^2 + i\beta\gamma^2 = 0.$$

Thus, apart from an overall negative sign in the squared length of the vector (x^μ) from the origin in eqn. (1.31) the Minkowski coordinate frame is a conventional orthogonal system in four dimensions. No physical significance is to be attached to the imaginary quantities appearing in the Minkowski format since these are merely the result of the artifice employed to force the fundamental element $(\varDelta s)^2$ into the conventional quadratic form of a squared vector length.†

1.4. The World-line Element

The invariant s^2 of eqn. (1.30) separates two events: passage of a photon through the origin of coordinates at time zero and passage of the photon through the point x, y, z at time t. We may similarly form an invariant interval $\varDelta s$ separating any arbitrarily selected pair of events. For events A and B, with coordinates t_A, x_A, y_A, z_A and t_B, x_B, y_B, z_B:

$$(\varDelta s_{AB})^2 = c^2(t_A - t_B)^2 - (x_A - x_B)^2 - (y_A - y_B)^2 - (z_A - z_B)^2 . \quad (1.33)$$

Clearly, for an arbitrary choice of events $(\varDelta s_{AB})^2$ may have any magnitude, and may be positive, negative, or zero. Event pairs which yield a positive $(\varDelta s_{AB})^2$ are called time-like; those which yield a negative value are space-like, and event pairs resulting in a null value of $(\varDelta s_{AB})^2$ are called light-like. We do not yet have any assurance that $(\varDelta s_{AB})^2$ is an invariant under Lorentz transformation for an arbitrary pair of events A and B in four-coordinate space, since the Lorentz transformation was derived above to satisfy the invariance property for *null* intervals $\varDelta s_{AB}$ only. We can demonstrate the form-invariance of $(\varDelta s_{AB})^2$ by direct transformation of eqn. (1.31) with use of the Lorentz transformation [eqns.

---

† There is a lack of uniformity in the literature on relativity concerning the sign to be employed in the definition of s^2 [eqn. (1.31)]. The practice is divided between the forms $s^2 = x^2 - c^2t^2$ and $s^2 = c^2t^2 - x^2$. Recent literature seems to favor the latter form, and therefore we shall use it throughout this book unless specifically stated otherwise. A survey of sign conventions used in the literature of relativity is given by D. R. Brill and R. C. Perisho, *Am. J. Phys.* **36**, 1 (1968).

(1.21 a)]. This substitution yields

$$(\Delta \bar{s}_{AB})^2 = c^2 \gamma^2 (\bar{t}_A - \bar{t}_B)^2 \left(1 - \frac{V^2}{c^2}\right) + \gamma^2 (\bar{x}_A - \bar{x}_B)^2 \left(\frac{V^2}{c^2} - 1\right)$$
$$- (\bar{y}_A - \bar{y}_B)^2 - (\bar{z}_A - \bar{z}_B)^2 \qquad (1.34)$$

where the product terms containing $(\bar{x}_A - \bar{x}_B)(\bar{t}_A - \bar{t}_B)$ cancel. Because of the definition of γ, eqn. (1.34) is equivalent to

$$(\Delta \bar{s}_{AB})^2 = c^2 (\bar{t}_A - \bar{t}_B)^2 - (\bar{x}_A - \bar{x}_B)^2 - (\bar{y}_A - \bar{y}_B)^2 - (\bar{z}_A - \bar{z}_B)^2. \qquad (1.34a)$$

This result verifies that $(\Delta \bar{s}_{AB})^2$ is identical in form in all inertial frames, for arbitrary event pairs under Lorentz transformation.

The form invariance of the interval $(\Delta s)^2$ between any two events implies also the invariance of its magnitude, by virtue of the Lorentz transformation, eqns. (1.21).† The aggregate of all the successive sets of coordinate points occupied by a particle or photon form the *world line* of the object. The element $(\Delta s)^2$ is called a world-line element, and its infinitesimal form, connecting the successive points (t, x, y, z) and $(t + dt, x + dx, y + dy, z + dz)$, is

$$ds^2 = c^2 dt^2 - dx^2 - dy^2 - dz^2. \qquad (1.35)$$

The spatial interval $-(dx^2 + dy^2 + dz^2)$ may with equal validity be expressed in curvilinear coordinates. Thus, alternate forms of eqn. (1.35) are

$$ds^2 = c^2 dt^2 - dr^2 - r^2 d\theta^2 - dz^2, \qquad (1.35a)$$

$$ds^2 = c^2 dt^2 - dr^2 - r^2 d\theta^2 - r^2 \sin^2 \theta \, d\phi^2 \qquad (1.35b)$$

for inertial systems in cylindrical and spherical coordinates, respectively. The differential form of Minkowski's line element [eqn. (1.31)] is also

$$ds^2 = -(dx^0)^2 - (dx^1)^2 - (dx^2)^2 - (dx^3)^2. \qquad (1.35c)$$

† See also Problem 1.5.

The fundamental interval ds^2 was retained as a basic element in the extension of relativity to the theory of the general relativity of all coordinate frames. The fundamental assumption of the general theory of relativity is that all coordinate systems, in arbitrary states of motion, should be equally suitable for the mathematical expression of the laws of physics. Therefore, means must be found for writing the physical laws in such a way that they do not change their form upon being subjected to an arbitrary transformation of coordinates. This is again an expression of the principle of general covariance, and the desired covariant behavior can be achieved by the use of tensor equations for the expressions of physical laws.

1.5. The Metric Tensor and Physical Law

The expressions for the world-line element ds^2 given by eqns. (1.35a, b) all have the form of a sum of terms, each containing a square of coordinate differentials, $(dx^\mu)^2$. Riemann, in 1854, investigating the properties of coordinate manifolds of general type, showed that manifolds could be characterized by the invariant element ds^2 measuring the infinitesimal interval between neighboring points in the coordinate space.

Riemann constructed this interval as a quadratic function of the coordinate differentials, having the form in four dimensions:

$$ds^2 = g_{00}(dx^0)^2 + g_{01}(dx^0)(dx^1) + \cdots + g_{33}(dx^3)^2 \qquad (1.36)$$

or, employing the summation convention,

$$ds^2 = g_{\mu\nu}\, dx^\mu\, dx^\nu \qquad (\mu, \nu = 0, 1, 2, 3) \qquad (1.37)$$

where the quantities $g_{\mu\nu}$ are in general functions of coordinates.

The coefficients $g_{\mu\nu}$ in an n-dimensional space form an $n \times n$ array of n^2 numbers, called the metric tensor of the coordinate space. In a three-dimensional Euclidean spatial region, described by coordinates $(x^1, x^2, x^3) = (x, y, z)$, the line element has the familiar form

$$ds^2 = (dx^1)^2 + (dx^2)^2 + (dx^3)^2.$$

Here the coefficients $g_{\mu\nu}$ are constants, having the values: $g_{11} = 1 = g_{22} = g_{33}$, with all other $g_{\mu\nu}$ zero, or

$$g_{\mu\nu} = \delta_{\mu\nu} \quad \text{(Euclidean space)}.$$

In three-dimensional physical space, the distance between the adjacent points (x, y, z) and $(x + dx, y + dy, z + dz)$ is assumed to have an objective reality that cannot be influenced by the choice of coordinate frame used to describe it. That is, the magnitude of ds^2 must be preserved under any valid coordinate transformation in the three-space of geometry. A scalar quantity having the property of invariance of magnitude under coordinate transformation is called a scalar invariant. The scalar invariants form an important class of elements in mathematical physics, usually being identifiable with physically significant quantities.

Our consideration of the characteristics of propagating light in inertial frames led us to define a four-dimensional space of events, in which the coordinate event-points (t, x, y, z) specify the time t of arrival of a photon at the space point (x, y, z). It was deduced in eqn. (1.30) that a scalar invariant element of this coordinate space is

$$ds^2 = c^2\, dt^2 - dx^2 - dy^2 - dz^2. \tag{1.30'}$$

The quantity on the right in eqn. (1.30') is not a (distance)^2 in the ordinary sense, and vanishes on the path of a photon, but it is an interval in the sense of the Riemannian geometry of the event space described by the coordinates t, x, y, z. As stated above, the concept of interval is extended beyond that of the arrival-events on the path of a photon, to include intervals of arbitrary kind. The succession of points generated by the successive positions in space-time of a given particle or photon compose the *world line* of the object, and intervals ds^2 on this line are correspondingly called world-line intervals.

The physical nature of event-space impresses a specific character upon the metric tensor of the world-line elements in the space. Examples of metric tensors of inertial spaces have been given in eqns. (1.35, 1.35a, 1.35b).

For the inertial-frame metrics of eqns. (1.35a, b) the metric tensor arrays are, respectively,

$$g_{\mu\nu} = \begin{bmatrix} c^2 & 0 & 0 & 0 \\ 0 & -1 & 0 & 0 \\ 0 & 0 & -1 & 0 \\ 0 & 0 & 0 & -1 \end{bmatrix}, \tag{1.35'}$$

$$g_{\mu\nu} = \begin{bmatrix} c^2 & 0 & 0 & 0 \\ 0 & -1 & 0 & 0 \\ 0 & 0 & -r^2 & 0 \\ 0 & 0 & 0 & -1 \end{bmatrix}, \tag{1.35a'}$$

$$g_{\mu\nu} = \begin{bmatrix} c^2 & 0 & 0 & 0 \\ 0 & -1 & 0 & 0 \\ 0 & 0 & -r^2 & 0 \\ 0 & 0 & 0 & -r^2\sin^2\theta \end{bmatrix}. \tag{1.35b'}$$

If the time coordinate in eqn. (1.35′) is defined to be $x^0 = ct$, the metric tensor becomes

$$g_{\mu\nu} = \begin{bmatrix} 1 & 0 & 0 & 0 \\ 0 & -1 & 0 & 0 \\ 0 & 0 & -1 & 0 \\ 0 & 0 & 0 & -1 \end{bmatrix}. \tag{1.35''}$$

The array of signs in eqn. (1.35″) is called the signature of the metric. It can be shown that a coordinate transformation can always be found that will bring any metric into a form having ± 1 on the diagonal, and that the total number of $+1$ and -1 members on the diagonal is an invariant under real coordinate transformations.†

† H. P. Robertson and T. W. Noonan, *Relativity and Cosmology*, p. 214, W. B. Saunders Co., Philadelphia, 1968.

The metric tensor of Minkowski space [eqn. (1.31)] has Euclidean character:

$$g_{\mu\nu} = \begin{bmatrix} -1 & 0 & 0 & 0 \\ 0 & -1 & 0 & 0 \\ 0 & 0 & -1 & 0 \\ 0 & 0 & 0 & -1 \end{bmatrix}. \qquad (1.31\,a)$$

The metric tensors illustrated above correspond to inertial coordinate frames in the absence of gravitational fields. Metric tensors can also be constructed to represent non-inertial (accelerated) coordinate frames and regions with gravitational fields.

The fundamental interval ds is an element of the world-line path followed by a mass point in the $(1 + 3)$-coordinate space–time domain of events. If a mass point is subjected to no external or restraining forces its path is a *geodesic line* of the coordinate space in which it exists. A geodesic line is the counterpart of the straight line of Euclidean geometry, and is defined to be a line the length of which has an extremal (maximum or minimum) value. Therefore the integral $\int ds$ has a stationary value under variation

$$\delta \int_A^B ds = 0. \qquad (1.38)$$

For a particle with the metric of eqn. (1.35), traveling along the x-axis $(dy = 0 = dz)$, the geodesic condition therefore is

$$\delta \int_A^B ds = \delta \int_A^B \sqrt{(c^2 \, dt^2 - dx^2)} = 0. \qquad (1.39)$$

Let us consider the path integral before variation, treating the time as a parameter.

$$\int ds = c \int_A^B dt \sqrt{\{1 - (\dot{x})^2/c^2\}}. \qquad (1.40)$$

If we assume that the particle velocity $\dot{x}$ is much less than the velocity of light, eqn. (1.40) may be written

$$\int ds \simeq c \int_A^B dt\left(1 - (\dot{x})^2/2c^2\right). \tag{1.41}$$

Integrating by parts in the second term, using $\dot{x}^2 \, dt = \dot{x}\dot{x} \, dt = \dot{x} \, dx$,

$$\int ds = ct\Big|_A^B - \frac{1}{2c}\left[\dot{x}x\Big|_A^B - \int_A^B x\ddot{x} \, dt\right]. \tag{1.42}$$

Assuming that the particle path values at the limits of integration undergo no variation, a variation of the first two terms above vanishes. The final term can be given an extremal value by taking $\ddot{x} = 0$. This is Newton's first law. Although a correct calculation of the extremum condition for a general path variation requires use of the Euler–Lagrange equation of the calculus of variations on eqn. (1.39), the result is the same as we have found. The outcome shows that the geodesic lines of mass particles in an inertial frame are straight-line paths at constant velocity (the solution of $\ddot{x} = 0$). This simple example of the generation of equations of motion of free mass points illustrates a typical application of the fundamental metric and the geodesic theorem. In order to deal with coordinate frames in more general states of motion, or with frames in gravitational fields, the tensor formulation of the geodesic equations will be required.

The equivalence of gravitational mass m_G and inertial mass m_A played a central role in the historical development of general relativity. This equivalence is embodied in the observation that Newton's second law, $F = ma$, takes the form $m_G g = m_A a$ for gravitational accelerations in a gravitational field of strength g. Because all objects are observed to accelerate at the same rate, $g = a$, in a gravitational field, Einstein undertook to investigate the hypothesis that gravitation was an essentially kinematic phenomenon involving a modification of the space and time coordinates in the neighborhood of the source of gravitational field. Thus, an observer in an "elevator", or laboratory room in space far from any sources of gravitational field, would observe the equivalent of a uniform gravitational field in his laboratory, if his room were given a steady linear acceleration in the direction normal to the ceiling. Objects released would appear to "drop" to the floor as it accelerated toward them, and all experiments would proceed as though they were being carried out in a uniform gravitational field. An inertial observer in the space outside the accelerated laboratory would reconcile the measurements being compiled by the accelerated observer as the necessary consequence of the latter's state of motion. He would further show that by applying a coordinate transformation to the observations of the accelerated observer to remove the components of accelerated motion, his observations would then correspond to the laws of physics for inertial frames.

It was shown by Einstein in the development of relativity theory, however, that the presence of a gravitating mass, or source of gravitational field, was enough to cause a modification of the space and time coordinates in its neighborhood and that this modification was of a type that could not be removed merely by a transformation of coordinates to a different coordinate network in the neighborhood of the gravitating object. The presence of the gravitating mass introduces an essential change into the metric $g_{\mu\nu}$ of the surrounding space. A measure of this change is given by the Riemann curvature tensor of the coordinate manifold. The Riemannian curvature has non-zero components in the presence of a gravitational field, when calculated in *any* valid system of coordinates. If the gravitational fields are regarded as disturbances on a background of Euclidean space, at sufficient distance from gravitating mass where all gravitational fields have fallen to zero, the components of the Riemann curvature tensor are zero, i.e. the space is "flat".

Problems

1.1. Solve the following on the basis of the assumption that light propagates with speed c in a medium stationary with respect to the observer's laboratory: an interferometer is constructed of two parallel glass plates with their planes 1 meter apart. The interferometer moves through the laboratory at speed V in a direction normal to the plane of the plates. Light from a source near the rearward plate travels through it and ahead to the forward plate, where it is reflected back and recombines with the light at the rear plate. Calculate the shift in the number of interference fringes occasioned in going from rest to motion at speed V. [*Suggestion*: calculate t_f, the laboratory time for the forward travel of light, and t_r, the time for the subsequent rearward travel. Then assuming angular frequency of the source to be ω, find the phase shift $\Delta\phi = \omega(t_f + t_r)$, and $\Delta n = \Delta\phi/2\pi$.]

1.2. Solve Problem 1.1 using the assumption that the length of the interferometer undergoes a Lorentz contraction in the direction of motion by a factor of $(1 - V^2/c^2)^{1\,2}$, and that the light source moving with the interferometer undergoes a frequency reduction by a factor of $(1 - V^2/c^2)^{1/2}$.

1.3. Show that Newton's laws retain their form under the assumed transformation to accelerated coordinates: $t = \bar{t}$, $x = \bar{x} + (1/2)\,a\bar{t}^2$, $y = \bar{y}$, $z = \bar{z}$, provided that a suitable fictitious (or, inertial) force is added.

1.4. A coordinate frame $\bar{E}$, with coordinates $(\bar{t}, \bar{x}, \bar{y}, \bar{z})$ is related to frame E, (t, x, y, z) by a Lorentz transformation [eqn. (1.21)]. A third coordinate frame $\bar{\bar{E}}$ with coordinates $\bar{\bar{t}}(, \bar{\bar{x}}, \bar{\bar{y}}, \bar{\bar{z}})$ moves at velocity U with respect to $\bar{E}$, in the direction of their mutual x-axes. Find by direct substitution the Lorentz transformation between $\bar{\bar{E}}$ and E, showing that it is not a Lorentz transformation between two frames moving with relative velocity $V + U$. Explain. What does the observer in E measure for the relative velocity of E and $\bar{\bar{E}}$?

1.5. An observer in coordinate frame E observes two events, A and B, having coordinates $(t_A, x_A, y_A, z_A) = (1\text{ sec}, 2\text{ m}, 3\text{ m}, 4\text{ m})$ and $(t_B, x_B, y_B, z_B) = (2\text{ sec}, 4\text{ m}, 5\text{ m}, 6\text{ m})$, respectively.

(a) Find the coordinates for the same two events as measured by an observer in frame $\bar{E}$, when E and $\bar{E}$ are related by a Lorentz transformation [eqn. (1.21)].
(b) Calculate the intervals $(\Delta s_{AB})^2$ and $(\Delta \bar{s}_{AB})^2$ found by the respective observers.

Chapter 2

Tensor Analysis

IN THE study of relativity we shall be concerned with physical and geo-metrical quantities, in general expressed as functions of the coordinates of the reference frames of interest. These quantities may be conveniently classified as:

1. Scalar invariants (tensors of zero rank).
2. Vectors (tensors of first rank).
3. Tensors (of second and higher rank).

In four dimensions, a tensor of nth rank is composed of a labeled set of 4^n functions.

It will frequently be necessary to transform tensors from expressions in terms of the coordinates of one system to corresponding expressions in the coordinates of another frame. For this purpose, a coordinate transformation law is required:

$$\bar{x}^\mu = \bar{x}^\mu(x^\nu). \tag{2.1}$$

The coordinate transformation may represent a shift from one rectilinear or curvilinear position-marker network to another at relative rest with respect to the first, or may give the relationship between the coordinates of two networks in some state of relative motion. We shall assume that the necessary coordinate transformation is available, at least in prin-ciple. (In actual fact, only one well-verified coordinate transformation law relating frames in relative motion is known. This is the Lorentz transformation between inertial frames. Numerous *ad hoc* transforma-tions, e.g. to rotating or linearly accelerated frames, have been proposed

23

in the literature.† These are, in most cases, approximately valid for low accelerations and low velocities, in the sense that the Galilean transformation is valid at low relative speeds.)

The components of a tensor are transformed to a new coordinate frame by the replacement of the old variables with the new, and the multiplication of the tensor components by transformation coefficients appropriate to their tensor character. Tensor components of two characters are defined: contravariant tensor components are identified by coordinate indices written as superscripts, e.g. A^μ, $B^{\mu\nu}$, and covariant tensor components are written with subscript indices, e.g. A_μ, $B_{\mu\nu}$. Tensors of second and higher rank may have mixed (combined covariant and contravariant) character, e.g. A^μ_ν, $B^{\alpha\beta}_{\gamma\delta}$, $C^{\varrho\sigma\pi\varkappa}_\tau$, etc. Covariant and contravariant tensors are distinguished by the manner in which they undergo coordinate transformation.

2.1. Coordinate Transformation of Tensors

(a) *Scalar invariants*

The general scalar invariant is a function $f(x^\nu)$ of $(1 + 3)$ coordinates that associates a scalar number with each point of four-space. Transformation of a scalar to new coordinates $\bar{x}$ is accomplished by the substitution of variables as in eqn. (2.1):

$$\bar{f}(\bar{x}^\mu) = f(x^\nu(\bar{x}^\mu)). \tag{2.2}$$

A typical scalar invariant is a time-dependent temperature distribution function which assigns a number, the temperature, to each space point at each time. As an example we may consider the one-dimensional distribution of temperature along a bar after an initial heat pulse at $(t, x) = (0, 0)$:

$$T(t, x) = 2(a\pi t)^{-1/2} \exp\left(-x^2/4at\right). \tag{2.3}$$

---

† C. Møller, *The Theory of Relativity*, pp. 240 ff., 251 ff., Oxford Univ. Press, London and New York, 1966; H. Lass, *Am. J. Phys.* **31**, 274 (1963); L. McL. Marsh, *ibid.* **33**, 934 (1965); M. G. Trocheris, *Phil. Mag.* **7**, 1143 (1949); H. Takeno, *Prog. Theoret. Phys.* **7**, 367 (1952); W. M. Irvine, *Physica* **30**, 1160 (1964).

If we now introduce a linear coordinate transformation,

$$t = p\bar{t} + q\bar{x},$$

$$x = m\bar{t} + n\bar{x},$$

the transformed temperature function [eqn. (2.3)] is

$$\bar{T}(\bar{t}, \bar{x}) = 2(a\pi p\bar{t} + a\pi q\bar{x})^{-1/2} \exp\left[-(m\bar{t} + n\bar{x})^2/4a(p\bar{t} + q\bar{x})\right]. \quad (2.4)$$

Equation (2.4) assigns the same temperature to a given physical point in space as does eqn. (2.3),† although the coordinate numbers used to identify the space–time points are different, in the two different coordinate frames.

(b) *Contravariant vectors*

A contravariant tensor of first rank, or contravariant vector, is a set of four quantities that undergo coordinate transformation according to the rule:

$$\bar{A}^\lambda(\bar{x}^\mu) = A^\alpha(x^\nu(\bar{x}^\mu))\frac{\partial \bar{x}^\lambda}{\partial x^\alpha} \quad (2.5)$$

where summation over α is implied ($\alpha = 0, 1, 2, 3$), and the change of variables in the unbarred components A^α is indicated explicitly.

The four coordinate differentials dx^μ form a prototype contravariant vector. This may be seen by differentiating eqn. (2.1):

$$d\bar{x}^\mu = \frac{\partial \bar{x}^\mu}{\partial x^\nu}dx^\nu. \quad (2.6)$$

Equation (2.6) represents the same transformation law as does eqn. (2.5).

(c) *Covariant vectors*

A covariant vector is a set of four quantities that undergo transformation according to

$$\bar{B}_\lambda = B_\alpha\frac{\partial x^\alpha}{\partial \bar{x}^\lambda} \quad (2.7)$$

† We assume for this example that the relative velocity V between the two systems is small: $V^2/c^2 \ll 1$.

where the coordinate dependence of B_α is omitted for simplicity. There is a close relationship between the covariant vectors and those vectors which are obtainable as the gradient of a scalar potential in Cartesian coordinates. The derivative of potential $V(\bar{x}^\mu)$ with respect to unbarred coordinates is obtained as:

$$\frac{\partial V(\bar{x}^\mu)}{\partial x^\nu} = \frac{\partial V(\bar{x}^\mu)}{\partial \bar{x}^\mu}\frac{\partial \bar{x}^\mu}{\partial x^\nu}. \tag{2.8}$$

In Cartesian coordinates we may define the vector X_λ from the gradients: $\partial V/\partial x^\nu = -X_\nu$, and $\partial V/\partial \bar{x}^\mu = -\bar{X}_\mu$, whereupon eqn. (2.8) becomes the transformation law for the covariant vector X_λ. It should be noted, however, that this analogy does not hold in curvilinear coordinate frames because, in general, physical vectors cannot be formed by differentiation with respect to the coordinates. In polar coordinates, for example, $\partial V/\partial \theta$ is not a component of the gradient of V. (We shall see further that the vectors E and B of the electromagnetic field transform correctly as components of a second-rank tensor (cf. Chapter 5).)

(d) *Tensors of higher rank*

The transformation of a tensor of higher rank is accomplished by multiplication by transformation coefficients of appropriate character for each tensor index:

$$\bar{T}^\mu_{\ \nu} = \frac{\partial \bar{x}^\mu}{\partial x^\alpha}\frac{\partial x^\beta}{\partial \bar{x}^\nu}T^\alpha_{\ \beta}, \qquad \bar{T}^\varrho_{\ \sigma\tau} = \frac{\partial \bar{x}^\varrho}{\partial x^\alpha}\frac{\partial x^\beta}{\partial \bar{x}^\sigma}\frac{\partial x^\gamma}{\partial \bar{x}^\tau}T^\alpha_{\ \beta\gamma},$$

$$\bar{T}^{\alpha\beta\cdots}_{\qquad \mu\nu\cdots} = \frac{\partial \bar{x}^\alpha}{\partial x^\varrho}\frac{\partial \bar{x}^\beta}{\partial x^\sigma}\cdots\frac{\partial x^\lambda}{\partial \bar{x}^\mu}\frac{\partial x^\varepsilon}{\partial \bar{x}^\nu}\cdots T^{\varrho\sigma\cdots}_{\qquad \lambda\varepsilon\cdots} \tag{2.9}$$

The form of the tensor transformation law follows naturally from the fact that one method of constructing tensors of higher rank is by forming *outer products* of vectors or lower-order tensors:

$$T^\alpha_{\ \beta} = A^\alpha B_\beta, \quad T^{\lambda\mu}_{\ \ \gamma\varepsilon} = A^{\lambda\mu}B_{\gamma\varepsilon}. \tag{2.10}$$

The outer product is composed of all products of all the elements of the component tensors, and is of rank $m + n$ if the component tensors are of rank m and n, respectively. It is important to preserve the identity of the indices in the product tensor, since in general $T^{12}_{\ \ 34} \neq T^{12}_{\ \ 43}$, etc.

We now define the process of tensor contraction in the following way: a tensor may be *contracted* by setting a covariant and a contravariant index equal and summing:

$$T^{\varrho\mu}_{\mu\sigma} = T^{\varrho}_{\sigma}. \qquad (2.11)$$

The contraction of a tensor over a pair of indices therefore reduces its rank by two. An *inner product* of two tensors is constructed by forming the outer product of the tensors and then contracting the result over a pair of indices:

$$A^{\mu\lambda}B_{\tau\lambda} = T^{\mu}_{\tau}.$$

The coordinate transformation represented by eqn. (2.1) may be of very general kind, subject only to the conditions that the derivatives $\partial\bar{x}^{\mu}/\partial x^{\nu}$ exist up to arbitrary order, and that the Jacobian of the transformation, $\det|\partial\bar{x}^{\mu}/\partial x^{\nu}|$, does not vanish. For the special case of a linear orthogonal transformation in Euclidean space:

$$x^{\alpha} = a^{\alpha}_{\lambda}\bar{x}^{\lambda}.$$

From eqn. (2.6) we see that

$$a^{\alpha}_{\lambda} = \frac{\partial x^{\alpha}}{\partial\bar{x}^{\lambda}}.$$

The orthogonality condition [eqn. (1.26)] then becomes

$$\sum_{v} \frac{\partial x^{\mu}}{\partial\bar{x}^{\nu}} \frac{\partial x^{\lambda}}{\partial\bar{x}^{\nu}} = \delta_{\mu\lambda}. \qquad (2.12)$$

But from $x^{\mu} = x^{\mu}(\bar{x}^{\nu})$, the inverse of eqn. (2.1), we may form the partial derivative

$$\frac{\partial x^{\mu}}{\partial x^{\lambda}} = \frac{\partial x^{\mu}}{\partial\bar{x}^{\nu}} \frac{\partial\bar{x}^{\nu}}{\partial x^{\lambda}} = \delta_{\mu\lambda} \qquad (2.13)$$

where the Kronecker delta function on the right arises from the character of the derivatives of the independent variables x^{μ} with respect to themselves.

Therefore, we deduce from eqns. (2.12) and (2.13) that for orthogonal transformations in Euclidean spaces

$$\frac{\partial x^{\lambda}}{\partial\bar{x}^{\nu}} = \frac{\partial\bar{x}^{\nu}}{\partial x^{\lambda}}.$$

Inspection of the consequence of this result in the transformation laws

$$A^\lambda = \frac{\partial x^\lambda}{\partial \bar{x}^\nu} \bar{A}^\nu, \qquad A_\lambda = \frac{\partial \bar{x}^\nu}{\partial x^\lambda} \bar{A}_\nu$$

shows that contravariant and covariant vectors transform in the same way, in rectangular orthogonal systems. In Euclidean coordinate frames, therefore, the contravariant and covariant components of a given vector are identical:

$$A^\lambda = A_\lambda \quad \text{Euclidean}. \tag{2.14}$$

In Minkowski coordinate frames, although they are orthogonal frames, the foregoing relationship does not hold because of the sign of the conventional definition of the world-line element. Consider the transformation of the product $\bar{g}_{\alpha\beta}\bar{A}^\alpha$ between two Minkowski frames, with coordinates x^μ and $\bar{x}^\nu$, respectively,

$$\bar{g}_{\alpha\beta}\bar{A}^\alpha = g_{\mu\nu} \frac{\partial x^\mu}{\partial \bar{x}^\alpha} \frac{\partial x^\nu}{\partial \bar{x}^\beta} A^\varrho \frac{\partial \bar{x}^\alpha}{\partial x^\varrho}. \tag{2.15}$$

We have seen in eqn. (1.35c) that Minkowski's metric tensor is $\bar{g}_{\alpha\beta} = -\delta_{\alpha\beta}$. Using this on the left above, and using also the fact that $(\partial x^\mu/\partial \bar{x}^\alpha)(\partial \bar{x}^\alpha/\partial x^\varrho) = \delta_{\mu\varrho}$, in carrying out the sums over α on the left and ϱ on the right, eqn. (2.15) becomes

$$-\bar{A}^\beta = \frac{\partial x^\nu}{\partial \bar{x}^\beta} (g_{\mu\nu}A^\mu). \tag{2.16}$$

The right-hand side of eqn. (2.16) represents the transformation expression for the ν component of a covariant vector, in parentheses, to its β-component in the barred coordinate frame. We identify this covariant vector as A_ν. Therefore, eqn. (2.16) shows that in a Minkowski manifold

$$-\bar{A}^\beta = \frac{\partial x^\nu}{\partial \bar{x}^\beta} A_\nu.$$

From which we infer that:

$$\bar{A}_\beta = -\bar{A}^\beta \quad \text{(Minkowski)}. \tag{2.17}$$

That is, in a Minkowski manifold, the covariant and contravariant components of a vector are related by (-1).

The tensor transformation laws that we stated in eqns. (2.5) and (2.7) suggest the question: What is the relationship of these quantities which we have defined as contravariant and covariant vectors with the conventional physical vectors with which we are familiar, such as velocity, force, and electric and magnetic fields? How are we to know whether a given physical vector should be transformed as a contravariant or a covariant vector? Before proceeding to answer these questions we must first observe that in the (1 + 3)-coordinate space-time continuum, the vectors A^α and B_λ necessarily possess four components, whereas the familiar physical vectors mentioned above are three-component vectors, defined in the three-coordinate space of ordinary experience. In order to treat the physical vectors as contravariant or covariant first-rank tensors in four dimensions they must be extended by the addition of a fourth component in some suitable manner. Unfortunately, no general prescription for making this extension can be given, and particular cases must be dealt with individually on the basis of what is known about the physical quantity. We shall find in some cases, notably that of the electromagnetic fields, that the physical vectors can be redefined as members of a two-dimensional array which is a tensor of second rank.

The terms contravariant and covariant as applied to vectors should preferably be modified to specify the contravariant and covariant *components* of the physical vectors. We can, in fact, transform from one set of components of a given vector to the other by use of the metric tensor, as is shown in the following section. The inner product of the covariant and contravariant components is equal to the squared amplitude of the physical vector:

$$A^\mu A_\mu = \pm |A^2|. \tag{2.18}$$

An example of the foregoing properties of vectors is given at the end of Section 2.2.

2.2. The Metric Tensor

The metric tensor $g_{\mu\nu}$ is a twice-covariant tensor of second rank. Its tensor character follows from the fact that the squared world-line element ds^2 is a scalar invariant resulting from the formation of the inner product of $g_{\mu\nu}$ with the two contravariant vectors dx^μ and dx^ν:

$$ds^2 = g_{\mu\nu}\, dx^\mu\, dx^\nu. \tag{2.19}$$

The metric tensor $g_{\mu\nu}$ is symmetric in its indices μ and ν. The properties of tensor symmetry are summarized as follows. A tensor may have symmetry with respect to the interchange of any pair of indices. The second-rank tensor $S_{\mu\nu}$ is symmetric if

$$S_{\mu\nu} = S_{\nu\mu}. \tag{2.20a}$$

A tensor is antisymmetric with respect to a pair of indices if its elements which are denoted by an interchange of indices are equal except for a change of sign:

$$A_{\mu\nu} = -A_{\nu\mu}. \tag{2.20b}$$

A general tensor $T_{\mu\nu}$ may be decomposed into the sum of its symmetric and antisymmetric components:

$$T_{\mu\nu} = S_{\mu\nu} + A_{\mu\nu} = \tfrac{1}{2}(T_{\mu\nu} + T_{\nu\mu}) + \tfrac{1}{2}(T_{\mu\nu} - T_{\nu\mu}). \tag{2.21}$$

If the metric tensor $g_{\mu\nu}$ contains any antisymmetric components, the contributions from these components will cancel out in the formation of the sum for ds^2 [eqn. (2.19)]. Therefore the metric tensor of Riemannian space is by its nature a symmetric tensor.

We have previously seen [eqn. (1.35c)] that the metric tensor of Minkowski coordinates for Cartesian inertial frames has the simple form

$$g_{\alpha\beta} = -\delta_{\alpha\beta}. \tag{2.22}$$

From this metric, we may derive a useful formula for the calculation of the elements of the metric $\bar{g}_{\mu\nu}$ of a general Riemannian coordinate frame, if we are in possession of a coordinate transformation relating the coordinates $\bar{x}^\mu$ of the given frame with the coordinates x^λ of a Minkowski frame:

$$x^\lambda = x^\lambda(\bar{x}^\mu).$$

Writing the transformation law for the metric tensor, we have

$$\bar{g}_{\mu\nu} = \frac{\partial x^\alpha}{\partial \bar{x}^\mu}\, \frac{\partial x^\beta}{\partial \bar{x}^\nu}\, g_{\alpha\beta}. \tag{2.23}$$

But, with use of eqn. (2.22), eqn. (2.23) becomes

$$\bar{g}_{\mu\nu} = -\sum_\alpha \frac{\partial x^\alpha}{\partial \bar{x}^\mu} \frac{\partial x^\alpha}{\partial \bar{x}^\nu}. \tag{2.24}$$

Equation (2.24) thus permits us to calculate the metric tensor from the coordinate transformation: $x^\lambda = x^\lambda(\bar{x}^\mu)$.

We may construct the twice-contravariant tensor associated with the metric tensor by the calculation:

$$g^{\varrho\sigma} = \frac{G^{\varrho\sigma}}{g} \tag{2.25}$$

where g is the determinant formed from the metric tensor

$$g = \text{Det } |g_{\mu\nu}| \tag{2.26}$$

and $G^{\varrho\sigma}$ is the cofactor of the element $g_{\varrho\sigma}$ in the determinant of the metric tensor. As a result of the properties of determinants,†

$$g^{\varrho\sigma} g_{\sigma\tau} = \delta^\varrho_\tau \tag{2.27}$$

where $\delta^\varrho_\tau = 1$ for $\varrho = \tau$, and $\delta^\varrho_\tau = 0$ for $\varrho \neq \tau$. The tensor δ^ϱ_τ is called the fundamental unit tensor of Riemannian coordinates.

An alternative calculation of the contravariant metric tensor is also available. From the properties of the determinant g, we have†

$$g^{\varrho\sigma} = \frac{1}{g} \frac{\partial g}{\partial g_{\varrho\sigma}}. \tag{2.28}$$

The metric tensor $g_{\mu\nu}$, with its contravariant form $g^{\mu\nu}$, may be used to obtain the covariant components of a tensor when the contravariant components of the tensor are known, and vice versa, in the process called the lowering and raising of indices:

$$A_\mu = g_{\mu\nu} A^\nu, \tag{2.29}$$

$$A^\mu = g^{\mu\nu} A_\nu, \tag{2.30}$$

$$T_\alpha{}^\beta{}_\gamma = g_{\alpha\varrho} g^{\beta\sigma} T^\varrho{}_{\sigma\gamma}, \text{ etc.} \tag{2.31}$$

† H. Margenau and G. Murphy, *The Mathematics of Physics and Chemistry*, pp. 161, 191, D. Van Nostrand, New York, 1943.

The proof of the raising and lowering theorems requires methods of differential geometry which we shall not introduce here, but we can present a justification for these processes in the following way. If we are in possession of a coordinate transformation from Minkowski coordinates x^λ to the Riemannian coordinates $\bar{x}^\mu$ of a given problem, the transformation of a vector $\bar{A}^\mu$ to the Minkowski frame is given by

$$A^\nu = \frac{\partial x^\nu}{\partial \bar{x}^\mu} \bar{A}^\mu. \tag{2.32}$$

But, in the Minkowski frame, from eqn. (2.17)

$$A_\nu = -A^\nu. \tag{2.33}$$

Transforming A_ν back to the coordinates $\bar{x}$, we obtain

$$\bar{A}_\lambda = \frac{\partial x^\nu}{\partial \bar{x}^\lambda} A_\nu. \tag{2.34}$$

Using eqns. (2.32) and (2.33), in eqns. (2.34), we find

$$\bar{A}_\lambda = -\frac{\partial x^\nu}{\partial \bar{x}^\lambda} \frac{\partial x^\nu}{\partial \bar{x}^\mu} \bar{A}^\mu \quad \text{(sum on } \nu\text{)}. \tag{2.35}$$

But the coefficient of $\bar{A}^\mu$ on the right in eqn. (2.35) is just $\bar{g}_{\mu\nu}$, from eqn. (2.24). Thus we see that this calculation has demonstrated the index-lowering operation:

$$\bar{A}_\lambda = \bar{g}_{\mu\lambda} \bar{A}^\mu. \tag{2.36}$$

We have reintroduced the Minkowski metric above, by reason of the analytical results which were conveniently available because of those properties of the Minkowski coordinate manifold which are common to orthogonal Euclidean coordinates. We recall that in Euclidean coordinates, the fundamental length, or world-line element ds^2, in four dimensions is by definition

$$ds^2 = (dx^1)^2 + (dx^2)^2 + (dx^3)^2 + (dx^4)^2. \tag{2.37}$$

The Riemannian metric tensor array for Euclidean space is therefore

$$g_{\mu\nu} = \begin{bmatrix} 1 & 0 & 0 & 0 \\ 0 & 1 & 0 & 0 \\ 0 & 0 & 1 & 0 \\ 0 & 0 & 0 & 1 \end{bmatrix}_{\text{Euclidean}} . \qquad (2.38)$$

We recall that we have seen the appearance of the Lorentz metric as a natural consequence of the postulates of special relativity:

$$ds^2 = c^2\,dt^2 - dx^2 - dy^2 - dz^2. \qquad (2.39)$$

With adoption of the coordinate notation, $(ct, x, y, z) = (x^0, x^1, x^2, x^3)$, the Lorentz metric takes the form

$$ds^2 = (dx^1)^2 - (dx^1)^2 - (dx^2)^2 - (dx^3)^2, \qquad (2.40)$$

with metric tensor array:

$$g_{\mu\nu} = \begin{bmatrix} 1 & 0 & 0 & 0 \\ 0 & -1 & 0 & 0 \\ 0 & 0 & -1 & 0 \\ 0 & 0 & 0 & -1 \end{bmatrix}_{\text{Lorentz}} . \qquad (2.41)$$

In physical terms, the Lorentz metric above is the metric appropriate to an inertial space–time coordinate region with rectangular spatial coordinates.

With the adoption of Minkowski's coordinate definitions, $(ict, x, y, a) = (x^0, x^1, x^2, x^3)$, the metric of the inertial frame becomes

$$ds^2 = -(ict)^2 - dx^2 - dy^2 - dz^2$$
$$= -[(dx^0)^2 + (dx^1)^2 + (dx^2)^2 + (dx^3)^2], \qquad (2.42)$$

and

$$g_{\mu\nu} = \begin{bmatrix} -1 & 0 & 0 & 0 \\ 0 & -1 & 0 & 0 \\ 0 & 0 & -1 & 0 \\ 0 & 0 & 0 & -1 \end{bmatrix}_{\text{Minkowski}} . \qquad (2.43)$$

In general relativity we shall be interested in metric of the more general form:

$$ds^2 = g_{\mu\nu} \, dx^\mu \, dx^\nu \qquad (2.44)$$

where in principle, all elements of the metric tensor may be functions of coordinates:

$$g_{\mu\nu} = \begin{bmatrix} g_{00} & g_{01} & g_{02} & g_{03} \\ g_{10} & g_{11} & g_{12} & g_{13} \\ g_{20} & g_{21} & g_{22} & g_{23} \\ g_{30} & g_{31} & g_{32} & g_{33} \end{bmatrix}. \qquad (2.45)$$

General Riemannian

In the case of metric tensors representing the physical world, however, symmetry arguments may be given against the appearance of off-diagonal terms in the metric tensor. It is a matter of experience that most equations of motion of mass particles are equally valid for the backward and for the forward evolution of time. If terms of the form: $g_{0\mu} \, dx^0 \, dx^\mu$ appear in ds^2, they will cause the value of ds^2 to depend upon the sign of dx^0. Hence terms $g_{0\mu}$ are rejected. In situations of central symmetry such as the gravitational field of a point mass, the inclusion of off-diagonal terms in a metric based on spherical space coordinates r, θ, ϕ would imply a preferred sense of angular rotation, which is unrealistic.[†] For these and related reasons we shall often, but not always, deal with metric tensors having diagonal form. The formalism which we shall develop is capable of dealing with the most general metrics and hence the most general possible space–time manifolds and off-diagonal $g_{\mu\nu}$ may be admitted when necessary.

The sequence of algebraic signs on the diagonal of a metric tensor in diagonal form is called the *signature* of the metric. In some literature, the sum of these, or the trace of the matrix, is called its signature. Using the latter definition, the signatures of the metrics of eqns. (2.38), (2.41) and (2.43) are $+4$, -2 and -4, respectively. The overall sign of the signature is, as we have noted, arbitrary, and dependent upon the sign employed in the definition of ds^2. As our foregoing discussion implies,

† R. Adler, M. Bazin and M. Schiffer, *Introduction to General Relativity*, p. 165, McGraw-Hill, New York, 1965.

nevertheless, the metric tensor occupies a central role in the development of relativity theory.

It will be helpful in gaining an appreciation of the practical significance of the concepts we have been developing to pause for consideration of a simple example illustrating vector character and the use of the metric in raising and lowering indices. Let us investigate a vector describing the static shear displacement ξ of a medium in rectangular coordinates

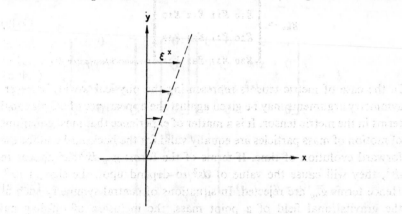

FIG. 2.1. Contravariant shear vector.

(Fig. 2.1). This displacement is assumed to occur in the x-direction only, and to depend on y according to

$$\xi^x = ay \tag{2.46}$$

where a is a constant. We thus *define* a four-component contravariant vector:

$$\xi^\lambda = (\xi^t, \xi^x, \xi^y, \xi^z) = (0, ay, 0, 0) \tag{2.46a}$$

and transform to a cylindrical space–coordinate frame under the assumed transformation given below, together with its inverse:

$$t = \bar{t} \qquad \bar{t} = t,$$

$$x = \bar{r} \cos \bar{\theta} \qquad \bar{r} = (x^2 + y^2)^{1/2}, \tag{2.46b}$$

$$y = \bar{r} \sin \bar{\theta} \qquad \bar{\theta} = \tan^{-1}(y/x),$$

$$z = \bar{z} \qquad \bar{z} = z.$$

In order to transform the vector as a contravariant and as a covariant vector, we calculate:

$$\xi^\mu = \frac{\partial \bar{x}^\mu}{\partial x^\sigma}\, \xi^\sigma \quad \text{and} \quad \xi_\mu = \frac{\partial x^\sigma}{\partial \bar{x}^\mu}\, \xi_\sigma. \tag{2.46c}$$

The coordinate derivatives are calculated from eqns. (2.46b), and may then be arrayed in matrix form, to yield the products

$$\xi^\mu = \begin{array}{c} \bar{t} \\ \bar{r} \\ \bar{\theta} \\ \bar{z} \end{array}
\begin{matrix} t & x & y & z \end{matrix} \\
\begin{bmatrix} 1 & 0 & 0 & 0 \\ 0 & x/r & y/r & 0 \\ 0 & -y/r^2 & x/r^2 & 0 \\ 0 & 0 & 0 & 1 \end{bmatrix}
\begin{bmatrix} 0 \\ ay \\ 0 \\ 0 \end{bmatrix}
= \begin{bmatrix} 0 \\ axy/r \\ -ay^2/r^2 \\ 0 \end{bmatrix}, \tag{2.46d}$$

$$\xi_\mu = (0, -ay, 0, 0) \quad
\begin{array}{c} t \\ x \\ y \\ z \end{array}
\begin{matrix} \bar{t} & \bar{r} & \bar{\theta} & \bar{z} \end{matrix} \\
\begin{bmatrix} 1 & 0 & 0 & 0 \\ 0 & x/r & -y & 0 \\ 0 & y/r & x & 0 \\ 0 & 0 & 0 & 1 \end{bmatrix}, \tag{2.46e}$$

$$= (0, -axy/r, ay^2, 0),$$

where the transformation matrices have been written in a mixture of "old" and "new" coordinates, for brevity.† The negative sign is used with the covariant component of ξ_σ on the left in eqn. (2.46e) [cf. eqn. (2.29)]. The summations indicated in eqn. (2.46c) may now be carried out by use of a modification of the procedure for matrix multiplication. Summation is carried out over columns in a given row of the transformation matrix $\partial \bar{x}^\mu/\partial x^\sigma$ in eqn. (2.46d), and over rows of the matrix $\partial x^\sigma/\partial \bar{x}^\mu$ in eqn. (2.46e). In carrying out tensor summations in this manner, it is essential to maintain proper identification of the rows and columns of the matrices of the tensor elements being multiplied. For this purpose it may be helpful to write in the coordinate identification along the margins of the matrices, as indicated in eqns. (2.46d) and (2.46e).

† For simplicity we drop the bar on coordinate r.

We now form the inner product of the vectors ξ^μ and ξ_λ, which is, by definition,

$$\xi^\mu \xi_\mu = \begin{bmatrix} 0 \\ axy/r \\ -ay^2/r^2 \\ 0 \end{bmatrix} \cdot (0, -axy/r, ay^2, 0), \qquad (2.46\text{f})$$

$$\xi^\mu \xi_\mu = -a^2 y^2$$

where we have used $x^2 + y^2 = r^2$. We have thus found that the inner product of the contravariant and covariant components of the vector yields the squared amplitude of the physical vector. This result illustrates the general rule stated in eqn. (2.18), and helps to clarify the relationship between the contravariant and covariant components of a vector. Having both sets of components at hand we may continue this example, to illustrate the use of the metric tensor for the raising and lowering of indices.

We assume an inertial metric with cylindrical spatial components like that of eqn. (1.35a):

$$\bar{g}_{\mu\nu} = \begin{bmatrix} c^2 & 0 & 0 & 0 \\ 0 & -1 & 0 & 0 \\ 0 & 0 & -r^2 & 0 \\ 0 & 0 & 0 & -1 \end{bmatrix}. \qquad (2.46\text{g})$$

Because of the diagonal character of the metric, the sums $\xi^\mu \bar{g}_{\mu\nu}$ for lowering the contravariant index reduce to single terms. Thus, using eqn. (2.46d) in eqn. (2.46g), we find

$$\xi_r = \bar{g}_{rr} \xi^r = (-1)(axy/r) = -axy/r,$$

$$\xi_\theta = \bar{g}_{\theta\theta} \xi^\theta = (-r^2)(-ay^2/r^2) = ay^2. \qquad (2.46\text{h})$$

The covariant components ξ_μ just found [eqn. (2.46h)] are seen to be in agreement with the known values [eqn. (2.46e)]. To perform the index-raising operation, we require the contravariant form of the metric tensor:

$$\bar{g}^{\mu\nu} = \frac{\bar{G}^{\mu\nu}}{g} = \begin{bmatrix} 1/c^2 & 0 & 0 & 0 \\ 0 & -1 & 0 & 0 \\ 0 & 0 & -(1/r^2) & 0 \\ 0 & 0 & 0 & -1 \end{bmatrix}.$$ (2.46i)

Then, calculating $\bar{g}^{\mu\nu}\xi_\mu$, we obtain

$$\xi^r = \bar{g}^{rr}\xi_r = -(-1)\,(axy/r) = axy/r,$$

$$\xi^\theta = \bar{g}^{\theta\theta}\xi_\theta = \left(-\frac{1}{r^2}\right)(ay^2) = -ay^2/r^2.$$

Thus the contravariant components of ξ^μ are confirmed.

2.3. Parallel Translation of a Tensor

In the application of tensor analysis, we require a covariant procedure corresponding to the differentiation of a tensor with respect to the coordinate variables x^μ. Ordinary partial differentiation is not a covariant procedure, that is, the partial derivative of a tensor does not undergo coordinate transformation as a tensor. This fact is readily shown by the following procedure: the transformation law for a contravariant vector is

$$\bar{A}^\mu = A^\nu \frac{\partial \bar{x}^\mu}{\partial x^\nu}.$$ (2.47)

Differentiation on both sides with respect to $\bar{x}^\lambda$ yields

$$\frac{\partial \bar{A}^\mu}{\partial \bar{x}^\lambda} = \frac{\partial A^\nu}{\partial \bar{x}^\lambda}\frac{\partial \bar{x}^\mu}{\partial x^\nu} + A^\nu \frac{\partial^2 \bar{x}^\mu}{\partial \bar{x}^\lambda \, \partial x^\nu}.$$ (2.48)

In the first term on the right, A^ν is a function of unbarred coordinates x^α. Therefore, eqn. (2.48) must be written

$$\frac{\partial \bar{A}^\mu}{\partial \bar{x}^\lambda} = \frac{\partial A^\nu}{\partial x^\alpha}\frac{\partial x^\alpha}{\partial \bar{x}^\lambda}\frac{\partial \bar{x}^\mu}{\partial x^\nu} + A^\nu \frac{\partial^2 \bar{x}^\mu}{\partial \bar{x}^\lambda \, \partial x^\nu}.$$ (2.49)

If we attempt to interpret eqn. (2.49) as the transformation law for a second-rank mixed tensor $t^\nu_\alpha = \partial A^\nu / \partial x^\alpha$, we see that the appearance of the second term on the right in eqn. (2.49) spoils the form of its transformation law. Therefore we deduce that $\partial A^\nu / \partial x^\alpha$ does not transform as a tensor and hence does not have tensor character.

In seeking the covariant procedure that corresponds to differentiation, we consider the factors which determine the difference between the components of a vector A^μ at coordinate points x^ν and at $x^\nu + dx^\nu$. In rectangular Cartesian coordinate frames, this difference is readily accounted for: any change in the components A^μ must be due to an explicit functional dependence of A^μ upon the coordinates:

$$dA^\mu = A^\mu(x^\nu + dx^\nu) - A^\mu(x^\nu) = \frac{\partial A^\mu}{\partial x^\nu} dx^\nu.$$

In curvilinear coordinate systems, however, the components which represent a given vector may vary in going from x^ν to $x^\nu + dx^\nu$, because of changing projections of the vector on the curvilinear coordinate lines.

The admission of the possibility of a coordinate-induced change in the components of a vector under displacement of position implies that we consider that the vector field itself has an objective reality, apart from the coordinate lines of the framework upon which we choose to measure its projections. This is the natural viewpoint for vector fields describing a physical quantity. This concept is relatively straightforward, and a simple illustration is shown in the three-dimensional example represented in Fig. 2.2. The vector A at point P in cylindrical coordinates has components $(A^r, A^\theta, A^z) = (0, A_0, 0)$. Upon transference to point P' through change of position-angle from θ to $\theta + \Delta\theta$, the *same* vector now is described by the new set of components $(A_0 \sin \Delta\theta, A_0 \cos \Delta\theta, 0)$.

In order to calculate the variation of the components of a vector with position we require a means for calculating the variation of the components of vector A^μ when evaluated at coordinates x^λ, then parallel-translated to $(x^\lambda + dx^\lambda)$:

$$\delta A^\mu(x^\lambda) = A^\mu(x^\lambda) - A^\mu(x^\lambda - dx^\lambda)|_{\text{translated}}. \tag{2.50}$$

We assume that the magnitude of this difference depends upon the values of the components A^μ themselves and also upon the coordinate changes dx^λ. Therefore we define the bilinear form:

$$\delta A^\mu = -\Gamma^\mu_{\nu\lambda} A^\nu \, dx^\lambda. \tag{2.51}$$

The quantities $\Gamma^\mu_{\nu\lambda}$ are called the coefficients of affine connection, and are evaluated at x^λ. We deduce that these coefficients must be symmetrical with respect to interchange of indices ν and λ, because if the

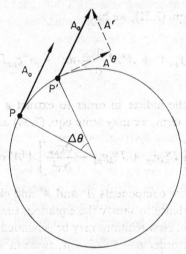

FIG. 2.2. Displacement of vector in curvilinear coordinates.

vector A^μ is the coordinate element Δx^μ, then in the limit in which $\Delta x^\mu \to dx^\mu$, the quantity $\Gamma^\mu_{\nu\lambda} \Delta x^\nu \, dx^\lambda$ must by symmetry be independent of interchange of ν and λ.†

In order to learn the analytic form of the coefficients $\Gamma^\mu_{\nu\lambda}$, we specify that they shall be of a nature such that the predicted value of the absolute length of a vector A^μ does not change during a displacement of position. The squared absolute length of A^μ is the invariant defined as the inner product $A^\mu A_\mu = A^\mu g_{\nu\mu} A^\nu$. Constancy of the invariant length of A^μ during

† This symmetry requires that we reach the same final coordinate point by displacing either dx^ν along dx^λ or dx^λ along dx^ν. This form of closure is not integrable, i.e. does not hold in general for finite displacements, but the symmetry of the $\Gamma^\mu_{\lambda\nu}$ remains.

displacement of position is specified by

$$\delta(A^\mu A_\mu) = 0. \tag{2.52}$$

After eliminating the covariant component A_μ from the parentheses, eqn. (2.52) becomes

$$\delta(A^\mu g_{\mu\nu} A^\nu) = \delta A^\mu g_{\mu\nu} A^\nu + A^\mu \frac{\partial g_{\mu\nu}}{\partial x^\lambda} dx^\lambda A^\nu + A^\mu g_{\mu\nu} \delta A^\nu = 0. \tag{2.53}$$

Substituting from eqn. (2.51), we have

$$0 = -\Gamma^\mu_{\alpha\lambda} A^\alpha \, dx^\lambda g_{\mu\nu} A^\nu + A^\mu A^\nu \frac{\partial g_{\mu\nu}}{\partial x^\lambda} dx^\lambda - A^\mu g_{\mu\nu} \Gamma^\nu_{\alpha\lambda} A^\alpha \, dx^\lambda. \tag{2.54}$$

Then, renaming cyclic indices in order to extract a common factor of $A^\mu A^\nu \, dx^\lambda$ from each term, we may write eqn. (2.54) as

$$0 = \left[\Gamma^\varrho_{\mu\lambda} g_{\varrho\nu} + \Gamma^\varrho_{\nu\lambda} g_{\mu\varrho} - \frac{\partial g_{\mu\nu}}{\partial x^\lambda} \right] A^\mu A^\nu \, dx^\lambda. \tag{2.55}$$

In eqn. (2.55) vector components A^μ and A^ν and elements dx^λ may be chosen arbitrarily. Hence to satisfy the equation, the quantity in square brackets must vanish. New relations may be generated from it by rotating indices in the cyclic order $\mu \to \nu \to \lambda \to \mu$, twice in succession, yielding the two new equations:

$$0 = \Gamma^\varrho_{\nu\mu} g_{\varrho\lambda} + \Gamma^\varrho_{\lambda\mu} g_{\nu\varrho} - \frac{\partial g_{\nu\lambda}}{\partial x^\mu}, \tag{2.56}$$

$$0 = \Gamma^\varrho_{\lambda\nu} g_{\varrho\mu} + \Gamma^\varrho_{\mu\nu} g_{\lambda\varrho} - \frac{\partial g_{\lambda\mu}}{\partial x^\nu}. \tag{2.57}$$

By adding eqns. (2.55) and (2.56) and subtracting eqn. (2.57) from the result, we obtain

$$g_{\nu\varrho} \Gamma^\varrho_{\mu\lambda} = \tfrac{1}{2} \left[\frac{\partial g_{\mu\nu}}{\partial x^\lambda} + \frac{\partial g_{\nu\lambda}}{\partial x^\mu} - \frac{\partial g_{\lambda\mu}}{\partial x^\nu} \right] \tag{2.58}$$

where again we related for convenience cyclic summation indices, and where the symmetry of $\Gamma^\varrho_{\nu\mu}$ in its subscripts has been used. The expression on the right side of eqn. (2.39) is called the Christoffel symbol of first kind:

$$\left[\begin{matrix} \nu \\ \mu\lambda \end{matrix}\right] \equiv \tfrac{1}{2}\left[\frac{\partial g_{\mu\nu}}{\partial x^\lambda} + \frac{\partial g_{\nu\lambda}}{\partial x^\mu} - \frac{\partial g_{\lambda\mu}}{\partial x^\nu}\right]. \tag{2.59}$$

The coefficient of the affine connection may be evaluated by multiplying eqn. (2.58) by $g^{\sigma\nu}$ and summing, to obtain

$$\Gamma^\sigma_{\mu\lambda} = \tfrac{1}{2} g^{\sigma\nu}\left[\frac{\partial g_{\mu\nu}}{\partial x^\lambda} + \frac{\partial g_{\nu\lambda}}{\partial x^\mu} - \frac{\partial g_{\mu\lambda}}{\partial x^\nu}\right] \tag{2.60}$$

where the delta-function property of $g_{\nu\varrho}g^{\sigma\nu}$ [eqn. (2.27)] has been used. Equation (2.60) has the alternate definition of Christoffel's symbol of second kind:†

$$\Gamma^\sigma_{\mu\lambda} = \left\{\begin{matrix} \sigma \\ \mu\lambda \end{matrix}\right\} \tag{2.61}$$

where

$$\left\{\begin{matrix} \sigma \\ \mu\lambda \end{matrix}\right\} \equiv \tfrac{1}{2} g^{\sigma\nu}\left[\frac{\partial g_{\mu\nu}}{\partial x^\lambda} + \frac{\partial g_{\nu\lambda}}{\partial x^\mu} - \frac{\partial g_{\mu\lambda}}{\partial x^\nu}\right]. \tag{2.62}$$

The Christoffel symbols of second kind play an important role in the tensor analysis for relativity, but they do not transform as tensors, although they enter all summations as though their indices were tensor indices. The transformation law of the Christoffel symbols is derived at the end of the next section.

We may illustrate the application of the Christoffel symbols in generating the variations of vector components under parallel translation by returning to the simple example discussed at the beginning of this section. For this case, we need the Christoffel symbols of an inertial frame in cylindrical coordinates (ct, r, θ, z). The world-line element of this system is

$$ds^2 = (c\,dt)^2 - dr^2 - r^2\,d\theta^2 - dz^2. \tag{2.63a}$$

---

† The coefficients of affine connection are defined in some literature with sign opposite to that used in eqn. (2.60), but the definitions of Christoffel's symbols are universal. See D. R. Brill and R. C. Perisho, *loc. cit.*

We wish to calculate the variations

$$\delta A^\mu = - \left\{ \begin{matrix} \mu \\ \nu\lambda \end{matrix} \right\} A^\nu dx^\lambda \qquad (2.63\,b)$$

and

$$\delta A_\mu = \left\{ \begin{matrix} \nu \\ \mu\lambda \end{matrix} \right\} A_\nu dx^\lambda$$

where the Christoffel symbols are given by eqn. (2.62). For the latter, we require the metric tensor $g_{\mu\nu}$ and its contravariant form $g^{\mu\nu}$, given by eqn. (2.25). From eqns. (2.63a) and (2.25), we find

$$g_{\mu\nu} = \begin{pmatrix} 1 & 0 & 0 & 0 \\ 0 & -1 & 0 & 0 \\ 0 & 0 & -r^2 & 0 \\ 0 & 0 & 0 & -1 \end{pmatrix}, \quad g^{\mu\nu} = \begin{pmatrix} 1 & 0 & 0 & 0 \\ 0 & -1 & 0 & 0 \\ 0 & 0 & -(1/r^2) & 0 \\ 0 & 0 & 0 & -1 \end{pmatrix}. \qquad (2.63\,c)$$

Due to the diagonal character of the metric tensors, most of the terms in eqn. (2.62) vanish for this metric. The only non-zero Christoffel symbols remaining are readily found to be:

$$\left\{ \begin{matrix} r \\ \theta\theta \end{matrix} \right\} = -r, \quad \left\{ \begin{matrix} \theta \\ r\theta \end{matrix} \right\} = \frac{1}{r}. \qquad (2.63\,d)$$

In order to complete the calculation of δA^μ and δA_μ using eqn. (2.63b), we need the cylindrical contravariant and covariant components of the vector given as A_0 in Fig. 2.2. To find these, we rotate the vector, and for simplicity define it as a vector initially in rectangular coordinates where its components are $(A^t, A^x, A^y, A^z) = (0, 0, A_0, 0)$. This will correspond to a vector in cylindrical coordinates, the components of which are $(A^t, A^r, A^\theta, A^z) = (0, 0, A_0, 0)$ at a position defined by $\theta = 0$. We may now transform the rectangular components to the cylindrical frame, first by use of the transformation matrix for contravariant vectors as already found in eqn. (2.46 d). Thus we have

$$
\bar{A}^\mu =
\begin{pmatrix}
1 & 0 & 0 & 0 \\
0 & x/r & y/r & 0 \\
0 & -y/r^2 & x/r^2 & 0 \\
0 & 0 & 0 & 1
\end{pmatrix}
\begin{pmatrix}
0 \\
0 \\
A_0 \\
0
\end{pmatrix}
=
\begin{pmatrix}
0 \\
A_0(y/r) \\
A_0(x/r^2) \\
0
\end{pmatrix}.
\tag{2.63e}
$$

Then, using the resulting components $\bar{A}^\mu$ in eqn. (2.63 b), with eqn. (2.63 d), we obtain the components of variation of the original vector due to a translation through an angle change $\Delta\theta$:

$$
\delta A^r = \begin{Bmatrix} r \\ \theta\theta \end{Bmatrix} A^\theta \Delta\theta = (-r)\frac{A_0 x}{r^2}\Delta\theta,
$$

$$
\tag{2.63f}
$$

$$
\delta A^\theta = \begin{Bmatrix} \theta \\ r\theta \end{Bmatrix} A^r \Delta\theta = \frac{1}{r}\frac{A_0 y}{r}\Delta\theta.
$$

Rewriting these results in terms of cylindrical coordinates r and θ, we have

$$
\delta A^r = -A_0 \cos\theta\,\Delta\theta,
$$

$$
\delta A^\theta = A_0\frac{\sin\theta}{r}\Delta\theta.
\tag{2.63g}
$$

To complete the calculation of the physical components of δA, we find the covariant components δA_μ. Proceeding as above, but with use of the transformation matrix $\partial x^\nu/\partial \bar{x}^\mu$ from eqn. (2.46e), we obtain

$$
\bar{A}_\mu = (0, A_r, A_\theta, A_z) = \big(0, A_0(y/r), A_0 x, 0\big).
\tag{2.63h}
$$

Then, calculating the components δA_μ, we find

$$
\delta A_r = \begin{Bmatrix} \theta \\ r\theta \end{Bmatrix} A_\theta\,\Delta\theta = \frac{1}{r}(A_0 x)(\Delta\theta) = A_0 \cos\theta\,\Delta\theta,
$$

$$
\delta A_\theta = \begin{Bmatrix} r \\ \theta\theta \end{Bmatrix} A_r\,\Delta\theta = (-r)(A_0 y/r)(\Delta\theta) = -A_0 r \sin\theta\,\Delta\theta.
\tag{2.63i}
$$

Combining eqns. (2.63 g) and (2.63 i), we find the squared amplitude of A:

$$\delta A^\mu \, \delta A_\mu = -[A_0^2 \cos^2 \theta (\varDelta\theta)^2 + A_0^2 \sin^2 \theta (\varDelta\theta)^2] \qquad (2.63\,\text{j})$$

from which

$$|(\delta A)|^2 = A_0^2 (\varDelta\theta)^2 \quad \text{or} \quad |\delta A| = A_0 (\varDelta\theta). \qquad (2.63\,\text{k})$$

Since this result is independent of the position angle θ, we see that it is in agreement with the result deduced from graphical construction in Fig. 2.2 for small θ:

$$A(\theta + \varDelta\theta) - A(\theta) = (A_0 \sin \varDelta\theta, \ A_0 \cos \varDelta\theta, \ 0) - (0, A_0, 0)$$

$$= (A_0 \, \varDelta\theta, 0, 0)$$

where we have used $\sin \varDelta\theta \doteq \varDelta\theta$, $\cos \varDelta\theta \doteq 1$, and the spatial components only are given. Thus we have verified in this simple example the comparison of a parallel-transported vector with the vector whose components were held constant relative to a background rectilinear coordinate frame in the example. With the affine connection, in the form of the Christoffel symbols, coordinate-induced shifts in a vector or tensor may be calculated in a routine way in more complex manifolds where elementary methods are not available.

A coordinate system, or manifold, which possesses a law of parallel transplantation of vectors is said to be affine, or affinely related. The Riemannian manifolds with which we shall deal in relativity are affinely related manifolds.

2.4. The Covariant Derivative

With the variation δA^μ of vector component A^μ under parallel translation known, the definition of the covariant derivative may now be completed. The covariant derivative DA^μ of a vector A^μ is composed of the change $(\partial A^\mu / \partial x^\lambda) \, dx^\lambda$ due to its explicit functional dependence on coordinates, and the change δA^μ due to its varying projections on the coordinate axes under parallel translation. We define the covariant derivative of the contravariant vector A^μ as

$$DA^\mu = \frac{\partial A^\mu}{\partial x^\lambda} dx^\lambda + \left\{ \begin{matrix} \mu \\ \nu\lambda \end{matrix} \right\} A^\nu \, dx^\lambda. \tag{2.64}$$

We shall employ notation in which the covariant derivative of A^μ with respect to coordinate x^λ is written

$$A^\mu_{;\lambda} = A^\mu_{,\lambda} + \left\{ \begin{matrix} \mu \\ \nu\lambda \end{matrix} \right\} A^\nu. \tag{2.65}$$

In this notation, the semicolon indicates covariant differentiation and the comma ordinary partial differentiation.

The covariant derivative of a scalar function of coordinates $f(x^\lambda)$ is the partial derivative of the function. As we have seen, differentiation of a scalar with respect to a coordinate variable yields a covariant vector, which transforms covariantly

$$f_{;\lambda} = f_{,\lambda} = F_\lambda. \tag{2.66}$$

The covariant derivative of a contravariant vector has been defined above by eqn. (2.65). Equation (2.66) may now be used to establish the form of the covariant derivative of a covariant vector. We utilize the fact that the squared amplitude $A^\mu A_\mu$ of a vector is a scalar function. Placing $f = A^\mu A_\mu$ in eqn. (2.66), we obtain, with use of the rule for differentiation of a product,

$$A^\mu_{;\lambda} A_\mu + A^\mu A_{\mu;\lambda} = A^\mu_{,\lambda} A_\mu + A^\mu A_{\mu,\lambda}. \tag{2.67}$$

Then, substitution for $A^\mu_{;\lambda}$ from eqn. (2.65) yields

$$\left(A^\mu_{,\lambda} + \left\{ \begin{matrix} \mu \\ \nu\lambda \end{matrix} \right\} A^\nu \right) A_\mu + A^\mu A_{\mu;\lambda} = A^\mu_{,\lambda} A_\mu + A^\mu A_{\mu,\lambda}. \tag{2.68}$$

After cancellation of terms, this becomes

$$\left\{ \begin{matrix} \mu \\ \nu\lambda \end{matrix} \right\} A^\nu A_\mu + A^\mu A_{\mu;\lambda} - A^\mu A_{\mu,\lambda} = 0. \tag{2.69}$$

In the last two terms above, μ is a cyclic index which is summed out. Therefore it may be replaced by index ν without changing the expression:

$$\left[\begin{Bmatrix} \mu \\ \nu\lambda \end{Bmatrix} A_\mu + A_{\nu;\lambda} - A_{\nu,\lambda} \right] A^\nu = 0. \tag{2.70}$$

In general A^ν is non-zero, so the covariant derivative of A_ν is

$$A_{\nu;\lambda} = A_{\nu,\lambda} - \begin{Bmatrix} \mu \\ \nu\lambda \end{Bmatrix} A_\mu. \tag{2.71}$$

The covariant derivative of a vector is a tensor of second rank. This may be verified for the case of the contravariant first-rank tensor, by rewriting eqn. (2.64) in the form

$$A^\mu{}_{;\lambda}\, dx^\lambda = dA^\mu - \delta A^\mu. \tag{2.72}$$

The right side of eqn. (2.72) is a contravariant vector composed of a differential increment of vector A^μ, and the variation of A^μ induced by parallel transport, itself a vector. The left side, which is the inner product of $A^\mu{}_{;\lambda}$ with contravariant vector dx^λ, must also be a contravariant vector. Therefore, $A^\mu{}_{;\lambda}$ is a tensor of second rank with one contravariant and one covariant index. We may similarly show that covariant differentiation of tensors of any rank yields a tensor of next higher rank by one covariant index. The *covariant divergence* operation consists of covariant differentiation with respect to an index, followed by contraction over that index, yielding a scalar.

$$A = A^\nu{}_{;\nu} \qquad (A_\nu){}_{;\nu} = (A^\alpha g_{\alpha\nu}){}_{;\nu}. \tag{2.73}$$

Covariant differentiation of tensors of higher rank is performed by carrying out operations like those of eqns. (2.65) and (2.71) on each tensor index:

$$T^{\varrho\sigma}{}_{\tau\gamma;\lambda} = T^{\varrho\sigma}{}_{\tau\gamma,\lambda} + \begin{Bmatrix} \varrho \\ \alpha\lambda \end{Bmatrix} T^{\alpha\sigma}{}_{\tau\gamma} + \begin{Bmatrix} \sigma \\ \alpha\lambda \end{Bmatrix} T^{\varrho\alpha}{}_{\tau\gamma} - \begin{Bmatrix} \alpha \\ \tau\lambda \end{Bmatrix} T^{\varrho\sigma}{}_{\alpha\gamma}$$

$$- \begin{Bmatrix} \alpha \\ \gamma\lambda \end{Bmatrix} T^{\varrho\sigma}{}_{\tau\alpha}. \tag{2.74}$$

We may now derive the coordinate-transformation law of the Christoffel symbols of second kind, which, although not tensors, undergo coordinate transformation in a definite way. Equation (2.65) is

$$A^\mu{}_{;\lambda} = A^\mu{}_{,\lambda} + \begin{Bmatrix} \mu \\ \nu\lambda \end{Bmatrix} A^\nu.$$

Replacing A^μ and $A^\mu{}_{;\lambda}$ with the corresponding quantities transformed from another (barred) coordinate frame, $\bar{x}^\alpha$, we obtain

$$\frac{\partial x^\mu}{\partial \bar{x}^\alpha} \frac{\partial \bar{x}^\beta}{\partial x^\lambda} \bar{A}^\alpha{}_{;\beta} = \frac{\partial}{\partial x^\lambda}\left(\frac{\partial x^\mu}{\partial \bar{x}^\alpha} \bar{A}^\alpha\right) + \begin{Bmatrix} \mu \\ \nu\lambda \end{Bmatrix} \frac{\partial x^\nu}{\partial \bar{x}^\alpha} \bar{A}^\alpha. \qquad (2.75)$$

Substituting for $\bar{A}^\alpha{}_{;\beta}$ from eqn. (2.65), and replacing the operator $\partial/\partial x^\lambda$ by $(\partial \bar{x}^\beta/\partial x^\lambda)\,\partial/\partial \bar{x}^\beta$, eqn. (2.75) becomes

$$\frac{\partial x^\mu}{\partial \bar{x}^\alpha} \frac{\partial \bar{x}^\beta}{\partial x^\lambda}\left[\bar{A}^\alpha{}_{,\beta} + \begin{Bmatrix} \alpha \\ \beta\gamma \end{Bmatrix} \bar{A}^\gamma\right] = \frac{\partial^2 x^\mu}{\partial \bar{x}^\alpha \partial \bar{x}^\beta} \frac{\partial \bar{x}^\beta}{\partial x^\lambda} \bar{A}^\alpha + \frac{\partial x^\mu}{\partial \bar{x}^\alpha} \frac{\partial \bar{x}^\beta}{\partial x^\lambda} \bar{A}^\alpha{}_{,\beta}$$

$$+ \begin{Bmatrix} \mu \\ \nu\lambda \end{Bmatrix} \frac{\partial x^\nu}{\partial \bar{x}^\alpha} \bar{A}^\alpha. \qquad (2.76)$$

After cancellation of like terms in eqn. (2.76), the cyclic indices α and γ may be interchanged on the left side, permitting cancellation of a common factor of $\bar{A}^\alpha$, with the result

$$\frac{\partial x^\mu}{\partial \bar{x}^\gamma} \frac{\partial \bar{x}^\beta}{\partial x^\lambda} \begin{Bmatrix} \gamma \\ \beta\alpha \end{Bmatrix} = \frac{\partial^2 x^\mu}{\partial \bar{x}^\alpha \partial \bar{x}^\beta} \frac{\partial \bar{x}^\beta}{\partial x^\lambda} + \begin{Bmatrix} \mu \\ \nu\lambda \end{Bmatrix} \frac{\partial x^\nu}{\partial \bar{x}^\alpha}. \qquad (2.77)$$

Equation (2.77) may be multiplied by $\partial \bar{x}^\varepsilon/\partial x^\mu$ and $\partial x^\lambda/\partial \bar{x}^\varkappa$. Then, by use of the delta-function properties of the coordinate derivatives:

$$\frac{\partial \bar{x}^\varepsilon}{\partial x^\mu} \frac{\partial x^\mu}{\partial \bar{x}^\gamma} = \delta^\varepsilon{}_\gamma, \qquad \frac{\partial \bar{x}^\beta}{\partial x^\lambda} \frac{\partial x^\lambda}{\partial \bar{x}^\varkappa} = \delta^\beta{}_\varkappa.$$

Equation (2.77) yields the transformation law for the Christoffel symbols:

$$\begin{Bmatrix} \varepsilon \\ \varkappa\alpha \end{Bmatrix} = \frac{\partial^2 x^\mu}{\partial \bar{x}^\alpha \partial \bar{x}^\varkappa} \frac{\partial \bar{x}^\varepsilon}{\partial x^\mu} + \begin{Bmatrix} \mu \\ \nu\lambda \end{Bmatrix} \frac{\partial x^\nu}{\partial \bar{x}^\alpha} \frac{\partial \bar{x}^\varepsilon}{\partial x^\mu} \frac{\partial x^\lambda}{\partial \bar{x}^\varkappa}. \qquad (2.78)$$

2.5. Tensor Products

The power of tensor notation and algebraic methods has become apparent through the foregoing proofs and derivations that have been possible with great economy of writing because of the use of tensor notation. We have also observed that the inner product of two tensors may be formed by use of a procedure that resembles matrix multiplication. This procedure must be applied with discrimination, however, to insure that the process called for by the tensor notation is actually being carried out.

Consider the inner product of two second-rank tensors $A_{\alpha\beta}$ and $B^{\mu}{}_{\nu}$. Setting two covariant (or two contravariant) indices equal and summing would give a meaningless result, but we may set $\beta = \mu$ in these tensors and sum

$$A_{\alpha\beta}B^{\beta}{}_{\nu} = \sum_{\beta} A_{\alpha\beta}B^{\beta\nu} = T_{\alpha\nu}. \tag{2.79}$$

The conventional rule for multiplying matrices A and B to obtain a product matrix C specifies that the ijth member of the product C_{ij} is formed as the sum of successive products of elements of the ith row in the first member of the product (A) with the elements of the jth column of B:

$$C_{ij} = \sum_{n} A_{in}B_{nj}. \tag{2.80}$$

Equation (2.80) may be represented diagrammatically:

$$\begin{pmatrix} a_{00} & a_{01} & a_{02} & a_{03} \\ \overrightarrow{a_{10}\ a_{11}\ a_{12}\ a_{13}} \\ a_{20} & a_{21} & a_{22} & a_{23} \\ a_{30} & a_{31} & a_{32} & a_{33} \end{pmatrix} \cdot \begin{pmatrix} b_{00} & b_{01} & b_{02} & b_{03} \\ b_{10} & b_{11} & b_{12} & b_{13} \\ b_{20} & b_{21} & b_{22} & b_{23} \\ b_{30} & b_{31} & b_{32} & b_{33} \end{pmatrix} = \begin{pmatrix} c_{00} & c_{01} & c_{02} & c_{03} \\ c_{10} & c_{11} & [c_{12}] & c_{13} \\ c_{20} & c_{21} & c_{22} & c_{23} \\ c_{30} & c_{31} & c_{32} & c_{33} \end{pmatrix}$$

$$\tag{2.81}$$

wherein

$$c_{12} = a_{10}b_{02} + a_{11}b_{12} + a_{12}b_{22} + a_{13}b_{32}. \tag{2.82}$$

Here, we have adopted the convention that the first subscript on the matrix symbol refers to its *row* position, the second to its *column*.

The same procedure as is illustrated in eqn. (2.81) may be used to systematize the process of forming the inner product $A_{\alpha\beta}B^{\beta}{}_{\sigma}$, if care is used to arrange the array of the tensor members of $A_{\alpha\beta}$ on the left, with indices α and β corresponding to rows and columns, respectively, and the array of $B^{\beta}{}_{\sigma}$ with β and σ corresponding to rows and columns, respectively.

It is well known that matrix multiplication is in general non-commutative. That is, $AB \neq BA$. This is illustrated by the simple example:

$$\begin{pmatrix} 1 & 0 \\ 1 & 2 \end{pmatrix} \cdot \begin{pmatrix} 1 & 1 \\ 1 & 1 \end{pmatrix} = \begin{pmatrix} 1 & 1 \\ 3 & 3 \end{pmatrix},$$

$$\begin{pmatrix} 1 & 1 \\ 1 & 1 \end{pmatrix} \cdot \begin{pmatrix} 1 & 0 \\ 1 & 2 \end{pmatrix} = \begin{pmatrix} 2 & 2 \\ 2 & 2 \end{pmatrix}.$$

For this reason, the matrices which are constructed to represent tensors in multiplication cannot be permuted indiscriminately, unless the rows and columns are rearranged to represent the contraction process originally called for. This statement should not be interpreted to mean that tensor multiplication is non-commutative, however. Both of the tensor products $A^{\beta}{}_{\alpha}B_{\beta\sigma}$ and $B_{\beta\sigma}A^{\beta}{}_{\alpha}$ are sets of instructions to carry out the *same process*, and if done correctly will both yield the same result.

As has been previously noted, ambiguity in tensor notation must be avoided when substituting a new symbol for a product of tensors. For example, in forming an inner product to yield a new tensor of low rank, in the representation

$$T_{\alpha\sigma} = A^{\beta}{}_{\alpha}B_{\beta\sigma}$$

it must be noted that, in general,

$$T_{30} = A^{\beta}{}_{3}B_{\beta0} \neq T_{03} = A^{\beta}{}_{0}B_{\beta3}.$$

Similarly, in forming an outer product, the identity of each index should be preserved (usually by preserving the order in which they are written), for example:

$$A^{\lambda}B^{\mu}C_{\nu}D^{\omega} = T^{\lambda\mu}{}_{\nu}{}^{\omega}.$$

2.6. Tensor Densities

An important class of quantities is generated by multiplying an ordinary tensor by $\sqrt{-g}$:

$$\mathfrak{T}^\mu_{\ \nu} = \sqrt{-g}\, T^\mu_{\ \nu}. \qquad (2.83)$$

These quantities, called tensor densities, are usually denoted by German-letter symbols, and have the rank of the original tensor. Tensor densities transform according to the law:

$$\overline{\mathfrak{T}}^\varrho_{\ \sigma} = \frac{\partial \bar{x}^\varrho}{\partial x^\mu} \frac{\partial x^\nu}{\partial \bar{x}^\sigma} \mathfrak{T}^\mu_{\ \nu} \left| \frac{\partial x^\alpha}{\partial \bar{x}^\beta} \right| \qquad (2.84)$$

wherein, in addition to being multiplied by the usual transformation coefficients appropriate to its tensor indices, the tensor density is multiplied by the determinant of transformation coefficients,† as indicated in eqn. (2.84), in order to accomplish coordinate transformation.

The tensor densities are a special case of the *relative tensors* of weight N. The latter must be multiplied by the Nth power of the transformation determinant during coordinate transformation. The tensor density is a relative tensor of rank 1, and is the only relative tensor which we shall need for our work in relativity.

As a consequence of the definition of the tensor density, eqn. (2.83), the quantity $\sqrt{-g}$ is a scalar density (tensor density of zero rank), since the scalar unity is a tensor of zero rank.

It should be noted that a tensor density is not a "density" in the ordinary-language sense. To illustrate, we may consider the following problem. A spherical container of radius R contains particles with a packing density of n_0 particles per cubic meter, in its own rest frame. However, if we multiply n_0 by the bare coordinate differentials $dt\, dr\, d\theta\, d\phi$, the result has no significance, and cannot be integrated to find the number of particles in the container. It is necessary to multiply the particle "density" n_0 by the determinant $r^2 \sin\theta$, relevant to spherical coordinates in an inertial frame, to obtain the *scalar density*, $n_0 c r^2 \sin\theta$ (tensor

---

† This determinant is the Jacobian determinant, in the terminology of calculus.

density of zero rank), which may be integrated

$$\int n_0 c r^2 \sin \theta \, dt \, dr \, d\theta \, d\phi$$

to calculate that the sphere contains $(4\pi/3)R^2 n_0 c \, dt$ particles. (The factor $c \, dt$ is an increment of no importance to this discussion.) This slight ambiguity in the terminology of tensor densities should ordinarily cause no difficulty.

2.7. The Riemann Curvature Tensor

The analytical treatment of relativity theory is carried out in the $(1 + 3)$-dimensional space–time coordinate manifold characterized by Riemann's metric tensor, $g_{\mu\nu}$. We have thus far seen some simple metric tensors that were known *a priori*, but in general a definite procedure is needed for finding the form of the metric tensors which correctly describe the physical world. The differential equation satisfied by the tensor $g_{\mu\nu}$ is needed. In the development of general relativity, Einstein was led, in the search for this differential equation, to the inclusion of Riemann's curvature tensor $R^\alpha{}_{\beta\gamma\alpha} = R_{\beta\gamma}$ in the differential equation for the metric tensor components. Thus we are led to the study of the tensor $R^\alpha{}_{\beta\gamma\delta}$, which gives a measure of the curvature of a coordinate space. It turns out further, that in the $(1 + 3)$-coordinate space–time manifolds of general relativity, a curvature of the space is produced by a gravitating mass. An illustration of a curved space of lower dimension is given by the two-dimensional space on the surface of a sphere. On the spherical surface, it is impossible to define a two-coordinate manifold (x^1, x^2) throughout the space such that the line element is given everywhere by the Euclidean form: $ds^2 = (dx^1)^2 + (dx^2)^2$. In the spherical surface, moreover, a vector having constant magnitude that is parallel-translated around a closed path will undergo a non-vanishing change in direction during the transport. The magnitude of the change in the vector components around the closed loop depends upon the path followed by the loop. An example is given by the vector V, initially at point P in the surface of the sphere illustrated in Fig. 2.3. The vector is parallel-transported around the loop *PQR*, being maintained everywhere locally parallel to its immediately previous positions, as observed in the two-dimensional domain of the spherical surface. If the path surrounds a quarter of a hemisphere, wherein the angles at *P*, *Q* and *R* are right angles, the components of the vector

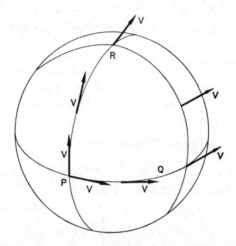

FIG. 2.3. Parallel translation of a vector in the surface of a sphere.

change from $(V^\theta, V^\phi) = (0, V)$ at the start of the circuit to (V^θ, V^ϕ) = $(V, 0)$ at its completion. This change is a consequence of the curvature of the surface, since a vector which is parallel-translated around a closed path on a plane surface is not found to have undergone any change of its components upon completion of the loop.

Riemann's curvature tensor may be obtained as a measure of the total variation of the components of a contravariant test vector V^μ which is translated through a closed circuit of infinitesimal extent. Let us consider the integral of the variation of vector V^μ under parallel transport around a loop of infinitesimal extent, as shown in Fig. 2.4,

$$\oint \delta V^\mu = - \oint \left\{ {\mu \atop \nu\lambda} \right\} V^\nu \, dx^\lambda. \tag{2.85}$$

We evaluate V^ν and $\left\{ \begin{matrix} \mu \\ \nu\lambda \end{matrix} \right\}$ at a general point on the loop at a small vector distance Δx^σ from the starting point at 0, by expanding these quantities

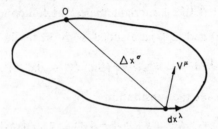

FIG. 2.4. Parallel transport of V^μ in closed path.

to first order about point 0. Thus we obtain

$$\left\{ \begin{matrix} \mu \\ \nu\lambda \end{matrix} \right\} = \left\{ \begin{matrix} \mu \\ \nu\lambda \end{matrix} \right\}(0) + \left[\frac{\partial}{\partial x^\sigma} \left\{ \begin{matrix} \mu \\ \nu\lambda \end{matrix} \right\} \right](0)\, \Delta x^\sigma, \qquad (2.86)$$

$$V^\nu = V^\nu(0) - \left\{ \begin{matrix} \nu \\ \beta\sigma \end{matrix} \right\}(0)\, V^\beta(0)\, \Delta x^\sigma \qquad (2.87)$$

where $V^\nu(0)$ and $\left\{ \begin{matrix} \mu \\ \nu\lambda \end{matrix} \right\}(0)$ are values of the corresponding quantities as evaluated at point 0. When these expansions are substituted into eqn. (2.85), and the higher-order term containing $(\Delta x^\sigma)^2$ is neglected, the result is

$$\oint \delta V^\mu = - \left\{ \begin{matrix} \mu \\ \nu\lambda \end{matrix} \right\}(0)\, V^\nu(0) \oint dx^\lambda$$

$$+ \left[\left\{ \begin{matrix} \mu \\ \nu\lambda \end{matrix} \right\} \left\{ \begin{matrix} \nu \\ \varrho\sigma \end{matrix} \right\} - \frac{\partial}{\partial x^\sigma} \left\{ \begin{matrix} \mu \\ \varrho\lambda \end{matrix} \right\} \right](0)\, V^\varrho \oint \Delta x^\sigma\, dx^\lambda. \qquad (2.88)$$

In eqn. (2.88), quantities evaluated at point 0, and hence constant through the integration, have been factored from the integrals. The first term in this equation necessarily vanishes, since $\oint dx^\lambda = 0$.

We now rewrite the remaining term, in the square bracket in eqn. (2.60), but with interchange of the cyclic indices σ and λ:

$$\oint \delta V^\mu = \left[\left\{ \begin{matrix} \mu \\ \nu\sigma \end{matrix} \right\} \left\{ \begin{matrix} \nu \\ \varrho\lambda \end{matrix} \right\} - \frac{\partial}{\partial x^\lambda} \left\{ \begin{matrix} \mu \\ \varrho\sigma \end{matrix} \right\} \right] V^\varrho \oint \Delta x^\lambda \, dx^\sigma. \quad (2.89)$$

Now, eqns. (2.88) and (2.89) are added, with the result

$$2 \oint \delta V^\mu = R^\mu{}_{\sigma\varrho\lambda} V^\varrho \oint (\Delta x^\lambda \, dx^\sigma - \Delta x^\sigma \, dx^\lambda) \quad (2.90)$$

where we have made the substitution

$$\oint \Delta x^\lambda \, dx^\sigma = \oint \Delta x^\lambda \, dx^\sigma - \tfrac{1}{2} \oint d(\Delta x^\lambda \, \Delta x^\sigma) = \tfrac{1}{2} \oint (\Delta x^\lambda \, dx^\sigma - \Delta x^\sigma \, dx^\lambda)$$

which utilizes the fact that the closed-path integral of the differential quantity $d(\Delta x^\lambda \, \Delta x^\sigma)$ vanishes. Also, from Fig. 2.4, $d(\Delta x^\sigma) = dx^\sigma$. In eqn. (2.90) we have also defined

$$R^\mu{}_{\sigma\varrho\lambda} \equiv \left\{ \begin{matrix} \mu \\ \nu\varrho \end{matrix} \right\} \left\{ \begin{matrix} \nu \\ \sigma\lambda \end{matrix} \right\} - \left\{ \begin{matrix} \mu \\ \nu\lambda \end{matrix} \right\} \left\{ \begin{matrix} \nu \\ \varrho\sigma \end{matrix} \right\} - \frac{\partial}{\partial x^\lambda} \left\{ \begin{matrix} \mu \\ \varrho\sigma \end{matrix} \right\} + \frac{\partial}{\partial x^\varrho} \left\{ \begin{matrix} \mu \\ \sigma\lambda \end{matrix} \right\}. \quad (2.91)$$

The integral in eqn. (2.90) is a measure of the area in the subsurface bounded by the loop of integration. We recognize this area by analogy with the three-dimensional example in which the surface bounded by a plane loop can be calculated by means of the integral:

$$(\text{Area}) = \tfrac{1}{2} \oint \mathbf{r} \times d\mathbf{r},$$

$$(\text{Area})_{xy} = \tfrac{1}{2} \oint (x \, dy - y \, dx),$$

wherein xy-plane projection of the area has been written in the last expression. Since the area element has the character of a twice-contravariant second-rank tensor, we deduce from the form of eqn. (2.90) that the quantity $R^\mu{}_{\sigma\varrho\lambda}$ is a tensor of fourth rank. The tensor $R^\mu{}_{\sigma\varrho\lambda}$ is Riemann's curvature tensor.

There are $4^4 = 256$ members in the tensor $R^\mu{}_{\sigma\varrho\lambda}$, but these are not all independent. Symmetry relations among the components of the curvature tensor reduce the number of distinct components greatly. By inspection of the defining eqn. (2.91), the tensor is seen to be antisymmetric in its final two indices:

$$R^{\mu}{}_{\sigma\varrho\lambda} = -R^{\mu}{}_{\sigma\lambda\varrho}. \tag{2.92a}$$

Other symmetry relations are conveniently written in terms of the wholly covariant Riemann curvature tensor† $R_{\nu\sigma\varrho\lambda} = g_{\mu\nu}R^{\mu}{}_{\sigma\varrho\lambda}$:

$$R_{\nu\sigma\varrho\lambda} = -R_{\sigma\nu\varrho\lambda}, \tag{2.92b}$$

$$R_{\nu\sigma\varrho\lambda} = R_{\varrho\lambda\nu\sigma}, \tag{2.92c}$$

$$R_{\alpha\alpha\beta\gamma} = 0 = R_{\alpha\beta\gamma\gamma} \quad \text{(no sum).} \tag{2.92d}$$

With these symmetries, the total number of independent components of $R_{\nu\sigma\varrho\lambda}$ is reduced to 20.

An alternative definition of the Riemann curvature tensor can be given in terms of the commutation properties of the process of covariant differentiation. In a coordinate manifold with non-vanishing Riemann curvature, successive covariant differentiations of a tensor with respect to two different independent variables do not commute. We find by direct differentiation that

$$A^{\varrho}{}_{;\tau;\sigma} - A^{\varrho}{}_{;\sigma;\tau} = R^{\varrho}{}_{\beta\tau\sigma}A^{\beta} \tag{2.93}$$

where $R^{\varrho}{}_{\beta\tau\sigma}$ is the Riemann tensor, as defined by eqn. (2.91). Similarly, for successive differentiations of a covariant vector,

$$B_{\varrho;\sigma;\tau} - B_{\varrho;\tau;\sigma} = R^{\beta}{}_{\varrho\tau\sigma}B_{\beta}. \tag{2.94}$$

A further important measure of the curvature of a coordinate space is the second-rank tensor formed by contraction of the Riemann tensor over its first and final indices. This is the tensor

$$R^{\lambda}{}_{\alpha\beta\lambda} = R_{\alpha\beta}. \tag{2.95}$$

The contracted tensor $R_{\alpha\beta}$ is symmetric in its indices, and therefore has only ten independent components. From eqn. (2.91) its full expression is

$$R^{\lambda}{}_{\alpha\beta\lambda} = -\begin{Bmatrix} \lambda \\ \varrho\lambda \end{Bmatrix}\begin{Bmatrix} \varrho \\ \alpha\beta \end{Bmatrix} + \begin{Bmatrix} \lambda \\ \varrho\beta \end{Bmatrix}\begin{Bmatrix} \varrho \\ \alpha\lambda \end{Bmatrix} - \begin{Bmatrix} \lambda \\ \alpha\beta \end{Bmatrix}_{,\lambda} + \begin{Bmatrix} \lambda \\ \alpha\lambda \end{Bmatrix}_{,\beta}. \tag{2.96}$$

† R. Adler, M. Bazin and M. Schiffer, *loc. cit.*

The contracted Christoffel symbol $\left\{ \begin{matrix} \lambda \\ \varrho\lambda \end{matrix} \right\}$ is obtainable from the compact expression (see Appendix II)

$$\left\{ \begin{matrix} \lambda \\ \varrho\lambda \end{matrix} \right\} = \tfrac{1}{2} \frac{\partial \ln (-g)}{\partial x^{\varrho}} \tag{2.97}$$

where g is the determinant formed from the metric tensor. With this expression, the two-index Riemann tensor is given by

$$R_{\alpha\beta} = \left\{ \begin{matrix} \lambda \\ \varrho\beta \end{matrix} \right\} \left\{ \begin{matrix} \varrho \\ \alpha\lambda \end{matrix} \right\} - \tfrac{1}{2} \left\{ \begin{matrix} \varrho \\ \alpha\beta \end{matrix} \right\} [\ln (-g)]_{,\varrho} - \left\{ \begin{matrix} \lambda \\ \alpha\beta \end{matrix} \right\}_{,\lambda} + \tfrac{1}{2} [\ln (-g)]_{,\alpha,\beta}.$$
$$\tag{2.98}$$

A still further contraction of this tensor leads to the Riemann curvature scalar:

$$R = g^{\alpha\beta} R_{\alpha\beta}. \tag{2.99}$$

2.8. The Bianchi Identities and Einstein's Tensor

An identity due to Bianchi results from the form of the Riemann tensor [eqn. (2.91)]. Bianchi's identity is

$$R_{\beta\lambda\mu;\nu} + R_{\beta\nu\lambda;\mu} + R_{\beta\mu\nu;\lambda} = 0. \tag{2.100}$$

Since the covariant derivative of the metric tensor vanishes, the first index in each term above can be lowered by multiplication through eqn. (2.100) by $g_{\alpha\sigma}$ and summing inside the differentiation. We then obtain

$$R_{\alpha\beta\lambda\mu;\nu} + R_{\alpha\beta\nu\lambda;\mu} + R_{\alpha\beta\mu\nu;\lambda} = 0. \tag{2.101}$$

By making use of the symmetry properties of the Riemann tensor [eqn. (2.92)], eqn. (2.101) may be written

$$R_{\alpha\beta\lambda\mu;\nu} - R_{\beta\alpha\nu\lambda;\mu} - R_{\alpha\beta\nu\mu;\lambda} = 0. \tag{2.102}$$

Then multiplying through eqn. (2.102) by $g^{\alpha\mu}g^{\beta\lambda}$ and raising indices, again inside the covariant differentiation operator, we obtain

$$g^{\beta\lambda} R^{\mu}_{\beta\lambda\mu;\nu} - g^{\alpha\mu} R^{\lambda}_{\alpha\nu\lambda;\mu} - g^{\beta\lambda} R^{\mu}_{\beta\nu\mu;\lambda}. \tag{2.103}$$

By use of the contraction operations [eqn. (2.95) and eqn. (2.99)], eqn. (2.103) is put into the form

$$R_{;\nu} - g^{\alpha\mu}R_{\alpha\nu;\mu} - g^{\beta\lambda}R_{\beta\nu;\lambda} = 0. \qquad (2.104)$$

The last two terms of eqns. (2.104) are identical, as is seen by relabeling cyclic indices. Therefore eqn. (2.104) is

$$R_{;\nu} - 2g^{\alpha\mu}R_{\alpha\nu;\mu} = 0. \qquad (2.105)$$

When the index is raised in the second term, eqn. (2.105) becomes

$$R_{;\nu} - 2R^{\mu}{}_{\nu;\mu} = 0. \qquad (2.106)$$

After multiplying the first term by the mixed tensor $g^{\mu}{}_{\nu} = \delta^{\mu}{}_{\nu}$, eqn. (2.106) may be written

$$(R^{\mu}{}_{\nu} - \tfrac{1}{2}g^{\mu}{}_{\nu}R)_{;\mu} = 0. \qquad (2.107)$$

The quantity in parentheses is Einstein's tensor

$$G^{\mu}{}_{\nu} = R^{\mu}{}_{\nu} - \tfrac{1}{2}g^{\mu}{}_{\nu}R, \qquad (2.108)$$

which has zero covariant divergence

$$G^{\mu}{}_{\nu;\mu} = 0. \qquad (2.109)$$

2.9. Calculation of a Curvature: Example

In order to overcome the apparent obscurity surrounding the physical meaning of the Riemann curvature tensor, it may be helpful to illustrate its application in a simple and familiar case. Let us consider the two-dimensional space on the surface of a sphere of radius a. The metric of this space is

$$ds^2 = a^2\,d\theta^2 + a^2\sin^2\theta\,d\varphi^2.$$

The covariant and contravariant metric tensors are

$$g_{\mu\nu} = \begin{pmatrix} a^2 & 0 \\ 0 & a^2\sin^2\theta \end{pmatrix}, \qquad g^{\mu\nu} = \begin{pmatrix} 1/a^2 & 0 \\ 0 & 1/(a^2\sin^2\theta) \end{pmatrix}$$

and $g = a^4\sin^2\theta$.

The Christoffel symbols are given by eqn. (2.62):

$$\left\{ \begin{matrix} \varrho \\ \sigma\tau \end{matrix} \right\} = \tfrac{1}{2} g^{\varrho\alpha}[g_{\sigma\alpha,\tau} + g_{\alpha\tau,\sigma} - g_{\sigma\tau,\alpha}].$$

By direct calculation, we find that the only non-zero symbols are

$$\left\{ \begin{matrix} \theta \\ \phi\phi \end{matrix} \right\} = \tfrac{1}{2} g^{\theta\alpha}[g_{\varphi\alpha,\varphi} + g_{\alpha\varphi,\varphi} - g_{\varphi\varphi,\alpha}];$$

when α takes the values θ and ϕ, this becomes

$$\left\{ \begin{matrix} \theta \\ \phi\phi \end{matrix} \right\} = -\tfrac{1}{2} g^{\theta\theta} g_{\phi\phi,\theta} = -\sin\theta\cos\theta.$$

We also find

$$\left\{ \begin{matrix} \phi \\ \theta\phi \end{matrix} \right\} = \tfrac{1}{2} g^{\varphi\alpha}[g_{\theta\alpha,\varphi} + g_{\varphi\alpha,\theta} - g_{\theta\varphi,\alpha}] = \tfrac{1}{2} g^{\varphi\varphi} g_{\varphi\varphi,\theta} = \cot\theta.$$

To calculate the contracted curvature tensor $R_{\alpha\beta}$, we require $(\ln g)_{,\theta}$, where the positive argument of the logarithm is used:

$$(\ln g)_{,\theta} = 2\cot\theta.$$

Then, using eqn. (2.98) we obtain

$$R_{\theta\theta} = \left\{ \begin{matrix} \lambda \\ \varrho\theta \end{matrix} \right\}\left\{ \begin{matrix} \varrho \\ \theta\lambda \end{matrix} \right\} - \tfrac{1}{2}\left\{ \begin{matrix} \theta \\ \theta\theta \end{matrix} \right\}(\cot\theta) - \left\{ \begin{matrix} \theta \\ \theta\theta \end{matrix} \right\}_{,\theta} + (\cot\theta)_{,\theta}$$

where all derivatives with respect to ϕ have been dropped since no quantity depends on ϕ. When λ and ϱ are summed, there remains

$$R_{\theta\theta} = \left\{ \begin{matrix} \phi \\ \theta\phi \end{matrix} \right\}\left\{ \begin{matrix} \phi \\ \theta\phi \end{matrix} \right\} + (\cot\theta)_{,\theta} = \cot^2\theta - \frac{1}{\sin^2\theta} = -1.$$

Proceeding similarly, we find

$$R_{\varphi\varphi} = -\sin^2\theta.$$

The curvature invariant R is then given by

$$R = g^{\theta\theta}R_{\theta\theta} + g^{\varphi\varphi}R_{\varphi\varphi} = -\frac{2}{a^2}.$$

It is known from the analytical geometry of surfaces that the function R here is equivalent to

$$R = \frac{2}{r_1 r_2}$$

where r_1 and r_2 are the two principal radii of curvature of the surface.[†] On the sphere these radii coincide and are equal to the spherical radius. Thus the Riemann curvature scalar bears a simple relationship to the radius of curvature of the two-dimensional space on the spherical surface.

The existence of curvature in the two-dimensional region of a surface is readily perceived. The distinguishing feature of a surface with curvature is that it is not developable upon the plane without deformation or splitting, this feature being characteristic of the problem of the cartography of the globe. It is more difficult to gain an intuitive notion of the nature of curvature in a three-dimensional region. The flat three-dimensional space of the physical world is so familiar that it is difficult to imagine a space of any other character. Three-dimensional spaces with curvature exist, however. The general (Cartesian coordinate) space in which the curvature is constant was shown by Riemann[‡] to have the metric:

$$ds^2 = \frac{dx^2 + dy^2 + dz^2}{[1 + (K/4)(x^2 + y^2 + z^2)]^2}. \tag{2.110}$$

In eqn. (2.110) K is the isotropic Gaussian curvature of the region. In a region where the Gaussian curvature is isotropic it is everywhere constant (Schur's Theorem). If $K \neq 0$, the space coordinate in eqn. (2.110) can be given an isotropic change of scale, in which (x, y, z) are redefined as $(x/R, y/R, z/R)$. The metric then becomes

$$ds^2 = \frac{R^2(dx^2 + dy^2 + dz^2)}{[1 + (k/4)(x^2 + y^2 + z^2)]^2} \tag{2.111}$$

where $k = KR^2$, and k may take the values ± 1 or zero. The quantity R is not a function of coordinates and will later (Chapter 7) be allowed to depend upon time, in the metric of the cosmological universe. It has the character of the radius of curvature of the three-space in question.

† I. S. Sokolnikoff, *Tensor Analysis*, J. Wiley & Sons, New York, 1952.
‡ L. P. Eisenhart, *Riemannian Geometry*, Princeton University Press, 1949.

It will be of interest to calculate the Riemann tensor curvature components $R_{\alpha\alpha}$ and $R = R^\alpha_\alpha$ for the metric of eqn. (2.111). In the present work we shall write the fully contracted Riemann scalar R [eqn. (2.99)] as R^α_α to distinguish it from the radius scale factor R in this metric. Let us define an abbreviated form of the metric with the definition

$$ds^2 = f\,dx^2 + f\,dy^2 + f\,dz^2 \tag{2.112}$$

where

$$f \equiv R^2[1 + (k/4)(x^2 + y^2 + z^2)]^{-2}. \tag{2.112a}$$

Proceeding in the standard way, we write†

$$\left(\frac{ds}{dq}\right)^2 = f\dot{x}^2 + f\dot{y}^2 + f\dot{z}^2. \tag{2.113}$$

Writing the Euler–Lagrange equations of eqn. (2.113), we may calculate the Christoffel symbols by the method given in Section 3.2, to find

$$\left\{\begin{matrix}1\\11\end{matrix}\right\} = \frac{f_x}{2f}, \quad \left\{\begin{matrix}1\\22\end{matrix}\right\} = -\frac{f_x}{2f}, \quad \left\{\begin{matrix}1\\33\end{matrix}\right\} = -\frac{f_x}{2f},$$

$$\left\{\begin{matrix}1\\12\end{matrix}\right\} = \frac{f_y}{2f}, \quad \left\{\begin{matrix}1\\13\end{matrix}\right\} = \frac{f_z}{2f},$$

$$\left\{\begin{matrix}2\\11\end{matrix}\right\} = -\frac{f_y}{2f}, \quad \left\{\begin{matrix}2\\22\end{matrix}\right\} = \frac{f_y}{2f}, \quad \left\{\begin{matrix}2\\33\end{matrix}\right\} = -\frac{f_y}{2f},$$

$$\left\{\begin{matrix}2\\12\end{matrix}\right\} = \frac{f_x}{2f}, \quad \left\{\begin{matrix}2\\32\end{matrix}\right\} = \frac{f_z}{2f},$$

$$\left\{\begin{matrix}3\\11\end{matrix}\right\} = -\frac{f_z}{2f}, \quad \left\{\begin{matrix}3\\22\end{matrix}\right\} = -\frac{f_z}{2f}, \quad \left\{\begin{matrix}3\\33\end{matrix}\right\} = \frac{f_z}{2f}$$

$$\left\{\begin{matrix}3\\13\end{matrix}\right\} = \frac{f_x}{2f}, \quad \left\{\begin{matrix}3\\23\end{matrix}\right\} = \frac{f_y}{2f}$$

† In eqn. (2.113) the symbol q is employed for the geodesic path parameter, with the dot overhead for d/dq, to avoid confusion with the curvature parameter of eqn. (2.111). Since this example utilizes methods of calculation introduced in the next chapter, it may be omitted until that material is covered. This example of calculation of curvature in a three-dimensional manifold is included in this section for completeness.

where

$$f_x = \frac{\partial f}{\partial x}, \quad f_y = \frac{\partial f}{\partial y}, \quad f_z = \frac{\partial f}{\partial z}.$$

The covariant second-rank Riemann tensor components $R_{\alpha\alpha}$ may be calculated from these Christoffel symbols by use of eqn. (2.98). Doing this, we find R_{11} to be

$$R_{11} = \frac{2f_{xx} + f_{yy} + f_{zz}}{2f} - \frac{4f_x{}^2 + f_y{}^2 + f_z{}^2}{4f^2}.$$

Components R_{22} and R_{33} are similar to R_{11} in form. They may be obtained from R_{11}, above, by rotating subscripts in order x, y, z, successively. The latter fact illustrates an advantage often to be gained from the use of Cartesian coordinates, in carrying out the explicit algebraic calculation of tensor quantities. The symmetry of the three Cartesian space coordinates allows of an economy of calculation by use of procedures such as the above. Alternatively, if component calculations are carried out in full, a check against the occurrence of algebraic errors is available through the necessity for formal agreement among quantities which differ only in the rotation of coordinate indices.

The Riemann curvature invariant $R^\alpha{}_\alpha$ may be calculated from the previous result by use of the relationship:

$$R^\alpha{}_\alpha = R_{\alpha\alpha} g^{\alpha\alpha}$$

where $g^{\alpha\alpha}$ is the contravariant form of the metric tensor:

$$g^{\alpha\beta} = \begin{pmatrix} 1/f & 0 & 0 \\ 0 & 1/f & 0 \\ 0 & 0 & 1/f \end{pmatrix}.$$

Calculation with eqn. (2.98) shows that $R_{\alpha\beta}$ does not have any non-zero off-diagonal components. Thus only terms $R_{\alpha\alpha}$ contribute to $R^\alpha{}_\alpha$. By carrying out the summation

$$R^\alpha{}_\alpha = g^{11} R_{11} + g^{22} R_{22} + g^{33} R_{33},$$

the Riemann curvature invariant is found to be

$$R^\alpha_{\ \alpha} = \frac{1}{f}\left[2\frac{f_{xx} + f_{yy} + f_{zz}}{f} - \frac{3}{2}\frac{f_x^2 + f_y^2 + f_z^2}{f^2}\right];$$

when $f(x, y, z)$ as given in eqn. (2.112a) is substituted above, the result is found to be

$$R^\alpha_{\ \alpha} = -\frac{6k}{f^2}\frac{1}{\left(1 + \dfrac{kr^2}{4}\right)^4}$$

where $r^2 = x^2 + y^2 + z^2$. Therefore,

$$R^\alpha_{\ \alpha} = -\frac{6K}{R^2}. \tag{2.114}$$

In an n-dimensional coordinate space, eqn. (2.114) assumes the form

$$R^\alpha_{\ \alpha} = -\frac{n(n-1)K}{R^2}.$$

Thus the Riemann curvature scalar corresponding to the metric of eqn. (2.111) is constant, and is proportional to the reciprocal square of the "radius of curvature" R of the region.

The coordinates x, y, z used in eqn. (2.111) were defined as dimensionless fractions of the radius R. The coordinate space is said to be spherical, flat, or hyperbolic when the constant k assumes the values $+1$, 0 or -1, respectively. In the hyperbolic case $(k = -1)$, the line element ds becomes singular at coordinate values for which $r^2 = x^2 + y^2 + z^2 = 4$. This case is not interpreted to correspond to any attainable physical situation.

Problems

2.1. In a coordinate frame having spherical spatial coordinates (x^0, x^1, x^2, x^3) $= (t, r, \theta, \phi)$, the components of the metric tensor are $g_{00} = (1 + ar^2)c^2$, $g_{11} = -1/(1 + ar^2)$, $g_{22} = -r^2$, $g_{33} = -r^2\sin^2\theta$, $g_{\mu\nu} = 0(\mu \neq \nu)$. The coordinates are transformed to a new frame having cylindrical spatial coordinates $(\bar{x}^0, \bar{x}^1, \bar{x}^2, \bar{x}^3)$

$= (\bar{t}, \bar{\varrho}, \bar{\alpha}, \bar{z})$. The coordinate-transformation is $\bar{t} = (0.1)t$, $\bar{\varrho} = r \sin \theta, \bar{\alpha} = \phi$, $\bar{z} = r \cos \theta$.

(a) Calculate the transformation matrix $d\bar{x}^\mu/\partial x^\nu$. Solve for $x^\alpha = x^\alpha(\bar{x}^\beta)$, and calculate $\partial x^\alpha/\partial \bar{x}^\beta$.

(b) Verify by direct summation that $(\partial \bar{x}^\mu/\partial x^\nu)(\partial x^\nu/\partial \bar{x}^\lambda) = \delta_{\mu\lambda}$, for any two pairs of indices μ and λ.

(c) Calculate the transformed metric by means of

$$\bar{g}_{\mu\nu}(\bar{x}^\lambda) = g_{\alpha\beta}[x^\varrho(x^\lambda)] \frac{\partial x^\alpha}{\partial \bar{x}^\mu} \frac{\partial x^\beta}{\partial \bar{x}^\nu}.$$

2.2. In a region where the metric tensor is Lorentzian with cylindrical spatial coordinates, $ds^2 = c^2 dt^2 - dr^2 - r^2 d\theta^2 - dz^2$, a twice-covariant second rank tensor $F_{\mu\nu}$ has only the components indicated:†

$$F_{\mu\nu} = \begin{pmatrix} 0 & -f & 0 & 0 \\ f & 0 & 0 & 0 \\ 0 & 0 & 0 & 0 \\ 0 & 0 & 0 & 0 \end{pmatrix}.$$

(a) Calculate the contravariant metric tensor $g^{\alpha\beta}$.

(b) By raising indices, calculate all components of the mixed tensor $F_\mu{}^\nu$.

(c) Calculate the twice-contravariant components $F^{\mu\nu}$.

(d) Using the results of parts (b) and (c), calculate:

$$T^{\alpha\beta} = F_\mu{}^\beta F^{\mu\alpha} + \tfrac{1}{4} F^{\mu\nu} F_{\mu\nu} g^{\alpha\beta}.$$

[Tensor $T^{\alpha\beta}$ is the energy tensor of the electromagnetic field (Chapter 5).]

2.3. Show by direct calculation that the covariant derivative of the metric tensor $g_{\mu\nu}$ vanishes.

2.4. Show that if $T^{\mu\nu}$ is antisymmetric, $T^{\mu\nu}{}_{;\mu;\nu} = 0$.

2.5. In the coordinate manifold of a gravitational field, with coordinates $(x^0, x^1, x^2, x^3) = (t, r, \theta, \phi)$, selected Christoffel symbols are known to be

$$\begin{Bmatrix} 0 \\ 01 \end{Bmatrix} = \tfrac{1}{2}\frac{f'}{1+f}, \quad \begin{Bmatrix} 1 \\ 00 \end{Bmatrix} = \frac{c^2}{2}f'(1+f), \quad \begin{Bmatrix} 1 \\ 11 \end{Bmatrix} = -\tfrac{1}{2}\frac{f'}{1+f}, \text{ and } \begin{Bmatrix} 1 \\ 22 \end{Bmatrix}, \begin{Bmatrix} 1 \\ 33 \end{Bmatrix},$$

$$\begin{Bmatrix} 2 \\ 12 \end{Bmatrix}, \begin{Bmatrix} 2 \\ 33 \end{Bmatrix}, \begin{Bmatrix} 3 \\ 13 \end{Bmatrix}, \begin{Bmatrix} 3 \\ 23 \end{Bmatrix} \text{ are non-zero. Here, } f = -2MG/c^2 r, \text{ where }$$

$G = 6.67 \times 10^{-11}$ m^3/kg sec^2, $c = 3 \times 10^8$ m/sec, and M is the mass of the gravitating object. Let M be the mass of the sun in the following calculation.

† Cf. eqn. (5.15) in Section 5.2.

(a) A radially oriented vector segment (Δx^1) which has unit length at the surface of the sun $(r = r_S)$ is parallel-translated radially outward to the earth's orbit, at r_{SE}. Calculate the shift in coordinate measurement of the length of this vector at the completion of this transport. [Neglect effect of change in (x^1) on its contribution to x^1, and consider only the gravitational field of the sun, neglecting that of the earth.]

(b) Carry out a similar calculation for a time interval (x^0) which measures one second in length at r_S, and is then parallel-translated radially to r_{SE}.

2.6. Verify by direct calculation that

$$A^\varrho_{;\sigma;\tau} - A^\varrho_{;\tau;\sigma} = R^\varrho_{\beta\sigma\tau}A^\beta.$$

Chapter 3

Equations of Motion of Free Particles

IN APPROACHING the task of constructing equations for the laws of physics that are independent of specific coordinate frames, and are thus in conformity with the principle of covariance, we begin with the laws of free-particle motion. In non-relativistic terms these are Newton's laws for point masses in a field-free region. We do not, however, proceed by attempting to generalize a particular statement of Newton's laws in some one coordinate frame, in the way that was used to put a conservation equation into more general form, in eqn. (1.11). We prefer instead to utilize a more general statement of principle as our starting point.

We have already mentioned in Chapter 1 the theorem stating that the length of the world-line path of a free particle between two event-points has an extremal value:

$$\delta \int ds = 0. \tag{3.1}$$

Equation (3.1) is in the form of a statement of the calculus of variations, wherein the value of an integral, in this case the integral $\int ds$, assumes an extremal (maximum or minimum) value under variations of coordinates about the final or "extremal" path of integration.† In the present case, the extremal path is the world line of the particle. A world-line path satisfying eqn. (3.1) is called a geodesic line.

It is not immediately self-evident why a free particle should follow a geodesic path in $(1 + 3)$-coordinate event-space. The statement of eqn. (3.1) is essentially a hypothesis, the geodesic hypothesis. Since we find

† See Appendix III.

that particle motions predicted by this hypothesis are found to be in agreement with observed particle trajectories, the hypothesis is retained as a principle. We can adduce, in an heuristic way, logical justification for the adoption of the geodesic principle, based on our knowledge of classical mechanics and guided by the requirements of the principle of covariance.

The world-line element was originally obtained as an invariant, among the inertial frames of special relativity. We carry over the assumption of invariance for ds^2 into general relativity. Then, since the geodesic principle [eqn. (3.1)] is stated in terms of the invariant ds, it is a covariant equation.

3.1. The Equation of the Geodesic Lines

For a specific justification in support of the assumption of the geodesic principle, we may turn to Hamilton's principle of classical mechanics.† Hamilton's principle states that the integral of the Lagrangian function, $L = T - V$, has an extremal value between any two instants in the motion of a mechanical system (or, along the path of a moving particle) where T and V are the kinetic and potential energies, respectively. For a particle moving under no external forces, $V = 0$, and hence $L = T = mv^2/2$. Hamilton's principle then takes the form

$$\delta \int_{t_1}^{t_2} T \, dt = 0, \qquad (3.2)$$

$$\delta \frac{m}{2} \int_{t_1}^{t_2} (\dot{x}^2 + \dot{y}^2 + \dot{z}^2) \, dt = 0. \qquad (3.3)$$

Utilizing the Lorentz metric

$$ds^2 = c^2 \, dt^2 - dx^2 - dy^2 - dz^2$$

† See, for example, J. B. Marion, *Classical Dynamics*, chap. 9, Academic Press, New York, 1965.

for illustration—which we may do, since special relativity must be obtainable as a special case of general relativity—we may write the integral of eqn. (3.2) in the form

$$\delta \int_{t_1}^{t_2} \frac{(ds^2 - c^2 \, dt^2)}{dt^2} \, dt = 0 \tag{3.4}$$

where constant multipliers and a negative sign have been cancelled. But $\delta \int dt$ vanishes between fixed end points, and therefore eqn. (3.4) is equivalent to

$$\delta \int_{t_1}^{t_2} \left(\frac{ds}{dt}\right)^2 dt = 0. \tag{3.5}$$

We have thus far regarded the time as a parameter of the problem, in the manner of classical mechanics. In our treatment of relativity, however, we wish to retain time as one of the four independent variables of the coordinate space. We shall therefore assume that we can set up a suitable parametric measure of intervals along the world line of a particle. This measure may be thought of as providing a series of marker points on the world line, possibly established by the "ticking" of a natural clock carried with the moving particle. Although we shall not here discuss the details of natural clocks suitable for this purpose, the markers may be thought of as being generated by the oscillations of an emitting atom or molecule, which we assume has a standard and reproducible behavior. Calling this marker parameter k, eqn. (3.5) then becomes

$$\delta \int_{1}^{2} \left(\frac{ds}{dk}\right)^2 dk = 0. \tag{3.6}$$

Equation (3.6) is not, however, in the form of our original statement of the geodesic principle [eqn. (3.1)]:

$$\delta \int ds = 0$$

which is, in fact, equivalent to

$$\delta \int \left[\left(\frac{ds}{dk} \right)^2 \right]^{1/2} dk = 0. \qquad (3.7)$$

We obtain the same result, however, whether we find the extremum condition for the integral with the integrand $(ds/dk)^2$, as in eqn. (3.6), or with the integrand $[(ds/dk)^2]^{1/2}$, as in eqn. (3.7), as long as the sign of ds^2 does not change. The latter change is impossible for a material particle, for which ds^2 is always positive. For a particle, ds^2 can never reach zero, as doing so would require a velocity of the speed of light. Therefore, since it is more convenient for the purposes of calculation to use the geodesic principle written in the form of eqn. (3.6), we shall write

$$\delta \int \left(\frac{ds}{dk} \right)^2 dk = 0.$$

The extremum condition of eqn. (3.6) is satisfied by the solutions of the Euler–Lagrange equation of the calculus of variations:[†]

$$\frac{d}{dk} \left[\frac{\partial}{\partial \dot{x}^\mu} (g_{\mu\nu} \dot{x}^\mu \dot{x}^\nu) \right] = \frac{\partial}{\partial x^\mu} (g_{\mu\nu} \dot{x}^\mu \dot{x}^\nu) \qquad (3.8)$$

where $\dot{x}^\mu = dx^\mu/dk$, and we have used

$$\left(\frac{ds}{dk} \right)^2 = g_{\mu\nu} \dot{x}^\mu \dot{x}^\nu.$$

When the differentiations in eqn. (3.8) are carried out, the result is found by a cumbersome but straightforward calculation[‡] to be

$$\frac{d^2 x^\mu}{dk^2} + \left\{ {\mu \atop \nu\lambda} \right\} \frac{dx^\nu}{dk} \frac{dx^\lambda}{dk} = 0. \qquad (3.9)$$

Equation (3.9), the equation for the geodesic lines, describes the motion of a unit mass point under no external forces of electrical or mechanical nature. The "inertial" forces such as the centrifugal and coriolis forces

[†] Cf. Appendix III.
[‡] See, for example, A. S. Eddington, *Relativity*, p. 59, Cambridge University Press, 1960.

acting on particles moving in curvilinear paths with respect to an inertial frame are introduced by the second term in eqn. (3.9), containing the Christoffel symbol. The inertial forces enter the equations of motion by reason of the form of the metric tensor $g_{\mu\nu}$ which, in turn, determines the Christoffel symbols. Gravitational forces, which are neither "external" nor inertial forces, also enter the equations of motion of mass points through their influence on the metric tensor of the space in which the gravitational fields exist. It is this incorporation of both inertial effects and gravitational forces into the geometry of the coordinate frame that characterizes Einstein's formulation of general relativity theory.

The geodesic equation [eqn. (3.9)] can be derived in an alternative way, based upon an extension of the classical mechanics of inertial frames. This second procedure has its origin in the property that the trajectories of free particles in an inertial frame are straight lines. For these trajectories, the velocity vector of the particle remains constant everywhere along its path. The counterpart of this property, in the four-dimensional Riemannian event-spaces of relativity, is that the geodesic lines are by definition those lines along which the covariant derivative of the geodesic velocity of the particle vanishes, where geodesic velocity is defined: $\dot{x}^{\mu} = dx^{\mu}/dk$. Then

$$0 = \frac{D\dot{x}^{\mu}}{Dx^{\nu}} = \frac{\partial \dot{x}^{\mu}}{\partial x^{\nu}} + \left\{ \begin{matrix} \mu \\ \nu\lambda \end{matrix} \right\} \dot{x}^{\lambda}. \qquad (3.9\,\text{a})$$

Then, multiplying by $\dot{x}^{\nu} = dx^{\nu}/dk$, and using $(\partial \dot{x}^{\mu}/\partial x^{\nu})\,(dx^{\nu}/dk) = d^2x^{\mu}/dk^2$, the result is seen to be equivalent to eqn. (3.9).

Here, the x^{μ} are the generalized coordinates of the system and may be distances or angles, or have arbitrary dimensions.

3.2. The Generation of Christoffel Symbols from the Euler Equations of the Geodesic Theorem

The fact that the Euler–Lagrange variational equations [eqn. (3.8)] must lead to the equations of the geodesic lines [eqn. (3.9)] furnishes us with a powerful tool for deriving the non-vanishing Christoffel symbols of any coordinate manifold for which the metric is known. After writing the variational equations [eqns. (3.8)] the Christoffel symbols may be read off from the result as:

$$\left\{ \begin{matrix} \mu \\ \nu\lambda \end{matrix} \right\} = \text{coefficient of } \dot{x}^\nu \dot{x}^\lambda \text{ in the equation of motion for } x^\mu.$$

It is, of course, necessary to put the variational equations into the standard form of eqns. (3.9) in order to make this identification.

This procedure for generating Christoffel symbols can be demonstrated by means of its use in the following simple examples.

(a) *Linearly accelerated frame*

We *assume* the following transformation to accelerated coordinates:†

$$\bar{t} = t \qquad\qquad \bar{y} = y,$$
$$\bar{x} = \tfrac{1}{2}at^2 + x \qquad \bar{z} = z. \tag{3.10a}$$

This transformation carries the inertial line element

$$d\bar{s}^2 = c^2\, d\bar{t}^2 - d\bar{x}^2 - d\bar{y}^2 - d\bar{z}^2$$

into

$$ds^2 = (c^2 - a^2 t^2)\, dt^2 - 2at\, dt\, dx - dx^2 - dy^2 - dz^2. \tag{3.10b}$$

Division by the factor $(dk)^2$ yields

$$\left(\frac{ds}{dk}\right)^2 = (c^2 - a^2 t^2)\, \dot{t}^2 - 2at\dot{t}\dot{x} - \dot{x}^2 - \dot{y}^2 - \dot{z}^2 \tag{3.10c}$$

where again we use a dot over the coordinate symbols to indicate differentiation with respect to k. Carrying out the procedure called for by eqn. (3.8) yields

$$\frac{d}{dk}[2(c^2 - a^2 t^2)\, \dot{t} - 2at\dot{x}] = -2a^2 t\dot{t}^2 - 2a\dot{t}\dot{x}, \tag{3.10d}$$

$$\frac{d}{dk}[-2at\dot{t} - 2\dot{x}] = 0. \tag{3.10e}$$

---

† The transformation of eqns. (3.10a) constitutes an *ad hoc* assumption of the same nature as was the classical Galilean transformation for uniform relative motion. We do not have any experimental evidence to verify that it would predict the results of observations in accelerated frames. Other more complex transformations have been proposed in the literature. See, for example, H. Lass, *Am. J. Phys.* **31**, 274 (1963); L. Marsh, *ibid.* **33**, 934 (1965).

Completing the Euler–Lagrange eqns. (3.10d) and (3.10e) we find

$$(c^2 - a^2t^2)\,\ddot{t} = a^2t\dot{t}^2 + at\ddot{x}, \qquad (3.10\text{f})$$

$$a\dot{t}^2 + at\ddot{t} + \ddot{x} = 0. \qquad (3.10\text{g})$$

Separating the second derivative terms, we find

$$\ddot{t} = 0, \qquad (3.10\text{h})$$

$$\ddot{x} + a\dot{t}^2 = 0. \qquad (3.10\text{i})$$

Equation (3.10h) indicates that all Christoffel symbols with upper index t vanish: eqn. (3.10i) shows that the single Christoffel symbol of this system is

$$\left\{ \begin{matrix} x \\ tt \end{matrix} \right\} = a. \qquad (3.10\text{j})$$

We can complete the solution of the equations of motion in the following way: eqn. (3.10h) shows that $\dot{t} =$ constant. For convenience, we may assume this constant to be $\dot{t} = 1/c$. The motivation for this assignment lies in the fact that in many cases we may identify the path parameter interval dk with the world-line length element ds itself. The latter may be expressed in terms of the proper time τ of a clock moving with the particle, in the ratio $ds = c\,d\tau$. For slow motion, $d\tau = dt$. With these assumptions, $dt/dk = 1/c$. Then, from eqn. (3.10i)

$$\frac{1}{c^2}\frac{d^2x}{dt^2} = -\frac{a}{c^2}$$

or

$$\frac{d^2x}{dt^2} = -a. \qquad (3.10\text{k})$$

Equation (3.10k) is the classically expected equation of motion for the given transformation [eqn. (3.10a)]. The approximation involved in this solution lies in the identification of coordinate time t with the proper time τ of the particle. A better approximation would be obtained by use of the special-relativistic relation: $dt/d\tau = (1 - V^2/c^2)^{-1/2}$.

(b) *Rotating-disc coordinates*

The rotating coordinate system presents a problem of particular interest, because of the obvious difficulty of relative velocity that increases indefinitely at large radius. Although numerous attempts have been made to find a suitable coordinate transformation from an inertial frame, or to construct a metric for the rotating frame, none of them has yet been verified by experiment.[†] In lieu of a verified coordinate transformation to rotating coordinates, we arbitrarily assume the rotating coordinate equivalent of a Galilean transformation:

$$\bar{t} = t \qquad \bar{\theta} = \theta + \omega t,$$
$$\bar{r} = r \qquad \bar{z} = z. \tag{3.11a}$$

We anticipate that this transformation will provide a reasonably good representation of the rotating frame for low relative velocities, or for small values of $\omega r/c$. When this transformation is applied to the worldline element for an inertial frame in cylindrical coordinates $d\bar{s}^2 = c^2\, d\bar{t}^2 - d\bar{r}^2 - \bar{r}^2\, d\bar{\theta}^2 - d\bar{z}^2$, the result is

$$ds^2 = (c^2 - r^2\omega^2)\, dt^2 - dr^2 - r^2\, d\theta^2 - 2r^2\omega\, d\theta\, dt - dz^2. \tag{3.11b}$$

Proceeding as before, we rewrite this equation as

$$\frac{ds^2}{dk^2} = (c^2 - r^2\omega^2)\, \dot{t}^2 - \dot{r}^2 - r^2\dot{\theta}^2 - 2r^2\omega\dot{\theta}\dot{t} - \dot{z}^2. \tag{3.11c}$$

By the use of eqn. (3.8), the coordinate equations of motion are found to be

$$\frac{d}{dk}[2\dot{t}(c^2 - r^2\omega^2) - 2r^2\omega\dot{\theta}] = 0,$$

$$\frac{d}{dk}(-2\dot{r}) = -2r\omega^2\dot{t}^2 - 2r\dot{\theta}^2 - 4r\omega\dot{\theta}\dot{t},$$

$$\frac{d}{dk}(-2r^2\dot{\theta} - 2r^2\omega\dot{t}) = 0, \tag{3.11d}$$

$$\frac{d}{dk}(-2\dot{z}) = 0.$$

[†] H. A. Atwater, *Nature*, **228**, 272 (1970); **230**, 197 (1971).

Solving for the second-derivative terms, we find

$$\ddot{t} = 0,$$

$$\ddot{r} - r\omega^2\dot{t}^2 - 2r\omega\dot{t}\dot{\theta} - r\dot{\theta}^2 = 0,$$

$$\ddot{\theta} + \frac{2}{r}\dot{r}\dot{\theta} + \frac{2\omega}{r}\dot{r}\dot{t} = 0, \qquad (3.11e)$$

$$\ddot{z} = 0.$$

Finally, we read off from eqns. (3.11e) the Christoffel symbols:

$$\left\{ \begin{matrix} r \\ tt \end{matrix} \right\} = -r\omega^2, \quad \left\{ \begin{matrix} r \\ t\theta \end{matrix} \right\} = -r\omega, \quad \left\{ \begin{matrix} \theta \\ rt \end{matrix} \right\} = \frac{\omega}{r},$$

$$\left\{ \begin{matrix} r \\ \theta\theta \end{matrix} \right\} = -r, \quad \left\{ \begin{matrix} \theta \\ r\theta \end{matrix} \right\} = \frac{1}{r}. \qquad (3.11f)$$

The factors of two in eqns. (3.11e) are omitted, above, since each term containing factors $\dot{x}^\mu\dot{x}^\nu$ stands for the *two* terms with the indices taken in order $\mu\nu$ and $\nu\mu$, because of the symmetry of the $\left\{ \begin{matrix} \lambda \\ \mu\nu \end{matrix} \right\}$ in the two lower indices.

A further computational aid is available in the literature for use in obtaining values of the Christoffel symbols. A tabulation has been made by H. Dingle[†] of all sixty-four Christoffel symbols of the general metric

$$ds^2 = D(dx^0)^2 - A(dx^1)^2 - B(dx^2)^2 - C(dx^3)^2,$$

where A, B, C, D are functions of the four coordinates. This tabulation is useful for metrics containing no off-diagonal components.

Let us now verify that the variational procedure has given the conventional Newtonian equations of motion for a free mass point observed from a coordinate frame which is in rotation. We limit our consideration to radii and angular speeds corresponding to low relative velocities ($\omega^2 r^2 \ll c^2$). With the first of eqns. (3.11e), we again employ the "nonrelativistic" assumption of universal time, namely that $\dot{t} = 1/c$. With

---

† H. Dingle, *Proc. Nat. Acad.* 19, 559 (1933), reprinted in R. Tolman, *Relativity, Thermodynamics, Cosmology*, Oxford University Press, 1934.

this assumption, the r and θ equations of motion in eqns. (3.11 e) become

$$\frac{d^2 r}{dt^2} = r\left(\omega + \frac{d\theta}{dt}\right)^2, \tag{3.11 g}$$

$$r\frac{d^2\theta}{dt^2} = 2\frac{dr}{dt}\left(\omega + \frac{d\theta}{dt}\right). \tag{3.11 h}$$

Equations (3.11 g) and (3.11 h) respectively represent the radial and angular accelerations due to the conventional centrifugal and coriolis forces of a unit point mass in rotational motion at a total angular velocity of $(\omega + d\theta/dt)$ with respect to inertial frames. The final equation of eqns. (3.11 e) indicates the conservation of the z-component of velocity under no external force.

We have limited ourselves in the foregoing to the assumption of low velocities, at which the Newtonian assumption of absolute time is expected to be valid. These are not necessary limitations. Relativistically exact equations of motion, as well as their solutions, are available in principle from the geodesic theorem and the variational theorem. If we should obtain the exact solutions of eqns. (3.10) and (3.11), however, they would represent the actual motions of point masses only in so far as our assumed coordinate transformations, eqns. (3.10a) and (3.11a), "correctly" represent the relationship between the coordinates of the inertial frame and the corresponding non-inertial frames. The problem of obtaining correct coordinate transformations is one of the principal tasks of relativity theory. Correct coordinate transformations are, of course, those which predict results of measurement that are later found to be in agreement with observations actually carried out. Relativity had its inception, as we know, in the attempt to find the correct coordinate transformation relating two inertial frames in relative linear motion. The Michelson–Morley experiment and related experiments proved the correctness of the Lorentz transformation and the incorrectness of the Galilean transformation. Until we have comparable experimental corroboration for other transformation laws, we cannot arbitrarily assume that such transformations as either eqns. (3.10a) or (3.11a) are correct in a relativistically exact sense, although we are assured of their approximate correctness at low velocities by their agreement with the familiar results of classical experiments.

3.3.   Gravitational Potentials and Fields

We have thus far restricted our attention to event-spaces having metrics which were generated by means of coordinate transformation from an inertial frame to a state of non-uniform motion. If we wish to attain a formulation of the static point-mass gravitational field through the metric tensor of $(1 + 3)$-coordinate event-space, we cannot do this by means of a transformation of coordinates to a new state of motion. It is, in fact, an absolute impossibility to find a coordinate transformation relating the coordinates of an inertial frame to those of a space having non-vanishing Riemannian curvature $R^\alpha{}_{\beta\gamma\delta}$. Regions in which there is a gravitational field produced by masses typically have non-zero Riemannian curvature tensor $R^\alpha{}_{\beta\gamma\delta}$. We may show the impossibility of such a transformation in the following way. The Riemann curvature tensor [eqn. (2.91)] is constructed from Christoffel symbols, which vanish when the components of the metric tensor are constants. The latter is true of the rectangular-coordinate inertial frame metric. Therefore all components of the curvature tensor vanish in an inertial frame. Therefore, if we write the explicit expression for the transformation of the curvature tensor from an inertial frame with coordinates x^μ to a frame with coordinates $\bar{x}^\lambda$ having non-vanishing curvature, we have

$$\bar{R}^\alpha{}_{\beta\gamma\varsigma} = \frac{\partial \bar{x}^\alpha}{\partial x^\mu} \frac{\partial x^\varrho}{\partial \bar{x}^\beta} \frac{\partial x^\sigma}{\partial \bar{x}^\gamma} \frac{\partial x^\tau}{\partial \bar{x}^\varsigma} R^\mu{}_{\varrho\sigma\tau}. \tag{3.12}$$

Clearly, no transformation coefficients $\partial x^\lambda / \partial \bar{x}^\nu$ can generate non-zero $\bar{R}^\alpha{}_{\beta\gamma\zeta}$ on the left in eqn. (3.12) from zero values of $R^\mu{}_{\varrho\sigma\tau}$ on the right.

We may take a different approach in seeking the form of a metric which will represent a centrosymmetric gravitational field. We may take advantage of the fact that, even in the gravitational field of the earth, mechanical phenomena proceed in much the same way as they would in an inertial frame, apart from the moderate and recognizable effects of the earth's gravitational force. We therefore anticipate that the metric of a weak gravitational field can be constructed by applying a slight perturbation to the metric tensor of an inertial frame. Let us postulate a metric representing a small fractional perturbation added to an inertial frame metric with spherical spatial coordinates:

$$
g_{\mu\nu} = \begin{pmatrix}
(1 + f_{00})\, c^2 & 0 & 0 & 0 \\
0 & -(1 + f_{11}) & 0 & 0 \\
0 & 0 & -(1 + f_{22})\, r^2 & 0 \\
0 & 0 & 0 & -(1 + f_{33})\, r^2 \sin^2 \theta
\end{pmatrix}. \quad (3.13)
$$

In eqn. (3.13) we assume that the perturbation is spherically symmetric and independent of the time coordinate. That is,

$$
f_{\mu\mu} = f_{\mu\mu}(r),
$$

and as stated above,

$$
|f_{\mu\mu}| \ll 1.
$$

Let us investigate the motion in the radial direction of a test particle of unit mass in the field of this metric. We write the geodesic equation for radial acceleration in the standard form of eqn. (3.9):

$$
\frac{d^2 r}{dk^2} + \left\{ \begin{matrix} r \\ \nu\lambda \end{matrix} \right\} \frac{dx^\nu}{dk} \frac{dx^\lambda}{dk} = 0. \quad (3.14)
$$

Writing d/dk as a dot over the coordinate symbol, and expanding the summation, this equation will have the form:

$$
\ddot{r} + \left\{ \begin{matrix} r \\ tt \end{matrix} \right\} \dot{t}^2 + \left\{ \begin{matrix} r \\ rr \end{matrix} \right\} \dot{r}^2 + \left\{ \begin{matrix} r \\ r\theta \end{matrix} \right\} \dot{r}\dot{\theta} + \cdots + \left\{ \begin{matrix} r \\ \phi\phi \end{matrix} \right\} \dot{\phi}^2 = 0. \quad (3.15)
$$

In keeping with our assumption that the motion is purely radial, we set $\dot{\theta} = 0 = \dot{\phi}$. Equation (3.15) then reduces to

$$
\ddot{r} + \left\{ \begin{matrix} r \\ rr \end{matrix} \right\} \dot{r}^2 + 2 \left\{ \begin{matrix} r \\ rt \end{matrix} \right\} \dot{r}\dot{t} + \left\{ \begin{matrix} r \\ tt \end{matrix} \right\} \dot{t}^2 = 0. \quad (3.16)
$$

The Christoffel symbols needed in this equation are [cf. eqn. (2.62)]:

$$\left\{ \begin{matrix} r \\ rr \end{matrix} \right\} = \tfrac{1}{2} g^{r\alpha}(2g_{r\alpha,r} - g_{rr,\alpha}),$$

$$\left\{ \begin{matrix} r \\ rt \end{matrix} \right\} = \tfrac{1}{2} g^{r\alpha}(g_{r\alpha,t} + g_{t\alpha,r} - g_{rt,\alpha}),$$

$$\left\{ \begin{matrix} r \\ tt \end{matrix} \right\} = \tfrac{1}{2} g^{r\alpha}(2g_{t\alpha,t} - g_{tt,\alpha}).$$

The metric tensor $g_{\mu\nu}$ [eqn. (3.13)] has no off-diagonal components and is assumed to be independent of time. Therefore when the summations over α are carried out, the expressions for the Christoffel symbols reduce to

$$\left\{ \begin{matrix} r \\ rr \end{matrix} \right\} = \tfrac{1}{2} g^{rr} g_{rr,r},$$

$$\left\{ \begin{matrix} r \\ rt \end{matrix} \right\} = 0,$$

$$\left\{ \begin{matrix} r \\ tt \end{matrix} \right\} = -\tfrac{1}{2} g^{rr} g_{tt,r}.$$

The contravariant metric tensor corresponding to eqn. (3.13) is

$$g^{\mu\nu} = \begin{pmatrix} (1 + f_{00})^{-1} c^{-2} & 0 & 0 & 0 \\ 0 & -(1 + f_{11})^{-1} & 0 & 0 \\ 0 & 0 & -(1 + f_{22})^{-1} r^{-2} & 0 \\ 0 & 0 & 0 & -(1 + f_{33})^{-1} r^{-2} \sin^{-2} \theta \end{pmatrix}.$$

$$(3.17)$$

The Christoffel symbols therefore take the form

$$\left\{ \begin{matrix} r \\ rr \end{matrix} \right\} = \tfrac{1}{2} \frac{f_{11,r}}{(1 + f_{11})},$$

$$\left\{ \begin{matrix} r \\ tt \end{matrix} \right\} = \tfrac{1}{2} \frac{c^2 f_{00,r}}{(1 + f_{11})}.$$

$$(3.18)$$

If the denominators above are expanded in powers of the small quantity f_{11}, and products of two or more factors of the $f_{\mu\mu}$ are neglected, eqns. (3.18) become: $\left\{\dfrac{r}{rr}\right\} = (1/2)f_{11,r}; \left\{\dfrac{r}{tt}\right\} = (c^2/2)f_{00,r}$. Substitution of these Christoffel symbols into eqn. (3.16) yields

$$\ddot{r} + \tfrac{1}{2}f_{11,r}\dot{r}^2 + \frac{c^2}{2}f_{00,r}\dot{t}^2 = 0. \tag{3.19}$$

Considering again the case of low particle velocity, for which $dk \simeq c\,dt$, the equation of radial motion becomes:

$$\frac{d^2r}{dt^2} = -\frac{c^2}{2}\left[f_{00,r} + \frac{v_r^2}{c^2}f_{11,r}\right] \tag{3.20}$$

where v_r is the radial velocity of the particle. Since we assume $v_r/c \ll 1$, eqn. (3.20) becomes

$$\frac{d^2r}{dt^2} \simeq -\frac{c^2}{2}f_{00,r}. \tag{3.21}$$

Equation (3.21) is the counterpart of the Newtonian equation for the radial motion of a particle of unit mass moving in a gravitational field of potential V_g:

$$\frac{d^2r}{dt^2} = -(\nabla V_g)_r \tag{3.22}$$

where

$$V_g = -\frac{MG}{r}. \tag{3.23}$$

Here, V_g is the potential due to the mass M, and $G = 6 \cdot 67 \times 10^{-11}$ nt m^2 kg^{-2} is the universal gravitational constant. Comparison of the Newtonian eqn. (3.22) with eqn. (3.21) shows

$$f_{00} = -\frac{2MG}{c^2 r}. \tag{3.24}$$

In the perturbed Lorentz metric [eqn. (3.13)], therefore, we have: $g_{00} = c^2(1 + f_{00})$. Thus we see that the metric

$$ds^2 = c^2\left(1 - \frac{2MG}{c^2 r}\right)dt^2 - d\sigma^2, \tag{3.25}$$

where $d\sigma^2$ is the squared three-space line element, exhibits a static, spherically symmetric gravitational field.

We have deduced in the foregoing calculation that the perturbation f_{00} has the character of a gravitational potential. We shall find in further work that the perturbed Lorentz metric

$$g_{\mu\nu} = g^{(0)}{}_{\mu\nu \text{ Lorentz}} + \gamma_{\mu\nu \text{ perturbation}}, \qquad (3.26)$$

together with the linearized theory in which we retain only first-order terms in the $\gamma_{\mu\nu}$ in calculation, constitutes a highly useful model for the investigation of weak gravitational fields. In such investigations the $\gamma_{\mu\nu}$ are regarded as the gravitational potentials of gravitational fields of more general form than in the simple case investigated above.

3.4. Differential Equations of the Metric Tensor in Empty Space

The methods we have used heretofore for finding the metric tensors of Riemannian coordinate spaces, of coordinate transformation, or of the use of a perturbed inertial metric are not sufficiently powerful or sufficiently general to serve us in the continued investigation of the description of physics in $(1 + 3)$-coordinate event-spaces. We now require the differential equation which is satisfied by the metric tensor $g_{\mu\nu}$. If we can solve this differential equation subject to given boundary or subsidiary conditions, we can then find the metric tensor for arbitrary coordinate spaces.

In the preceding section we found that the components of the tensor $g_{\mu\nu}$ have the character of gravitational potentials. From our experience with the classical Newtonian gravitational field we know that its scalar gravitational potential V_g satisfies Laplace's equation in empty space:

$$\nabla^2 V_g = 0.$$

In the presence of a distribution of matter of volume density ϱ, the potential satisfies Poisson's equation:

$$\nabla^2 V_g = 4\pi G\rho.$$

The metric tensor $g_{\mu\nu}$ is a symmetrical second-rank tensor having ten independent components. We anticipate therefore that the $g_{\mu\nu}$ will be the solutions not of a single differential equation, but rather of a set of ten differential equations. In seeking the differential equations to be satisfied by the $g_{\mu\nu}$, Einstein turned to the Riemannian curvature tensor. The simplest equation which can be formed from this tensor

$$R^{\mu}_{\ \alpha\beta\gamma} = 0$$

is too restrictive, being satisfied only by the metric of "flat" inertial spaces. A more useful equation can be formed by use of the contracted Riemann tensor $R_{\alpha\beta} = R^{\mu}_{\ \alpha\beta\mu}$ [eqn. (2.98)]. The equation

$$R_{\alpha\beta} = 0 \qquad (3.27)$$

is satisfied by the metrics of regions wherein a gravitational field exists in empty space. The contracted curvature tensor $R_{\alpha\beta}$ is symmetric in its subscripts, and therefore eqn. (3.27) represents ten independent equations, and will be sufficient to determine the $g_{\mu\nu}$ in empty space.

We may verify that the field equation $R_{\alpha\beta} = 0$ leads to Laplace's equation for the gravitational potential, using the example of the simple metric investigated in the preceding section [eqn. (3.25)]. Writing the spatial part of the metric in rectangular coordinates, we have

$$ds^2 = (1 + f_{00}) c^2 \, dt^2 - dx^2 - dy^2 - dz^2. \qquad (3.28)$$

In the form given in eqn. (2.96), the Riemann tensor is

$$R_{\alpha\beta} = - \left\{ {\lambda \atop \varrho\lambda} \right\} \left\{ {\varrho \atop \alpha\beta} \right\} + \left\{ {\lambda \atop \varrho\beta} \right\} \left\{ {\varrho \atop \alpha\lambda} \right\} - \left\{ {\lambda \atop \alpha\beta} \right\}_{,\lambda} + \left\{ {\lambda \atop \alpha\lambda} \right\}_{,\beta}. \qquad (3.29)$$

We recall that the Christoffel symbols are given by the expression

$$\left\{ {\lambda \atop \varrho\alpha} \right\} = \tfrac{1}{2} g^{\lambda\sigma}(g_{\varrho\sigma,\alpha} + g_{\alpha\sigma,\varrho} - g_{\varrho\alpha,\sigma}). \qquad (3.30)$$

Because of the differentiations acting upon the $g_{\mu\nu}$ in the parenthesis on the right in eqn. (3.30) this parenthesis is at most of the order of $f_{00,\lambda}$ in magnitude. The contravariant metric tensor is

$$g^{\lambda\sigma} = \begin{pmatrix} c^{-2}(1+f_{00})^{-1} & 0 & 0 & 0 \\ 0 & -1 & 0 & 0 \\ 0 & 0 & -1 & 0 \\ 0 & 0 & 0 & -1 \end{pmatrix}. \tag{3.30a}$$

Since we assume that $f_{00,\lambda}$ is of the same order of smallness compared with unity as is f_{00}, we deduce from eqns. (3.28) and (3.30a) that the magnitudes of the Christoffel symbols [eqn. (3.30)] are at most of the order of f_{00}. Therefore we neglect the terms containing products of Christoffel symbols in eqn. (3.29). The field equation then reduces to the form

$$R_{\alpha\beta} = -\left\{ \begin{matrix} \lambda \\ \alpha\beta \end{matrix} \right\}_{,\lambda} + \left\{ \begin{matrix} \lambda \\ \alpha\lambda \end{matrix} \right\}_{,\beta} = 0. \tag{3.31}$$

In Appendix II the second term above is shown to have a simpler form, leading to

$$R_{\alpha\beta} = -\left\{ \begin{matrix} \lambda \\ \alpha\beta \end{matrix} \right\}_{,\lambda} + \tfrac{1}{2}[\ln(-g)]_{,\alpha,\beta} = 0. \tag{3.32}$$

In the metric of eqn. (3.28), $g = -(1 + f_{00})c^2$. A Taylor expansion of $\ln(-g)$ to first order in f_{00} yields

$$\ln(-g) = \ln c^2 + f_{00}. \tag{3.33}$$

Using eqns. (3.33) and (3.30), eqn. (3.32) may be written

$$R_{\alpha\beta} = -\tfrac{1}{2}[g^{\lambda\sigma}(g_{\alpha\sigma,\beta} + g_{\beta\sigma,\alpha} - g_{\alpha\beta,\sigma})]_{,\lambda} + \tfrac{1}{2}f_{00,\alpha,\beta}. \tag{3.34}$$

Thus the component R_{00} is

$$R_{00} = -\tfrac{1}{2}[g^{\lambda\sigma}(2g_{0\sigma,0} - g_{00,\sigma})]_{,\lambda} + \tfrac{1}{2}f_{00,0,0}. \tag{3.35}$$

By our assumption g_{00} is independent of time. All time differentials therefore vanish, and eqn. (3.35) becomes

$$R_{00} = \tfrac{1}{2}[g^{ij}g_{00,j}]_{,i} \quad (i,j = 1,2,3). \tag{3.36}$$

Since g^{ij} is diagonal, [eqn. (3.30a)], summation over j in eqn. (3.36) yields

$$R_{00} = \tfrac{1}{2} \sum_i g_{00,i,i} = -\frac{c^2}{2} \nabla^2 f_{00} = 0 \qquad (3.37)$$

or

$$\nabla^2 f_{00} = 0.$$

Calculation of R_{ii} by similar procedures for $i = 1, 2, 3$ yields

$$R_{ii} = \tfrac{1}{2} f_{00,i,i} \qquad (i = 1, 2, 3) \text{ (no sum)}.$$

Then, the sum of the equations $R_{ii} = 0$ leads again to Laplace's equation. Thus we have verified the correspondence of the field equation

$$R_{\alpha\beta} = 0$$

with the Newtonian gravitational field equation, when the perturbation f_{00} is regarded as a gravitational potential.

In the weak-field theory we have used to obtain this verification, a gravitational potential which is formed as the sum of contributions of the fields produced by separate masses is still a solution of the field equation, just as is true in the non-relativistic Newtonian theory. In Section 3.3 we found a metric for the gravitational field of a point mass M

$$ds^2 = c^2 \left(1 - \frac{2MG}{c^2 r} \right) dt^2 - d\sigma^2 \qquad (3.38)$$

where $d\sigma^2$ is the Euclidean three-space metric.

By extension of this result, the metric established by a pair of masses M_1 and M_2 at distances r_1 and r_2 from the point where ds^2 is being calculated would be

$$ds^2 = c^2 \left(1 - \frac{2M_1 G}{c^2 r_1} - \frac{2M_2 G}{c^2 r_2} \right) dt^2 - d\sigma^2. \qquad (3.39)$$

Carrying the analogy further, the metric due to a continuous distribution of matter characterized by a volume density of mass ϱ would be written

$$ds^2 = c^2 \left(1 - \frac{2G}{c^2} \int \frac{\varrho \, dV'}{r'} \right) dt^2 - d\sigma^2 \qquad (3.40)$$

where r' is measured from the volume element dV' to the position of ds^2.

It must be emphasized, however, that the approximate metrics given by eqns. (3.39) and (3.40) are not solutions of the exact field equation [eqn. (3.29)]. The latter contains products of two or more $g_{\mu\nu}$ and their derivatives, and consequently a sum of two different $g_{\mu\nu}$ which are separately solutions of the equation is itself no longer a solution. An exact metric for a given assumed field symmetry can be found by solving the field equations (3.29) exactly. This was first done by Schwarzschild in 1916 for the centrosymmetric, static field. Schwarzschild's solution is discussed in Chapter 4.

3.5. Field Equations in the Presence of Matter

We have obtained in Chapter 2 the divergenceless tensor [eqn. (2.108)] constructed from Riemann's curvature tensor:

$$G_{\alpha\beta} = R_{\alpha\beta} - \tfrac{1}{2}g_{\alpha\beta}R;$$

since the curvature scalar R is constructed from $R_{\alpha\beta}$, the vanishing of $R_{\alpha\beta}$ ensures the vanishing of R. Consequently, the equations

$$R_{\alpha\beta} = 0$$

and

$$G_{\alpha\beta} = 0 \tag{3.41}$$

are equivalently valid as field equations for the metric tensor $g_{\mu\nu}$ in empty space.

We now wish to proceed to find the differential equations to be satisfied by the metric tensor in a region occupied by a non-zero density of mass or energy. Knowledge of the metric of matter-filled regions is of course necessary in studies such as those of astrophysics wherein it is desired to know the gravitational forces within the masses of stars, or, in the construction of metrics for models of the universe in which the matter in the galaxies is typically assumed to be equivalent to a uniform distribution of dust spread throughout the universe. We seek, therefore, the relativistic counterpart of the classical Poisson equation for the gravitational potential:

$$\nabla^2 V_G = -4\pi\varrho G.$$

In its relativistic form, the left side of Poisson's equation can be represented by the tensor $G_{\alpha\beta}$. On the right, therefore, we must have a second-rank tensor representing the matter and energy density in the given region. Let us designate this tensor as $T_{\alpha\beta}$. That is, we postulate an equation of the form

$$G_{\alpha\beta} = AT_{\alpha\beta} \qquad (3.42)$$

where A is a constant to be determined. Because of the fact that the tensor $G_{\alpha\beta}$ is divergenceless, the matter tensor $T_{\alpha\beta}$ must also have a vanishing covariant divergence. Anticipating later requirements, we define a tentative form for the matter tensor of inert matter

$$T^{\alpha\beta} = \varrho_0 \frac{dx^\alpha}{ds} \frac{dx^\beta}{ds} \qquad (3.43)$$

where ϱ_0 is the volume density of mass, as measured in the rest frame of the particles making up the matter. Here, ds is an element of the world lines of the particles, and the (dx^μ/ds) are the quantities we have called world-line velocities. Equation (3.43) defines the contravariant components of the matter tensor.

We may evaluate the constant of proportionality A by consideration of an example in which we assume a uniform continuous distribution of matter in the form of a stationary dust cloud to exist over a large region with spherical symmetry. In any neighborhood within this region the metric is isotropic and differs only slightly from a Lorentz metric. We may utilize the weak-field gravitational metric calculated in the last section. Equation (3.42) may be put into a form suitable for this calculation. With $G_{\alpha\beta}$ written in full, the equation is

$$R_{\alpha\beta} - \tfrac{1}{2} g_{\alpha\beta} R = AT_{\alpha\beta}. \qquad (3.44)$$

Multiplication by $g^{\alpha\gamma}$ yields

$$g^{\alpha\gamma} R_{\alpha\beta} - \tfrac{1}{2} g^{\alpha\gamma} g_{\alpha\beta} R = A g^{\alpha\gamma} T_{\alpha\beta}. \qquad (3.45)$$

After summation over index α, eqn. (3.45) becomes

$$R^\gamma_\beta - \tfrac{1}{2} \delta^\gamma_\beta R = AT^\gamma_\beta \qquad (3.46)$$

where $\delta^\gamma_\beta = g^\gamma_\beta$ is the fundamental unit tensor. Setting γ equal to β and contraction yields

$$R - \tfrac{4}{2} R = AT \tag{3.47}$$

where the trace of the fundamental tensor is equal to four, and $T = T^{\beta}_{\beta}$ is defined as the matter scalar. Consequently we have

$$R = - AT. \tag{3.48}$$

With this result, eqn. (3.44) becomes

$$R_{\alpha\beta} = A(T_{\alpha\beta} - \tfrac{1}{2} g_{\alpha\beta} T). \tag{3.49}$$

Equation (3.49) is an alternate and equivalent form of eqn. (3.44). We utilize this equation to evaluate the as yet undetermined constant A by requiring that it reduce to the classical Poisson equation. It will be sufficient to construct the (0,0) component of eqn. (3.49). Since we assume a stationary dust cloud, eqn. (3.43) shows that the only non-zero member of $T^{\alpha\beta}$ is T^{00}, which has the value $T^{00} = \varrho_0/c^2$, since $dt/ds = 1/c$. For this case, $T_{00} = (g_{00})^2 T^{00} = c^2 \rho_0$, and also $T = g_{00} T^{00} = \rho_0$, where we neglect the product of the small quantities ρ_0 and f_{00}. We thus obtain from eqn. (3.49):

$$-\frac{c^2}{2} \nabla^2 f_{00} = A(c^2 \varrho_0 - \tfrac{1}{2} c^2 \varrho_0),$$

$$\nabla^2 f_{00} = -A\varrho_0 \tag{3.50}$$

where eqn. (3.37) has been employed for R_{00}. We also found in the preceding section that for the static, spherically symmetric weak gravitational field, $f_{00} = - 2V_g/c^2$, where V_g is the Newtonian gravitational potential. We may apply this result in the present case, whereupon eqn. (3.50) becomes:

$$\nabla^2 V_g = \frac{c^2 A}{2} \varrho_0. \tag{3.51}$$

Equation (3.51) is identical with Poisson's equation $\nabla^2 V_g = - 4\pi G \varrho_0$ if we set

$$A = - \frac{8\pi G}{c^2}.$$

In summary, we obtain for the field equations for the metric $g_{\mu\nu}$ in the presence of matter:

$$R^{\alpha\beta} - \tfrac{1}{2}g^{\alpha\beta}R = -\frac{8\pi G}{c^2}T^{\alpha\beta} \tag{3.52}$$

where $T^{\alpha\beta}$ has the form given in eqn. (3.43), for ponderable matter.

3.6. The Matter–Energy Tensor

We have defined the energy tensor of a distribution of non-interacting mass particles as

$$T^{\alpha\beta} = \varrho_0 \frac{dx^\alpha}{ds}\frac{dx^\beta}{ds}.$$

In a Lorentz frame having coordinates $x^\mu = (t, x, y, z)$, the metric is

$$ds^2 = c^2\,dt^2 - dx^2 - dy^2 - dz^2 = c^2\,dt^2(1 - V^2/c^2).$$

In the inertial frame therefore we write

$$(dt/ds)^2 = (1/c^2)\,\gamma^2$$

where $\gamma = (1 - V^2/c^2)^{-1/2}$.

Therefore, in a Lorentz manifold the components of $T^{\mu\nu}$ are

$$T^{\mu\nu} = \frac{\varrho_0\gamma^2}{c^2}\begin{pmatrix} 1 & \dot{x} & \dot{y} & \dot{z} \\ \dot{x} & \dot{x}^2 & \dot{x}\dot{y} & \dot{x}\dot{z} \\ \dot{y} & \dot{y}\dot{x} & \dot{y}^2 & \dot{y}\dot{z} \\ \dot{z} & \dot{z}\dot{x} & \dot{z}\dot{y} & \dot{z}^2 \end{pmatrix} \tag{3.53}$$

where a dot over a coordinate symbol here indicates differentiation with respect to the *time* coordinate, t. The factor $\varrho_0\gamma^2$ in eqn. (3.28) may be justified with reference to the results of special relativity by the statement that one factor of γ corresponds to the relativistic mass increase of the particles at velocity V.† The second factor of γ may be regarded as being due to the Lorentz–Fitzgerald contraction of volume elements in the direction of V, which increases the effective volume density of particles

† See Chapter 9.

as seen in the surrounding manifold. In the latter frame we define, for brevity,

$$\varrho = \varrho_0 \gamma^2. \tag{3.54}$$

The mass–energy tensor must have vanishing covariant divergence, or

$$T^{\mu\nu}{}_{;\nu} = 0. \tag{3.55}$$

In the rectangular Lorentz frame in which we have written $T^{\mu\nu}$ in eqn. (3.53), the Christoffel symbols vanish, and the covariant derivative becomes the ordinary partial derivative

$$T^{\mu\nu}{}_{,\nu} = 0. \tag{3.56}$$

With eqn. (3.56) the calculation of the divergence of $T^{\mu\nu}$, eqn. (3.53), assuming $(V^2/c^2) \ll 1$, yields

$$c^2 T^{0\nu}{}_{,\nu} = \frac{\partial \varrho}{\partial t} + \frac{\partial}{\partial x}(\varrho v_x) + \frac{\partial}{\partial y}(\varrho v_y) + \frac{\partial}{\partial z}(\varrho v_z) = 0, \tag{3.57a}$$

$$c^2 T^{1\nu}{}_{,\nu} = \frac{\partial}{\partial t}(\varrho v_x) + \frac{\partial}{\partial x}(\varrho v_x{}^2) + \frac{\partial}{\partial y}(\varrho v_x v_y) + \frac{\partial}{\partial z}(\varrho v_x v_z) = 0 \tag{3.57b}$$

where only the first two of the four divergence equations have been written, the remainder being similar to (3.57b) for v_y and v_z. Equation (3.57a) is the continuity equation of fluid flow, which has the vector form:

$$\nabla \cdot (\varrho v) = -\dot{\varrho}. \tag{3.58}$$

After carrying out the differentiations in eqn. (3.57b) this equation may be expressed in the form

$$\varrho \frac{\partial v_x}{\partial t} + v \cdot \nabla(\varrho v_x) = 0 \tag{3.59}$$

which is the x-component equation of motion of a fluid under no external forces (Euler's equation). The remaining component equations of fluid motion are provided by the remaining divergence equations from eqn. (3.55).

The vanishing of the covariant divergence of $T^{\mu\nu}$ is thus verified by the requirement of correspondence with the known non-relativistic equations of fluid mechanics. The condition $T^{\mu\nu}{}_{;\nu} = 0$ is therefore a phenomenological description of the behavior of matter, expressing the conservation laws for mass, energy and momentum.

The restriction of non-interaction among the particles of the fluid may be partially lifted by the addition of a term to $T^{\mu\nu}$ proportional to fluid pressure. This must be done in such a way that the resulting matter–energy tensor is covariant, and remains divergenceless. A form which satisfies these requirements is

$$T^{\mu\nu} = \left(\varrho_0 + \frac{p}{c^2}\right)\frac{dx^\mu}{ds}\frac{dx^\nu}{ds} - \frac{p}{c^2}g^{\mu\nu} \tag{3.60}$$

where p is the pressure measured in the proper frame of the moving fluid, and $g^{\mu\nu}$ is the contravariant metric tensor.

An energy density is associated with the presence of electric and magnetic fields in free space: $w_E = \varepsilon_0 E^2/2$ and $w_M = B^2/2\mu_0$, respectively. Charged free particles can exchange energy with the fields, their forces of interaction with the fields being given, in vector form, by the Lorentz force formula:

$$\mathscr{F} = qE + qv \times B.$$

We expect, moreover, that the equivalent mass corresponding to the energy content of the electromagnetic field should give rise to a gravitational field.† The energy contribution of the electromagnetic field can be incorporated into the mass–energy tensor by the addition of a suitable divergence-free tensor to the $T^{\mu\nu}$ of the matter field discussed above:

$$T^{\mu\nu} = \varrho_0\frac{dx^\mu}{ds}\frac{dx^\nu}{ds} + \varepsilon_0(F^{\mu\sigma}F_\sigma{}^\nu + \tfrac{1}{4}g^{\mu\nu}F^{\varkappa\lambda}F_{\varkappa\lambda}). \tag{3.61}$$

In eqn. (3.61) the zero-pressure form of the matter tensor has been used for simplicity, and $F^{\mu\nu}$ and $F^\mu{}_\nu$ are contravariant and mixed tensor forms of the electromagnetic field tensor $F_{\mu\nu}$ (see Chapter 5). With this modi-

† The metric of the Coulomb field was first calculated by H. Reissner, *Ann. Physik* **50**, 106 (1916) (see Chapter 4).

fication, $T^{\mu\nu}$ remains divergenceless, the components $T^{\mu\nu}{}_{;\nu} = 0$ of the divergence equation expressing the equation of motion of the mass particles of the matter distribution under the Lorentz electromagnetic forces cited above.

3.7. Deviation of Geodesic Lines in a Space with Curvature

We have defined the geodesic lines of a Riemannian coordinate manifold as those lines whose length $\int ds = \int (g_{\mu\nu} \, dx^\mu \, dx^\nu)^{1/2}$ has an extremal value. In flat spaces, or spaces of zero curvature, the geodesic lines are straight lines. In both flat and curved spaces, the geodesic lines are the paths, i.e. event-histories, of free mass particles. We have employed in Section 3.1 the constancy of the geodesic-velocity vector $\dot{x}^\mu = \partial x^\mu / \partial k$ under covariant differentiation as a criterion of geodesic-line character:

$$\frac{D\dot{x}^\mu}{Dx^\sigma} = \frac{\partial \dot{x}^\mu}{\partial x^\sigma} + \left\{ \begin{matrix} \mu \\ \sigma\nu \end{matrix} \right\} \dot{x}^\nu = 0.$$

Therefore,

$$\frac{\partial \dot{x}^\mu}{\partial x^\sigma} = - \left\{ \begin{matrix} \mu \\ \sigma\nu \end{matrix} \right\} \dot{x}^\nu \tag{3.62}$$

where the parameter k is a measure of position along the geodesic lines. The components $\dot{x}^\nu$ may be regarded as the components of the tangent vectors of the geodesics. Let us now consider the existence of a densely distributed one-parameter family of geodesic lines, passing through the space region of interest. Let the various members of the family be distinguished by a parameter h, which assumes a unique value on each of the geodesic lines. We now define a vector y^ν "normal" to the geodesic lines by means of the relation

$$y^\nu = \frac{\partial x^\nu}{\partial h}. \tag{3.63}$$

The vectors y^ν are a measure of the separation between neighboring geodesics, at constant value of the parameter k which measures distance along all of the geodesics. Since each geodesic line is described by the two parameters k and h, $\dot{x}^\nu = \dot{x}^\nu(k, h)$ and $y^\nu = y^\nu(k, h)$. Therefore, because of the interchangeability of the order of partial differentiation,

$$\frac{\partial^2 x^\nu}{\partial k\, \partial h} = \frac{\partial \dot{x}^\nu}{\partial h} = \frac{\partial y^\nu}{\partial k}. \tag{3.64}$$

We now calculate Dy^ν/Dk, the covariant geodesic-path derivative of y^ν, in the manner employed in eqn. (3.62):

$$\frac{Dy^\nu}{Dk} = \frac{\partial y^\nu}{\partial k} + \left\{ \begin{matrix} \nu \\ \mu\lambda \end{matrix} \right\} y^\mu \frac{\partial x^\lambda}{\partial k} \tag{3.65}$$

$$= \frac{\partial \dot{x}^\nu}{\partial h} + \left\{ \begin{matrix} \nu \\ \mu\lambda \end{matrix} \right\} y^\mu \dot{x}^\lambda. \tag{3.66}$$

The derivative [eqn. (3.66)] is a contravariant vector. We perform a second geodesic-path derivative upon it:

$$\frac{D^2 y^\nu}{Dk^2} = \frac{\partial}{\partial k} \left(\frac{Dy^\nu}{Dk} \right) + \left\{ \begin{matrix} \nu \\ \varrho\sigma \end{matrix} \right\} \dot{x}^\varrho \left(\frac{Dy^\sigma}{Dk} \right). \tag{3.67}$$

Substituting for Dy^ν/Dk from eqn. (3.66), and eliminating the term $\partial \dot{x}^\nu/\partial k = \partial^2 x^\nu/\partial k^2$ by the use of eqn. (3.9), leads to†

$$\frac{D^2 y^\nu}{Dk^2} = R^\nu{}_{\alpha\beta\gamma} y^\gamma \dot{x}^\alpha \dot{x}^\beta \tag{3.68}$$

where eqn. (2.91) for the Riemann tensor has been used. Equation (3.68) is a second-order differential equation for the deviation y^ν, between adjacent geodesic lines passing through a medium with non-zero Riemannian curvature. It is this deviation which is responsible for the apparent "tidal" gravitational forces experienced by a rigid framework in free fall in a point-mass gravitational field and, as we shall see, for the forces carried by gravitational waves.

† Cf. R. Adler, M. Bazin and M. Schiffer, *Introduction to General Relativity*, p. 161, McGraw-Hill, New York, 1969.

3.8. Tangent Flat Spaces

We shall be largely interested in the properties of spaces having curvature, in our continued study of relativity. In the early development of relativity, much use was made of the concept of the equivalence principle, outlined at the end of Chapter 1, in expressing the kinematic character of the gravitational field, but this concept is necessarily of limited utility.

The force field observed by an observer in a uniformly accelerating coordinate frame is everywhere constant, i.e. is independent of position within his reference frame Fig. 3.1(a). The force field seen by an observer

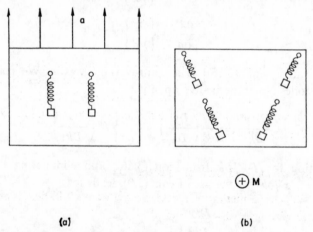

(a)   (b)

FIG. 3.1. (a) Force field of uniform acceleration. (b) Gravitational field of a mass point M.

at rest in the gravitational field of a mass point M varies in direction and magnitude throughout any finite region Fig. 3.1(b). The increments of force observed with change of position are called tidal forces of gravity. The distribution of forces appearing in the "laboratory" of Fig. 3.1(b) could not be produced by the acceleration, in the ordinary sense, of any rigid coordinate frame of finite extent.

If the necessary distribution of masses could be suitably contrived so as to produce parallel lines of gravitational field over a limited region, an observer in that region could not decide by means of any experiment whether he was in fact in the gravitational field of massive objects, or in a coordinate space undergoing uniform acceleration with respect to the inertial frame of the fixed stars. The philosopher E. Mach enunciated the hypothesis that all inertial forces were ultimately due to effects produced by non-constant motions relative to the mass distributions of the universe (Mach's Principle), but little quantitative use has been made of this idea.

If the laboratory space in Fig. 3.1(b) is allowed to move in free fall in the gravitational field of point M, the "downward" components of force, directed toward the center of mass, will vanish. Mass points situated on the center line of the figure in free fall with the laboratory will seem to be under no forces, with respect to the laboratory frame.† Mass points to the right and left will move toward the center of figure under the influence of the tidal forces of gravity, their velocities of inward motion being greater in proportion to their distances from the center line of fall. The region in the immediate vicinity of the line of fall of the laboratory will be observed to have the properties of an inertial frame, with respect to laboratory-fixed coordinates.

The concept that in the neighborhood of *any* space–time point a "flat" or inertial coordinate space can be defined is given concrete expression by the definition of geodesic coordinates. Geodesic coordinates are a local inertial frame of reference defined over a restricted region in the immediate vicinity of a given point in a general Riemannian coordinate manifold. That such a local frame is definable can be made plausible in the following way. Assume that at a point 0 the coordinates $\bar{x}^\mu$ of the Riemannian manifold are related to the coordinates x^α of the local frame of inertia by the linear orthogonal transformation

$$dx^\alpha = p^\alpha{}_\beta d\bar{x}^\beta \tag{3.69}$$

where the $p^\alpha{}_\beta$ are constants. We further assume the local inertial frame to be defined such that $p^\beta{}_\alpha = p^\alpha{}_\beta$. Thus the matrix of coefficients $p^\alpha{}_\beta$ is symmetric, and there are $4(4 + 1)/2 = 10$ independent coefficients $p^\alpha{}_\beta$ in four-dimensional space. Substitution from eqn. (3.69) into eqn. (2.24) for the metric tensor yields

$$\bar{g}_{\mu\nu(0)} = -\sum_\alpha p^\alpha{}_\mu p^\alpha{}_\nu. \tag{3.70}$$

† The extent of the vertical, or radial, domain is assumed small.

The metric $g_{\mu\nu}(0)$ is calculated at point 0, where the coordinate matching is being accomplished. Because of the symmetry of the $\bar{g}_{\mu\nu}$ there are ten independent equations (3.70). These ten equations may be solved in principle for the unknown coefficients $p^\alpha{}_\beta$, demonstrating that the coordinate transformation can be determined at point 0.

A more useful expression is the transformation to a local frame of inertia which is valid over a small neighborhood about 0. The transformation law may be constructed as an expansion in powers of $(\bar{x}^\nu - \bar{x}^\nu(0))$:

$$x^\lambda = (\bar{x}^\nu - \bar{x}^\nu(0))\frac{\partial x^\lambda}{\partial \bar{x}^\nu} + \frac{1}{2!}\frac{\partial^2 x^\lambda}{\partial \bar{x}^\nu \partial \bar{x}^\mu}(\bar{x}^\nu - \bar{x}^\nu(0))(\bar{x}^\mu - \bar{x}^\mu(0)). \quad (3.71)$$

The origin of geodesic coordinates is taken at point 0, so that $x^\lambda(0) = 0$.

In a Riemannian coordinate space, it is always possible to find a system of coordinates in which all $\partial g_{\alpha\beta}/\partial x^\gamma$ vanish at a given point. We define the geodesic coordinate frame to have this property, at the matching point 0. Consequently the Christoffel symbols will vanish in the geodesic coordinates at this point. In simplest terms, the geodesic frame has Cartesian character at 0. A point in which the Christoffel symbols vanish is called a pole of the coordinate frame.

At the point of tangency of the geodesic frame with the embedding Riemannian frame, we further require

$$\left.\frac{\partial x^\lambda}{\partial \bar{x}^\nu}\right|_0 = \delta^\lambda{}_\nu. \quad (3.72)$$

This condition [eqn. (3.72)] specifies the parallel alignment of corresponding coordinate axes at point 0, and the matching of the scales of measure. Equation (3.71) thus becomes

$$x^\lambda = (\bar{x}^\lambda - \bar{x}^\lambda(0)) + \tfrac{1}{2}\frac{\partial^2 x^\lambda}{\partial \bar{x}^\nu \partial \bar{x}^\mu}(\bar{x}^\nu - \bar{x}^\nu(0))(\bar{x}^\mu - \bar{x}^\mu(0)). \quad (3.73)$$

The coordinate transformation law [eqn. (2.78)] for the Christoffel symbols is

$$\begin{Bmatrix} \tau \\ \mu\nu \end{Bmatrix} = \begin{Bmatrix} \alpha \\ \beta\gamma \end{Bmatrix}\frac{\partial \bar{x}^\tau}{\partial x^\alpha}\frac{\partial x^\beta}{\partial \bar{x}^\mu}\frac{\partial x^\gamma}{\partial \bar{x}^\nu} + \frac{\partial^2 x^\sigma}{\partial \bar{x}^\mu \partial \bar{x}^\nu}\frac{\partial \bar{x}^\tau}{\partial x^\sigma}.$$

Setting $\begin{Bmatrix} \alpha \\ \beta\gamma \end{Bmatrix} = 0$ in the geodesic frame, and multiplying both sides of the

equation by $\partial x^\lambda / \partial \bar{x}^\tau$, with use of eqn. (3.72), yields

$$\frac{\partial^2 x^\lambda}{\partial x^\mu \, \partial \bar{x}^\nu} = \begin{Bmatrix} \lambda \\ \mu\nu \end{Bmatrix}\Bigg|_0. \qquad (3.74)$$

With this result, the transformation to geodesic coordinates becomes

$$x^\lambda = \left(\bar{x}^\lambda - \bar{x}^\lambda(0)\right) + \tfrac{1}{2}\begin{Bmatrix} \lambda \\ \mu\nu \end{Bmatrix}_0 \left(\bar{x}^\nu - \bar{x}^\nu(0)\right)\left(\bar{x}^\mu - \bar{x}^\mu(0)\right). \qquad (3.75)$$

The availability of this transformation to the local geodesic coordinate frame, which has inertial-frame characteristics, provides a conceptual convenience for general relativity. Any law of nature, the form of which is known in inertial coordinates, can in principle be written in a non-inertial frame if we construct the transformation, as in eqn. (3.75), to the non-inertial frame. This has the effect of enabling us to express in covariant form physical laws which are known in an inertial frame.

The foregoing derivation of course does not imply that all physics is inertial-frame physics, in small regions. It is necessary to actually carry out the coordinate transformation (3.75), in order to learn the detailed physical laws of the non-inertial frame. For example, transformation of the inertial frame metric to a given accelerated frame will result in a metric which predicts force fields that are not present in the inertial frame.†

---

† A simple illustration of the concept of local frame of inertia, or geodesic frame, is that associated with a steeply banked turn on an automobile speedway, around which a racing car is traveling at high speed. An automobile traveling just outside the racing pavilion along a straight and level roadway tangent to the banked curve, at a velocity instantaneously equal to that of the banking racing car, represents the local inertial frame of the racing vehicle. The observer in the uniformly traveling automobile finds himself in a force-free region (aside from the downward pull of gravity) and observes that light rays travel in straight lines in any direction. The driver of the racing car, on the other hand, observes an abnormally strong "downward" gravitational field, in which complex coriolis forces appear, and he observes that light travels in curved paths in his frame, bending toward the floor of the vehicle. In these respects, the physical observations in the two coordinate frames are different.

Problems

3.1. In Section 1.5 an approximate solution was made for the equation of motion arising from the geodesic, $ds^2 = c^2 dt^2 - dx^2$, or $(ds/dk)^2 = c^2 \dot{t}^2 - \dot{x}^2$, where the dot indicates (d/dk). By use of Euler's equation, verify that the metric predicts constant geodesic velocity, $\ddot{x} = 0$, and that $\ddot{t} = 0$.

3.2. Given the metric, $ds^2 = x\, dt^2 - t\, dx^2$, show that the Christoffel symbols are

$$\begin{Bmatrix} 0 \\ 01 \end{Bmatrix} = \frac{1}{2x} = \begin{Bmatrix} 0 \\ 11 \end{Bmatrix}, \quad \begin{Bmatrix} 1 \\ 00 \end{Bmatrix} = \frac{1}{2t} = \begin{Bmatrix} 1 \\ 01 \end{Bmatrix}.$$

3.3. A metric proposed for the cosmological universe by Einstein has the form

$$ds^2 = c^2 dt^2 - \frac{dr^2}{1 - br^2} - r^2 d\theta^2 - r^2 \sin^2\theta\, d\phi^2$$

where b is a constant. Show that the geodesic equation of motion for the radial coordinate in the equatorial plane ($\theta = \pi/2$) has the form

$$\ddot{r} + br(1 - br^2)^{-1} \dot{r}^2 - r^2(1 - br^2) \dot{\phi}^2 = 0.$$

Derive also the expressions showing conservation of angular momentum in orbital motion, in this metric.

3.4. Carry out in detail the calculations leading from eqn. (3.67) to eqn. (3.68).

3.5. In the gravitational field of a point mass, the radial lines through the mass point at the origin are the spatial paths of a class of geodesic lines (those for which $\dot{\theta} = 0 = \dot{\phi}$). For an observer moving along a radial line (see Fig. 4.1), show that the geodesic deviation in the tangential (θ) direction is given by

$$\frac{D^2(y^2)}{Dk^2} = R^2{}_{121}(y^2) \left(\frac{dr}{dk} \right)^2$$

where y^2 is the deviation in the θ direction.

(a) Using Christoffel symbols:

$$\begin{Bmatrix} 2 \\ 21 \end{Bmatrix} = \frac{1}{r}, \quad \begin{Bmatrix} 1 \\ 11 \end{Bmatrix} = -\frac{f'}{2(1 + f)},$$

where $f = -2MG/c^2 r$, calculate the rate of geodesic deviation as a function of the rate of fall.

3.6. A metric of the universe proposed by deSitter is equivalent to that of eqn. (3.25), with $f_{00} = -ar^2$.

(a) Using this $f(r)$ calculate all $R_{\alpha\alpha}$.

(b) By use of the contravariant metric tensor $g^{\mu\nu}$ raise indices to calculate $R^{\alpha}{}_{\alpha}$. Summing, then show that $R = 12a$.

(c) Calculate $G_{\alpha\alpha} = R_{\alpha\alpha} - (1/2)g_{\alpha\alpha}R$. Verify that the mixed tensor $G^{\alpha}{}_{\alpha}$ is equal to $-3a$, for all α.

3.7. Form the geodesic equation of motion for the radial coordinate r, for DeSitter's metric as in Problem 3.6, and show that free test particles undergo an acceleration radially away from the origin proportional to $c^2 ar$.

3.8. Calculate $G^{\alpha\beta}$ for the metric: $ds^2 = (1 + h)(c^2 dt^2 - dx^2 - dy^2 - dz^2)$. Assume: $h = \varepsilon r = \varepsilon(x^2 + y^2 + z^2)^{1/2}$, with $\varepsilon \ll 1$.

Chapter 4

Solutions of the Field Equations

IN THE course of the development of a system for the expression of the laws of mechanics in terms of the coordinate geometry of the $(1 + 3)$-dimensional event space of one time-like and three space-like coordinates, we have adopted Riemann's geometry and the concept of the invariance of the event-interval

$$ds^2 = g_{\mu\nu}\, dx^\mu\, dx^\nu \tag{4.1}$$

under coordinate transformation.

We have enunciated the differential equation to be satisfied by the components of the metric tensor $g_{\mu\nu}$ as an equation relating two divergenceless tensors:

$$G^{\mu\nu} = -\frac{8\pi G}{c^2}\, T^{\mu\nu} \tag{4.2}$$

or

$$R^{\mu\nu} - \tfrac{1}{2}g^{\mu\nu}R = -\frac{8\pi G}{c^2}\, T^{\mu\nu}. \tag{4.3}$$

In empty space, including the space regions surrounding, but not occupied by, gravitating matter or electromagnetic fields, the right side of eqns. (4.2) and (4.3) vanishes. In these regions the curvature $R^{\mu\nu}$ and the scalar R vanish, but this may be accompanied by the appearance of gravitational fields.

We have discussed a method of approximation for finding solutions of the field equations for the case of weak gravitational fields, in the form of a perturbed Lorentz metric:

$$g_{\mu\nu} = g^{(0)}{}_{\mu\nu} + \gamma_{\mu\nu}. \tag{4.4}$$

Using this metric in eqn. (4.2) and the assumption of time-independence, we found correspondence with the Newtonian equation of potential:

$$\nabla^2 V = 4\pi G\rho. \tag{4.5}$$

In order to obtain a correct description of gravitational fields of arbitrary strength, however, we must find exact solutions for eqn. (4.2). This was first done for the case of the static, spherically symmetric field by Schwarzschild in 1916.† It was later shown by Birkhoff‡ that the assumption of static character was unnecessary, and that all spherically symmetric solutions for the field eqn. (4.2) that vanish at infinity are equivalent. The centrosymmetric metric has the form

$$ds^2 = c^2(1+f)\,dt^2 - (1+h)\,dr^2 - r^2\,d\theta^2 - r^2\sin^2\theta\,d\phi^2 \tag{4.6}$$

where f and h are functions of r only, satisfying

$$(1+h) = (1+f)^{-1} \tag{4.7}$$

or

$$h = -\frac{f}{1+f}. \tag{4.8}$$

4.1. The Static Spherically Symmetric Gravitation Field

Because of the close approach to spherical symmetry of most of the large gravitating masses of the physical world, great interest attaches to the static, spherically symmetric solutions of the gravitational field equations [eqn. (4.3)]. The requirement of a static field implies that the components $g_{\mu\nu}$ of the metric tensor shall not depend upon the time

† K. Schwarzschild, *Berichte Preuss. Akad. Wiss.*, Berlin, 1961.
‡ G. D. Birkhoff, *Relativity and Modern Physics*, Harvard University Press, 1923. See also W. B. Bonnor in *Recent Developments in General Relativity*, p. 167, Pergamon Press, New York, 1962.

coordinate. This is a natural specification for the gravitational field in the coordinates of the rest frame of the point mass acting as source of the field. The requirement of spherical symmetry can be expressed by writing the metric to be determined in the form

$$ds^2 = g_{00}(r)\, dt^2 + g_{11}(r)\, dr^2 - r^2(d\theta^2 + \sin^2\theta\, d\phi^2). \quad (4.9)$$

In writing the metric in the form of eqn. (4.9), the metric coefficients g_{22} and g_{33} have already been chosen to be equal to $-r^2$ and $-r^2\sin^2\theta$. We consider the gravitational field to be a perturbation on a background of "flat" space. Therefore we assume that the introduction of the gravitating point mass cannot alter the symmetrical disposition of the θ and ϕ coordinate lines of the original Lorentzian metric, and angular measures will be unchanged. The retention of the factor r^2 in g_{22} and g_{33} impresses a condition upon the ratio of the coordinate distance from the origin of an object subtending a given angle from the origin to the width of the object.

It will be convenient to put $g_{00}(r)$ into a form showing its relationship with the metric in the limiting condition of weak gravitational field, by employing the form $g_{00}(r) = (1 + f(r))\, c^2$, as was done previously in Section 3.3. Further, utilizing Birkhoff's theorem, we take g_{00} in reciprocal relation with g_{11}:

$$g_{00} = (1 + f), \quad g_{11} = \frac{-1}{(1 + f)}. \quad (4.10)$$

Thus, we wish to verify that the metric

$$ds^2 = (1 + f)\, c^2\, dt^2 - \frac{dr^2}{(1 + f)} - r^2\, d\theta^2 - r^2\sin^2\theta\, d\phi^2 \quad (4.11)$$

is a solution of the field equation [eqn. (4.3)], and to find the form of $f(r)$. To carry out the calculation, we require the Christoffel symbols of this metric. Hence we write the Euler–Lagrange equations for

$$\left(\frac{ds}{dk}\right)^2 = (1 + f)\, c^2\dot{t}^2 - \frac{\dot{r}^2}{(1 + f)} - r^2\dot{\theta}^2 - r^2\sin^2\theta\, \dot{\phi}^2 \quad (4.12)$$

where, as before, a dot over a coordinate symbol indicates d/dk. The variational equations are

$$\frac{d}{dk}[2c^2(1 + f)\,\dot{t}] = 0, \tag{4.13}$$

$$\frac{d}{dk}\left[-\frac{2\dot{r}}{(1 + f)}\right] = c^2 f'\dot{t}^2 + \frac{f'}{(1 + f)^2}\dot{r}^2 - 2r(\dot{\theta}^2 + \sin^2\theta\dot{\phi}^2), \tag{4.14}$$

$$\frac{d}{dk}[-2r^2\dot{\theta}] = -2r^2\sin\theta\cos\theta\dot{\phi}^2, \tag{4.15}$$

$$\frac{d}{dk}[-2r^2\sin^2\theta\dot{\phi}] = 0. \tag{4.16}$$

In eqn. (4.14), $f' = \partial f/\partial r$, and we shall use: $df/dk = (df/dr)(dr/dk)$ $= f'\dot{r}$.

From eqns. (4.13) to (4.16), we obtain

$$\ddot{t} + \frac{f'}{(1 + f)}\dot{r}\dot{t} = 0, \tag{4.17}$$

$$\ddot{r} + \frac{c^2}{2}f'(1 + f)\dot{t}^2 - \frac{f'}{2(1 + f)}\dot{r}^2 - r(1 + f)(\dot{\theta}^2 + \sin^2\theta\dot{\phi}^2) = 0, \tag{4.18}$$

$$\ddot{\theta} + \frac{2}{r}\dot{r}\dot{\theta} - \sin\theta\cos\theta\dot{\phi}^2 = 0, \tag{4.19}$$

$$\ddot{\phi} + \frac{2}{r}\dot{r}\dot{\phi} + 2\cot\theta\dot{\theta}\dot{\phi} = 0. \tag{4.20}$$

Integrating eqns. (4.13) and (4.16), we obtain the two subsidiary equations:

$$\dot{t} = \frac{dt}{dk} = \frac{a}{(1 + f)}, \tag{4.21}$$

$$r^2\dot{\phi}\sin^2\theta = b \tag{4.22}$$

where a and b are constants of integration.

From eqns. (4.17) to (4.20) we read the Christoffel symbols for this metric, with $(x^0, x^1, x^2, x^3) = (t, r, \theta, \phi)$:

$$\begin{Bmatrix} 0 \\ 01 \end{Bmatrix} = \tfrac{1}{2} \frac{f'}{1+f},$$

$$\begin{Bmatrix} 1 \\ 00 \end{Bmatrix} = \tfrac{1}{2} c^2 f'(1+f) \qquad \begin{Bmatrix} 1 \\ 22 \end{Bmatrix} = -r(1+f),$$

$$\begin{Bmatrix} 1 \\ 11 \end{Bmatrix} = -\tfrac{1}{2} \frac{f'}{1+f} \qquad \begin{Bmatrix} 1 \\ 33 \end{Bmatrix} = -r(1+f)\sin^2\theta, \qquad (4.23)$$

$$\begin{Bmatrix} 2 \\ 12 \end{Bmatrix} = \frac{1}{r} \qquad \begin{Bmatrix} 2 \\ 33 \end{Bmatrix} = -\sin\theta\cos\theta,$$

$$\begin{Bmatrix} 3 \\ 13 \end{Bmatrix} = \frac{1}{r} \qquad \begin{Bmatrix} 3 \\ 23 \end{Bmatrix} = \cot\theta.$$

We employ the expression for the Riemann curvature [eqn. (2.98)]:

$$R_{\alpha\beta} = p_{,\alpha,\beta} - \begin{Bmatrix} \varrho \\ \alpha\beta \end{Bmatrix} p_{,\varrho} - \begin{Bmatrix} \varrho \\ \alpha\beta \end{Bmatrix}_{,\varrho} + \begin{Bmatrix} \varrho \\ \alpha\sigma \end{Bmatrix} \begin{Bmatrix} \sigma \\ \varrho\beta \end{Bmatrix} \qquad (4.24)$$

where we have used $p = \ln\sqrt{-g}$, and $p_{,\mu} = \partial p/\partial x^\mu$. After summation over ϱ and σ, $R_{\alpha\beta}$ takes the form

$$R_{\alpha\beta} = p_{,\alpha,\beta} - \begin{Bmatrix} 0 \\ \alpha\beta \end{Bmatrix}_{,0} - \begin{Bmatrix} 1 \\ \alpha\beta \end{Bmatrix}_{,1} - \begin{Bmatrix} 2 \\ \alpha\beta \end{Bmatrix}_{,2} - \begin{Bmatrix} 3 \\ \alpha\beta \end{Bmatrix}_{,3}$$

$$- \begin{Bmatrix} 0 \\ \alpha\beta \end{Bmatrix} p_{,0} - \begin{Bmatrix} 1 \\ \alpha\beta \end{Bmatrix} p_{,1} - \begin{Bmatrix} 2 \\ \alpha\beta \end{Bmatrix} p_{,2} - \begin{Bmatrix} 3 \\ \alpha\beta \end{Bmatrix} p_{,3}$$

$$+ \begin{Bmatrix} 0 \\ 0\alpha \end{Bmatrix}\begin{Bmatrix} 0 \\ 0\beta \end{Bmatrix} + \begin{Bmatrix} 0 \\ 1\alpha \end{Bmatrix}\begin{Bmatrix} 1 \\ 0\beta \end{Bmatrix} + \begin{Bmatrix} 0 \\ 2\alpha \end{Bmatrix}\begin{Bmatrix} 2 \\ 0\beta \end{Bmatrix} + \begin{Bmatrix} 0 \\ 3\alpha \end{Bmatrix}\begin{Bmatrix} 3 \\ 0\beta \end{Bmatrix}$$

$$+ \begin{Bmatrix} 1 \\ 0\alpha \end{Bmatrix}\begin{Bmatrix} 0 \\ 1\beta \end{Bmatrix} + \begin{Bmatrix} 1 \\ 1\alpha \end{Bmatrix}\begin{Bmatrix} 1 \\ 1\beta \end{Bmatrix} + \begin{Bmatrix} 1 \\ 2\alpha \end{Bmatrix}\begin{Bmatrix} 2 \\ 1\beta \end{Bmatrix} + \begin{Bmatrix} 1 \\ 3\alpha \end{Bmatrix}\begin{Bmatrix} 3 \\ 1\beta \end{Bmatrix} \qquad (4.25)$$

$$+ \begin{Bmatrix} 2 \\ 0\alpha \end{Bmatrix}\begin{Bmatrix} 0 \\ 2\beta \end{Bmatrix} + \begin{Bmatrix} 2 \\ 1\alpha \end{Bmatrix}\begin{Bmatrix} 1 \\ 2\beta \end{Bmatrix} + \begin{Bmatrix} 2 \\ 2\alpha \end{Bmatrix}\begin{Bmatrix} 2 \\ 2\beta \end{Bmatrix} + \begin{Bmatrix} 2 \\ 3\alpha \end{Bmatrix}\begin{Bmatrix} 3 \\ 2\beta \end{Bmatrix}$$

$$+ \begin{Bmatrix} 3 \\ 0\alpha \end{Bmatrix}\begin{Bmatrix} 0 \\ 3\beta \end{Bmatrix} + \begin{Bmatrix} 3 \\ 1\alpha \end{Bmatrix}\begin{Bmatrix} 1 \\ 3\beta \end{Bmatrix} + \begin{Bmatrix} 3 \\ 2\alpha \end{Bmatrix}\begin{Bmatrix} 2 \\ 3\beta \end{Bmatrix} + \begin{Bmatrix} 3 \\ 3\alpha \end{Bmatrix}\begin{Bmatrix} 3 \\ 3\beta \end{Bmatrix}.$$

Substitution of the Christoffel symbols [eqn. (4.23)] into eqn. (4.25), with use of $p = \frac{1}{2}\ln(c^2 r^4 \sin^2\theta)$, yields

$$R_{00} = -\frac{c^2}{2}(1+f)\left[f'' + \frac{2f'}{r}\right], \tag{4.26a}$$

$$R_{11} = \frac{1}{2(1+f)}\left[f'' + \frac{2f'}{r}\right], \tag{4.26b}$$

$$R_{22} = f + rf', \tag{4.26c}$$

$$R_{33} = \sin^2\theta(rf' + f), \tag{4.26d}$$

$$R_{\alpha\beta} = 0, \ \alpha \neq \beta. \tag{4.26e}$$

The Riemann scalar $R = g^{\mu\nu}R_{\mu\nu}$, calculated with the contravariant metric $g^{\alpha\beta}$, is

$$R = -\left[f'' + \frac{4f'}{r} + \frac{2f}{r^2}\right]. \tag{4.27}$$

4.2. The Schwarzschild Metric

The static, spherically symmetric metric [eqn. (4.11)]

$$ds^2 = c^2(1+f)\,dt^2 - \frac{dr^2}{(1+f)} - r^2(d\theta^2 + \sin^2\theta\,d\phi^2) \tag{4.28}$$

is required to be a solution for the field equation for empty space [eqn. (4.2)]

$$G_{\mu\nu} = 0.$$

An equivalent condition for empty space is the shorter form:

$$R_{\mu\nu} = 0. \tag{4.29}$$

We satisfy the latter requirement by equating the components of $R_{\alpha\beta}$ found in eqn. (4.26) to zero. The solution of the resulting equations is readily found to be

$$f = \frac{\bar{\mu}}{r} \tag{4.30}$$

where $\bar{\mu}$ is a constant.

We anticipate by comparing eqn. (4.30) with eqn. (3.24) that $\bar{\mu} = -2MG/c^2$ for the gravitational field of a point mass M. We may verify this expectation by substituting eqn. (4.30) into the geodesic equation for purely radial motion, after setting $\theta = 0 = \dot{\phi}$ in eqn. (4.18). With the latter conditions, eqn. (4.18) becomes

$$\ddot{r} + \frac{c^2}{2}f'(1 + f)\left[\dot{t}^2 - \frac{\dot{r}^2}{c^2(1 + f)^2}\right] = 0. \tag{4.31}$$

With use of eqn. (4.21), eqn. (4.31) may be written

$$\ddot{r} + \frac{a^2c^2}{2}\frac{f'}{(1 + f)}\left[1 - \frac{\dot{r}^2}{c^2a^2}\right] = 0. \tag{4.32}$$

For low particle velocity $(dr/dt \ll c)$ we may replace (d/dk) by

$$(d/ds) = (1/c)(d/d\tau) \simeq (1/c)\,d/dt.$$

In this limit, for small f, eqn. (4.21) shows that $a \simeq 1/c$. Therefore, in the low velocity limit with $f \ll 1$, eqn. (4.32) becomes

$$\frac{d^2r}{dt^2} \simeq -\frac{c^2}{2}f'. \tag{4.33}$$

By analogy with the Newtonian gravitational equation, we deduce from eqn. (4.33)

$$\bar{\mu} = -\frac{2MG}{c^2}. \tag{4.34}$$

For the gravitational field at the surface of the earth ($M = 6 \times 10^{24}$ kg, $G = 6\cdot7 \times 10^{-11}$ mt m^2/kg^2, $r = 6\cdot4 \times 10^9$ m), $f \simeq 4 \times 10^{-6}$. In the field of most celestial objects, $f = \bar{\mu}/r$ is a small quantity, justifying the approximation we have made for the purpose of deducing the numerical value of $\bar{\mu}$. This approximation does not constitute a limitation upon the solution we have found, however. The result, the Schwarzschild metric, is, as we have shown, an exact solution for the field equation $R_{\alpha\beta} = 0$, for all r. In summary, the Schwarzschild metric has the form

$$ds^2 = c^2\left(1 - \frac{2MG}{c^2r}\right)dt^2 - \frac{dr^2}{\left(1 - \frac{2MG}{c^2r}\right)} - r^2(d\theta^2 + \sin^2\theta\,d\phi^2). \tag{4.35}$$

The Schwarzschild metric has a singularity at radius $r_s = (2MG/c^2)$. This metric applies to the field in free space in the neighborhood of a point mass M. For most physical objects, the Schwarzschild radius is much smaller than the radius of the exterior surface of the object, so that all of the mass of the object is not concentrated within a sphere of radius less than r_s, and a singularity is never formed. Moreover, the conditions for the Schwarzschild metric do not apply in the interior of matter. (For the earth, $r_s = 2MG/c^2 = 0.89$ cm.) The properties of this metric are discussed in Chapter 6.

The Schwarzschild metric constitutes an important achievement in relativistic theory, since it is one of the few known exact solutions of the field equations. It has provided a foundation for much of our present understanding of gravitation, as well as the basis for many of the experimental verifications for general relativity theory that have been devised.

4.3. Precession of Orbital Perihelion

We have written the equation of motion of a mass point in the Schwarzschild field, in eqns. (4.17) to (4.20). Let us now investigate the motion in a planar orbit. We consider the plane $\theta = \pi/2$. Equation (4.19) shows that if we have initial conditions of $\theta = \pi/2$ and $\dot{\theta} = 0$, then $\ddot{\theta} = 0$ for all time, and the particle continues to orbit in the same plane.

Let us now write the Schwarzschild metric [eqn. (4.35)] for motion in the plane $\theta = \pi/2$, and adopt the geodesic path length increment ds as the path parameter dk. Then, with $ds = dk$, eqn. (4.35) becomes

$$1 = c^2 \left(1 - \frac{2MG}{c^2 r}\right) \dot{t}^2 - \frac{\dot{r}^2}{\left(1 - \frac{2MG}{c^2 r}\right)} - r^2 \dot{\phi}^2. \qquad (4.36)$$

We eliminate $\dot{t}$ from eqn. (4.36) by use of eqn. (4.21), and using eqn. (4.22) we write: $dr/ds = (r^2/b)(dr/d\phi)$. Using this relation to remove $\dot{r}$ from eqn. (4.36), we obtain

$$\frac{b^2}{r^4} \left(\frac{dr}{d\phi}\right)^2 = c^2 a^2 - \left(1 - \frac{2MG}{c^2 r}\right)\left(1 + \frac{b^2}{r^2}\right). \qquad (4.37)$$

Making the substitution $u = 1/r$, eqn. (4.37) is given the form

$$\left(\frac{du}{d\phi}\right)^2 = \frac{c^2 a^2}{b^2} - \frac{1}{b^2}\left(1 - \frac{2MG}{c^2}u\right)(1 + b^2 u^2)$$ (4.38)

$$= \frac{c^2 a^2}{b^2} - \left(\frac{1}{b^2} + u^2 - \frac{2MG}{c^2 b^2}u - \frac{2MG}{c^2}u^3\right).$$

Equation (4.38) can be simplified by differentiation with respect to ϕ:

$$\frac{d^2 u}{d\phi^2}\frac{du}{d\phi} = -\left(u - \frac{MG}{c^2 b^2} - 3\frac{MG}{c^2}u^2\right)\frac{du}{d\phi}.$$ (4.39)

The case $du/d\phi = 0$ corresponds to the solution for a circular orbit. We wish to investigate the elliptical orbit, $du/d\phi \neq 0$, and therefore may divide eqn. (4.39) by $du/d\phi$, to obtain

$$\frac{d^2 u}{d\phi^2} + u = \frac{MG}{c^2 b^2} + 3\frac{MG}{c^2}u^2.$$ (4.40)

Equation (4.40) without the term $3(MG/c^2)u^2$ would be the equation for a Newtonian elliptical orbit. The solution for the Newtonian equation is

$$u = \frac{MG}{c^2 b^2}[1 + e\cos(\phi - \phi_0)]$$ (4.41)

where e is the eccentricity of the orbit ($e = F/2a$, where F is the distance between foci and a is the half length of the major axis of the ellipse) (Fig. 4.1). Here ϕ_0 is the angle at which perihelion occurs. Equation (4.40)

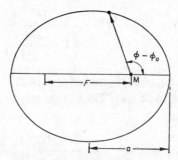

Fig. 4.1. Elliptical orbit about mass point M.

can be solved by use of the approximation in which the u^2 term on the right is replaced with the square of the unperturbed solution [eqn. (4.41)]:

$$\frac{d^2u}{d\phi^2} + u = \frac{MG}{c^2b^2} + \frac{3M^3G^3}{c^6b^4} [1 + e \cos (\phi - \phi_0)]^2. \qquad (4.42)$$

An approximate solution for eqn. (4.42) is

$$u = \frac{MG}{c^2b^2} [1 + e \cos (\phi - \phi_0 - \Delta\phi)] \qquad (4.43)$$

where

$$\Delta\phi = (3M^2G^2/c^4b^2) \phi \qquad (4.44)$$

and terms in powers of (MG/c^2b) higher than the second are neglected. The form of the solution [eqn. (4.44)] shows that since $\Delta\phi$ increases with ϕ, it may be regarded as a constantly increasing correction to ϕ_0, or precession of the position of perihelion of the orbit. The planet Mercury possesses the most readily observable $\Delta\phi$ of the solar planets, and in fact the astronomer Leverrier had discovered in 1845 that Mercury exhibited an "anomalous" precession of perihelion of about $43''$ per century that could not be accounted for by the known perturbations acting on the planet. This is almost equal to the relativistically predicted $\Delta\phi$ per century. The precession of the perihelion of Mercury was therefore regarded as an early verification of the correctness of general relativity theory. The proof is not an unequivocal one, however, due to uncertainties in the measurement of the position of the perihelion of Mercury, and in accounting for poorly known external perturbations.†

4.4. Deflection of Light Rays in a Gravitational Field

Since light rays travel along null geodesic lines, the propagation of light will be influenced by the presence of gravitational fields in the co-ordinate manifold. The expectation of this effect led to one of the first tests performed to verify general relativity theory. The measurement of

† For a discussion see R. H. Dicke, *Experimental Tests of General Relativity*, p. 27, Gordon & Breach, New York, 1964.

the deflection of light rays from the stars by the gravitational field of the sun was first performed in 1919.

The equation of the geodesic lines of a Schwarzschild metric was calculated as eqn. (4.38). In this equation, a unit term which originated from the quotient $(ds/dk)^2$ must be omitted, for a null geodesic. This omission causes the term MG/c^2b^2 to be eliminated from eqn. (4.39), resulting in the "orbital" equation for light rays:

$$\frac{d^2u}{d\phi^2} + u = \frac{3MG}{c^2}u^2.$$ (4.45)

This equation can be solved by the method of approximation as before, where the term on the right is small. The solution of the equation

$$\frac{d^2u}{d\phi^2} + u = 0$$

is

$$u = U_0 \cos \phi.$$

We substitute this approximation for u on the right in eqn. (4.45):

$$\frac{d^2u}{d\phi^2} + u = \frac{3MG}{c^2}U_0^2\cos^2\phi.$$ (4.46)

A solution for eqn. (4.46) is

$$u = U_0 \cos \phi + \frac{MG}{c^2}U_0^2(2 - \cos^2\phi).$$ (4.47)

In eqn. (4.47) let $\cos \phi = x$, $U_0 = a$, $(MG/c^2)U_0^2 = b$. The equation becomes

$$u = ax + b(2 - x^2).$$ (4.48)

With coordinates as in Fig. 4.2, at $\phi = \pi/2$, $x = 0$, the trajectory of the beam is assumed to be in grazing incidence with the sun at $u = 1/R_0$,

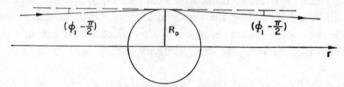

FIG. 4.2. Trajectory of light ray.

where R_0 is the radius of the sun. Then, from eqn. (4.48),

$$b = \frac{1}{2R_0}.$$

At $r \to \infty$, $u = 0$, the solutions for x are

$$x = \frac{a}{b}, \quad -\frac{2b}{a} \qquad (4.49)$$

where the approximation $b/a \ll 1$ has been used. The second root, $\cos \phi = -(2b/a)$, corresponds to

$$\phi = \pm \left(\frac{\pi}{2} + \frac{2b}{a} \right).$$

Therefore the angle of deflection of the outgoing light ray with respect to the ingoing ray is $4b/a$ radians. In the gravitational field of the sun, $4b/a \simeq 8 \times 10^{-6}$ radians, or approximately $1 \cdot 77''$. Deflection of star images seen near the sun's disc in agreement with this value have been observed during eclipses.

4.5. Gravitational Red Shift of Spectral Lines

A free particle momentarily at rest in a Schwarzschild field is described by a metric with $dr = 0 = d\theta = d\phi$:

$$ds^2 = \left(1 - \frac{MG}{c^2 r} \right) c^2 \, dt^2. \qquad (4.50)$$

If the free particle is a clock, e.g. an atom or molecule, whose natural vibrations are unaffected by gravitational forces, its world-line increments are intervals of its proper time $d\tau = ds/c$:

$$d\tau = \left(1 - \frac{MG}{c^2 r} \right)^{1/2} dt. \qquad (4.51)$$

In eqn. (4.51), dt is an increment of coordinate time, which is assumed to be measured on a fixed measuring scale common to the entire coordinate manifold, in a way such that dt has the same magnitude in all parts of the coordinate space.†

The ratio of the clock-time intervals $d\tau_1$ and $d\tau_2$ between a given pair of events separated by the coordinate time interval dt, measured by observers located at radii r_1 and r_2 in a Schwarzschild field, therefore is

$$\frac{d\tau_1}{d\tau_2} = \left[\frac{g_{00}(r_1)}{g_{00}(r_2)} \right]^{1/2}$$

$$= \left[\frac{1 - 2MG/c^2 r_1}{1 - 2MG/c^2 r_2} \right]^{1/2}. \tag{4.52}$$

For $2MG \ll c^2 r$, and $\Delta r = r_1 - r_2 \ll r_1$, eqn. (4.37) may be expanded to take the form

$$d\tau_2 = d\tau_1 \left[1 - \frac{G}{c^2} \left(\frac{M}{r_2} - \frac{M}{r_1} \right) \right]. \tag{4.53}$$

Equation (4.53) shows that if $M/r_2 > M/r_1$, then $d\tau_2 < d\tau_1$. The clock at r_2 shows a smaller reading in a given interval dt than the clock at r_1. This is interpreted to mean that the clock at smaller radius runs more slowly than the other. By the same token, atomic processes are expected to proceed more slowly at points that are relatively "deeper" in a gravitational potential. This behavior is experimentally observed, in the case of light emitted by atoms in the gravitational field of massive stars, and in the gamma rays emitted by nuclei in the field of the earth. Light signals are assumed to propagate in such a way that the coordinate time intervals between successive signals remain constant.

If $d\tau_2$ in eqn. (4.52) is the period of the light waves emitted by hydrogen atoms on the surface of a star of radius r_S and mass M_S, and received on earth (radius r_E, mass m_E), then eqn. (4.52) leads to the wavelength-shift relation

$$\frac{\Delta\lambda}{\lambda} = \frac{G}{c^2} \left(\frac{M_S}{r_S} - \frac{M_E}{r_E} \right). \tag{4.54}$$

The red shift of the hydrogen spectrum of the white dwarf star 40 Eridani B was measured by Popper,‡ who reported $\Delta\lambda/\lambda = 7 \times 10^{-5}$. He

---

† For a discussion of methods for setting up a coordinate time scale, see Section 6.1.
‡ D. M. Popper, *Astrophys. J.* **120**, 316 (1954).

estimated the mass of the star to be 0·43 solar masses, and its radius was estimated as 0·016 solar radii. With these data, eqn. (4.54) predicts $\Delta\lambda/\lambda$ = 5·6 × 10^{-5}, which is in agreement with the experimental value within the errors involved in the determination of the mass and radius of the star. Other sources of red shift of spectral lines are superposed upon the shift caused by the gravitational field of the star upon which an emitting atom is located. These other sources are cosmological in origin, and include a Doppler shift due to a presumed expansion of the universe, and the influence of the overall metric tensor of the universe upon light signals received from great distances.

More accurate measurements of the gravitational red shift are possible in terrestrial laboratories by use of the Mössbauer effect. This effect accurately measures variations in frequency of the gamma rays emitted from radioactive nuclei by selectively Doppler-shifting the gamma rays relative to the energy levels of an absorber containing nuclei of the same species as in the emitter. Equation (4.53) is in the appropriate form for calculation of a Mössbauer shift in the earth's field, with mass $M = M_E$. The experiment was carried out by Pound and Rebka[†] using the 14·4 keV gamma ray from Fe^{57} nuclei, with source and absorber separated by 21·6 m vertically in the earth's field. They found $\Delta\nu/\nu = 2\cdot56 \times 10^{-15}$, as compared with a prediction by eqn. (4.53) of

$$\frac{\Delta\nu}{\nu} = \frac{GM_E}{c^2}\frac{\Delta r}{r^2_E} = 2\cdot46 \times 10^{-15}, \qquad (4.55)$$

in good agreement with the measured shift. In eqn. (4.55) we have used $\Delta r = r_1 - r_2$, and $r_1 r_2 \simeq r^2_E$.

4.6. Application of the Centrosymmetric Metric in Non-empty Space

We have applied the static, centrally symmetric metric investigated in Section 4.1,

$$ds^2 = (1 + f)\, c^2\, dt^2 - \frac{dr^2}{(1 + f)} - r^2(d\theta^2 + \sin^2\theta\, d\phi^2), \quad (4.56)$$

[†] R. V. Pound and G. A. Rebka, *Phys. Rev. Letters* 4, 337 (1960).

only to the empty space surrounding a point mass. In this case the metric was required to satisfy $R_{\alpha\beta} = 0$, giving rise to the Schwarzschild solution. Because of its point symmetry, with $f = f(r)$, eqn. (4.56) finds natural application in spaces symmetrically occupied by matter, or in the Coulomb electric field. In these cases, the metric must satisfy

$$R_{\alpha\beta} - \tfrac{1}{2}g_{\alpha\beta}R = -\frac{8\pi G}{c^2}T_{\alpha\beta} \tag{4.57}$$

where $T_{\alpha\beta}$ is the matter–energy tensor for the problem under consideration. We have written eqn. (4.57) in terms of its covariant components since we have calculated, in eqn. (4.26), the covariant components of the Riemann tensor $R_{\alpha\beta}$. We can find solutions for eqn. (4.57) in the form of the metric of eqn. (4.56) with $f = a_m r^m$, $(m = \pm 2)$, for some problems of interest which we discuss in the following sections.

4.7. DeSitter's Cosmological Metric

DeSitter proposed a metric for the cosmological universe,† based on eqn. (4.56) with

$$f = ar^2 \tag{4.58}$$

where a is a constant. To illustrate the mode of utilization DeSitter's metric of the universe, we may tentatively assume a simple configuration in which all of the matter of the universe is assumed to be distributed evenly throughout space, constituting a dust cloud of particles of mass density ϱ_0, characterized by a uniform pressure p. The matter–energy tensor [eqn. (3.60)] then has the components

$$T^{00} = \varrho_0 \left(\frac{dt}{ds}\right)^2, \tag{4.59}$$

$$T^{ii} = -\frac{p}{c^2}g^{ii} \quad (i = 1, 2, 3). \tag{4.60}$$

Assuming the matter to be at rest relative to the coordinate frame, its metric becomes $ds^2 = c^2(1 + f)\, dt^2$. Then, calculating the covariant

† W. DeSitter, *Proc. Akad. Wetensch. Amsterdam* **19**, 1217 (1917).

components $T_{\mu\mu} = (g_{\mu\mu})^2\, T^{\mu\mu}$, we obtain

$$T_{00} = \varrho_0 c^2 (1 + f),$$

$$T_{ii} = -\frac{p}{c^2}\, g_{ii}.$$

(4.61)

Substitution of DeSitter's function $f = ar^2$ into eqn. (4.26) yields the Riemann tensor components:

$$R_{00} = -3a(1 + f)\, c^2,$$

$$R_{11} = \frac{3a}{(1 + f)},$$

$$R_{22} = -3ar^2,$$

$$R_{33} = -3ar^2 \sin^2 \theta,$$

$$R = -12a.$$

(4.62)

Equations (4.62) are equivalent to

$$R_{\mu\mu} = -3a g_{\mu\mu},$$

$$R = -12a.$$

(4.63)

Constructing the field equations [eqn. (4.57)] from eqns. (4.61) and (4.63), we obtain, from the G_{00} equation,

$$3a = -\frac{8\pi G \varrho_0}{c^2}$$

(4.64)

and from the G_{ii} equations ($i = 1, 2, 3$),

$$3a = \frac{8\pi G}{c^4}\, p.$$

(4.65)

Equations (4.64) and (4.65) imply

$$p = - \varrho_0 c^2. \tag{4.66}$$

Since the matter density ϱ_0 is a positive quantity, eqns. (4.64) and (4.65) imply that the DeSitter model predicts a negative pressure in the dust cloud of matter. Since this seems to be an unphysical requirement, we may attempt to avoid this conclusion by setting density and pressure separately to zero, corresponding to an empty universe:

$$\varrho_0 = 0, \quad p = 0. \tag{4.67}$$

The latter assumption would cause the constant a in eqn. (4.65) to vanish, however, destroying DeSitter's solution.

In some cosmological theories, the differential equation for the metric $g_{\mu\nu}$ in the presence of matter is modified by the addition of a term containing a "cosmological constant", Λ:

$$R^{\alpha\beta} - \tfrac{1}{2} g^{\alpha\beta} R + \Lambda g^{\alpha\beta} = - \frac{8\pi G}{c^2} T^{\alpha\beta}. \tag{4.68}$$

Although the new term is introduced in an *ad hoc* manner, its inclusion can be given the mathematical justification that the most general tensor having zero covariant divergence which can be constructed from the metric tensor and its first and second derivatives is the linear combination

$$t^{\alpha\beta} = A R^{\alpha\beta} + B g^{\alpha\beta} R + C g^{\alpha\beta}$$

where A, B, and C are constants, with $B/A = -1/2$ and C arbitrary. If we set $C/A = \Lambda$ and $A = 1$, the left side of the field equation [eqn. (4.68)] is seen to be the most general divergenceless tensor involving $g_{\mu\nu}$ and its derivatives.

With the field equation in the form of eqn. (4.68), the conditions for DeSitter's universe with zero pressure and zero mass density [eqns. (4.64) and (4.65)] become

$$3a + \Lambda = 0. \tag{4.69}$$

DeSitter's metric then takes the form

$$ds^2 = (1 - r^2\Lambda/3)\, c^2\, dt^2 - \frac{dr^2}{(1 - r^2\Lambda/3)} - r^2(d\theta^2 + \sin^2\theta\, d\phi^2). \quad (4.70)$$

The structure of eqn. (4.70) shows that Λ must have dimensions of (length)$^{-2}$. Assuming that the characteristic length of this problem is the radius of the universe, of the order of 10^{10} light years, then Λ has the value $\Lambda \simeq 10^{-52}$ m^{-2}. A cosmologic constant of this small size in eqn. (4.68) would not modify the equation in any way observable in regions of the order of magnitude of the solar system. We shall later see in Chapter 7 that abandonment of the assumption of a static universe, with the adoption of an expanding model of the universe, allows us to satisfy the field equations without the inclusion of the cosmological term.

4.8. Field of a Charged Mass Point

We have seen that electromagnetic fields add a contribution to the mass energy tensor, in the form:

$$(T^{\mu\nu})_{\text{electromagnetic}} = \varepsilon_0(F_\alpha{}^\mu F^{\alpha\nu} + \tfrac{1}{4}g^{\mu\nu}F^{\alpha\beta}F_{\alpha\beta}) \quad (4.71)$$

where $F^{\alpha\beta}$ is the tensor of the electromagnetic field, discussed in Chapter 5. We therefore expect an electromagnetic field to exert a gravitational effect. The metric of the region surrounding a point mass with charge was calculated by Reissner.† Reissner found a metric in the centrosymmetric form of eqn. (4.56) with

$$f + \frac{\bar\mu}{r} + \frac{\varkappa}{r^2} \quad (4.72)$$

where $\bar\mu$ and $\varkappa$ are constants.

The first term on the right in eqn. (4.72) corresponds to the Schwarzschild potential, due to the contribution of the inert mass of the particle to the metric. The second term represents the contribution due to the energy density of the electromagnetic field. Let us determine the character of the coefficient $\varkappa$.

† H. Reissner, *Ann. Physik*, **50**, 106 (1916).

Since we know that the term $\bar{\mu}/r$ is a solution of the equation $R_{\alpha\beta} = 0$, we ignore it for the moment, and investigate $f = \varkappa/r^2$ as a solution of the field equation [eqn. (4.57)] for non-empty space.†

The Coulomb field is a purely radial electrostatic field, and its electromagnetic field tensor is therefore [eqn. (5.17)]:

$$F_{\mu\nu} = \begin{pmatrix} 0 & -E_r & 0 & 0 \\ E_r & 0 & 0 & 0 \\ 0 & 0 & 0 & 0 \\ 0 & 0 & 0 & 0 \end{pmatrix}. \qquad (4.73)$$

Writing the electromagnetic energy tensor in covariant form, we have

$$T_{\varkappa\lambda} = \varepsilon[g^{\alpha\sigma}F_{\varkappa\sigma}F_{\alpha\lambda} + \tfrac{1}{4}g_{\varkappa\lambda}g^{\varrho\alpha}g^{\beta\sigma}F_{\varrho\alpha}F_{\alpha\beta}]. \qquad (4.74)$$

When the energy tensor is evaluated with the $g_{\mu\nu}$ of the centrosymmetric metric,

$$ds^2 = (1 + f)\,c^2\,dt^2 - \frac{dr^2}{(1 + f)} - r^2(d\theta^2 + \sin^2 d\phi^2), \qquad (4.75)$$

using the tensor of the Coulomb field [eqn. (4.73)], we obtain

$$T_{00} = \frac{\varepsilon_0}{2c^2}\,E_r{}^2 g_{00},$$

$$T_{11} = \frac{\varepsilon_0}{2c^2}\,E_r{}^2 g_{11},$$

$$(4.76)$$

$$T_{22} = -\frac{\varepsilon_0}{2c^2}\,E_r{}^2 g_{22},$$

$$T_{33} = -\frac{\varepsilon_0}{2c^2}\,E_r{}^2 g_{33}.$$

† The separation of the two components of f is valid when both $\bar{\mu}/r$ and $\varkappa/r$ remain much less than unity in magnitude, which is true in all real cases.

Substitution of the function $f = \varkappa/r^2$ into eqns. (4.26) yields the Riemann tensor components:

$$R_{00} = -\frac{\varkappa}{r^4} g_{00},$$

$$R_{11} = -\frac{\varkappa}{r^4} g_{11},$$

$$R_{22} = \frac{\varkappa}{r^4} g_{22}, \qquad (4.77)$$

$$R_{33} = \frac{\varkappa}{r^4} g_{33},$$

$$R = 0.$$

From the last of eqns. (4.77) we see that the field equation [eqn. (4.57)] to be satisfied reduces to

$$R_{\alpha\beta} = -\frac{8\pi G}{c^2} T_{\alpha\beta}. \qquad (4.78)$$

With eqns. (4.76) and (4.77), this yields

$$\varkappa = \frac{4\pi G \varepsilon_0}{c^4} r^4 E_r{}^2. \qquad (4.79)$$

But the (mks) Coulomb field of a point charge q is: $E_r = q/(4\pi\varepsilon_0 r^2)$. Consequently $\varkappa$ has the value

$$\varkappa = \frac{q^2 G}{4\pi\varepsilon_0 c^4}. \qquad (4.80)$$

Therefore the gravitational potential function of the charged mass point is

$$f = -\frac{2MG}{c^2 r} + \frac{q^2 G}{4\pi\varepsilon_0 c^4 r^2}. \qquad (4.81)$$

The metric tensor [eqn. (4.75)] therefore has the components

$$g_{00} = \left(1 - \frac{2MG}{c^2 r} + \frac{q^2 G}{4\pi\varepsilon_0 c^4 r^2}\right)c^2,$$

$$g_{11} = \frac{-1}{\left(1 - \frac{2MG}{c^2 r} + \frac{q^2 G}{4\pi\varepsilon_0 c^4 r^2}\right)}, \qquad (4.82)$$

$$g_{22} = -r^2,$$

$$g_{33} = -r^2 \sin^2 \theta.$$

The gravitational force of the field of the charged mass is proportional to $-\partial f/\partial r$:

$$-\frac{\partial f}{\partial r} = -\frac{2MG}{c^2 r^2} + \frac{2q^2 G}{4\pi\varepsilon_0 C^4 r^3}. \qquad (4.83)$$

This result shows the curious property that the gravitational force due to electrostatic energy is repulsive, falling off as the inverse third power of distance. The ratio η of the "electrical" component of the gravitational force to that of the component due to the inert mass is

$$\eta = -\frac{q^2}{4\pi\varepsilon_0 r(Mc^2)}. \qquad (4.84)$$

The ratio of forces is clearly equal to the ratio of the electrostatic potential energy at radius r to the energy Mc^2 of the rest mass of the particle. At the "surface" of a proton, using a nominal radius of $r = 10^{-15}$ m, this ratio of gravitational force components is $\eta = 0.0016$. Therefore, the electrical contributions to the point-charge metric probably cannot have any observable consequences, since the primary gravitational force, due to the inert mass, is itself much less than the Coulomb force and forces of nuclear binding, in most of the possible interactions of charged elementary particles.

Problems

4.1. Show that in a spherically symmetric dust cloud composed of non-interacting particles at a density of ϱ_0 kg/m^3, the Newtonian gravitational potential is $V_g = -(4\pi\rho_0 Gr^2/6)$, with origin of spherical coordinates at the center of the cloud. Prove that this potential is a solution of Poisson's equation: $\nabla^2 V_g = -4\pi G\varrho_0$.

4.2. By use of eqns. (4.23) and (4.25), verify any one of the curvature components $R_{\mu\mu}$, eqn. (4.26).

4.3. Form the geodesic equation of motion for the radial coordinate r, for DeSitter's metric [eqn. (4.70)], and show that free test particles undergo an acceleration radially away from the origin proportional to $ar^2(1 - a^2r^2)$. (The velocity resulting from this acceleration was proposed as the origin of Doppler shift seen as the red shift of light from distant galaxies.)

4.4. Verify the magnitude of the precession of the perihelion of the orbit of Mercury, by calculation from eqn. (4.44). Note that the angular momentum b is defined in eqn. (4.22) as $b = r^2 \sin^2 \theta(d\phi/dk) \simeq (r^2/c) \sin^2 \theta(d\phi/dt)$.

4.5. The planet Jupiter (mass $M_J = 1\cdot 91 \times 10^{27}$ kg) has a satellite Io (mass $m_{\text{Io}} = 7\cdot 28 \times 10^{22}$ kg) that has a slightly elliptical orbit with an orbital period of $0\cdot 00484$ yr $\simeq 1\cdot 52 \times 10^5$ sec and mean orbital radius of $r \simeq 4\cdot 13 \times 10^8$ m. Calculate the rate of precession of the perihelion of Io's orbit due to general-relativistic perturbation. Would this precession be measurable? See note in Problem 4.4.

4.6. It is postulated that neutron stars can exist having mass of $3\cdot 1 \times 10^{30}$ kg and radius of $9\cdot 3 \times 10^3$ m. If a hydrogen atom at the surface of such a star emitted a photon from the transition in the Balmer series that has wavelength $\lambda_0 = 6\cdot 562 \times 10^{-7}$ m when emitted on earth, what wavelength would the light be observed to have upon its arrival at the earth?

Chapter 5

Electromagnetism in General Relativity

WE HAVE seen that with the geodesic theorem of Riemannian geometry we may calculate the equations of motion of free mass points under the influence of gravitational and inertial "forces":

$$\ddot{x}^\mu + \left\{ {\mu \atop \nu\lambda} \right\} \dot{x}^\nu \dot{x}^\lambda = 0.$$

The character of the geodesic equations is determined by the metric tensor of the coordinate manifold in which the mass points move.

Much effort has been expended in attempts to incorporate electrical and magnetic forces into the coordinate description of the space–time manifold so as to thereby create a unified geometrical theory of the motion of particles with charge and mass in electromagnetic and gravitational fields. These efforts have not succeeded, however, in correctly reproducing electromagnetic forces by means of the same analytical procedure as is used in introducing the gravitational forces into the equations of motion. Lacking this achievement, however, the electromagnetic forces may still be brought into the equations of motion in a covariant way by adding an electromagnetic force term f^μ to the geodesic equation, in the form†

$$\ddot{x}^\mu + \left\{ {\mu \atop \nu\lambda} \right\} \dot{x}^\nu \dot{x}^\lambda = f^\mu. \tag{5.1}$$

It has been found possible, moreover, to express the equations of the electromagnetic field, "Maxwell's equation", in covariant form. There-

† Cf. eqn. (5.28).

120

fore they may be written in any Riemannian coordinate manifold for which the metric tensor is known. In addition, the energy and momentum of the electromagnetic field can be introduced into the stress–energy tensor $T^{\mu\nu}$ by use of a suitable supplementary tensor form. By these means the electromagnetic field may be dealt with in general relativity, although it does not play an integral role in the theory as does the gravitational field.

5.1. The Electromagnetic Potential and Four-current

The covariant expression of the electromagnetic field equations requires the definition of two vectors, or tensors of first rank: the four-potential A_μ and the four-current J^μ. These may be illustrated in terms of their components in an inertial frame of reference in rectangular coordinates (t, x, y, z) as

$$A_\mu = (-\phi, A_x, A_y, A_z), \tag{5.2}$$

$$J^\mu = (\varrho, J_x, J_y, J_z), \tag{5.3}$$

where ϕ is the ordinary scalar potential, A_x, A_y, A_z are the components of the electromagnetic vector potential and ϱ and J_x, J_y, J_z are the charge and current densities, respectively.† The potentials are defined in classical electromagnetic theory by the formulae‡

$$B = \nabla \times A, \tag{5.4}$$

$$E = -\dot{A} - \nabla\phi, \tag{5.5}$$

$$\nabla \cdot A = -\frac{1}{c^2}\dot{\phi}. \tag{5.6}$$

We use a dot over a symbol to indicate time differentiation here. (The operation d/dk will not be used in this chapter, so there should be no danger of confusion in the use of this convention.) In eqn. (5.3) ϱ is the volume density of charge, related to the current density J by the classical

---

† We use the symbol ϱ, volume density of electric charge (coul m^{-3}), at small hazard of confusion with mass density, ϱ, introduced in Section 3.4.

‡ MKS units. The mks system of units will be used in the treatment of electromagnetic fields in this book.

conservation law:

$$\nabla \cdot J = -\dot{\varrho}. \tag{5.7}$$

The current density J^μ can be expressed covariantly as

$$J^\mu = \varrho_0 \frac{dx^\mu}{ds} \tag{5.8}$$

where ϱ_0 is the volume density of charge measured in the rest frame of the moving charge, and ds is an element of the world line of the charge. In covariant form, eqns. (5.6) and (5.7) are

$$A^\mu{}_{;\mu} = 0, \tag{5.9}$$

$$J^\mu{}_{;\mu} = 0 \tag{5.10}$$

where the contravariant components of A_μ are used in eqn. (5.9).

5.2. The Tensor of Electromagnetic Fields and the Field Equations

An antisymmetric second-rank tensor composed of the vectors of the electromagnetic field is derived from the potential A_μ by means of the definition

$$F_{\mu\nu} = A_{\nu;\mu} - A_{\mu;\nu}. \tag{5.11}$$

From eqn. (5.11) and in keeping with eqns. (5.4) and (5.5), we identify the components of $F_{\mu\nu}$ as

$$F_{\mu\nu} = \begin{pmatrix} 0 & -E_1 & -E_2 & -E_3 \\ E_1 & 0 & B_3 & -B_2 \\ E_2 & -B_3 & 0 & B_1 \\ E_3 & B_2 & -B_1 & 0 \end{pmatrix} \tag{5.12}$$

where indices 1, 2, 3 refer to the space coordinates x, y, z.

The field equations may now be constructed from the tensor $F_{\mu\nu}$. The equations are given by

$$F_{\mu\nu,\lambda} + F_{\lambda\mu,\nu} + F_{\nu\lambda,\mu} = 0, \tag{5.13}$$

$$(\sqrt{-g} . F^{\mu\nu})_{,\nu} = \mu_0 \sqrt{-g} . J^\mu. \tag{5.14}$$

The field equations are covariant although the differentiations are indicated as only partial derivatives, because the terms containing Christoffel symbols in covariant differentiation cancel as a result of the antisymmetry of $F_{\mu\nu}$. The constant μ_0 in eqn. (5.14) is the vacuum permeability in the mks system of units ($\mu_0 = 4\pi \times 10^{-7}$). Equation (5.13) stands for the set of four equations obtained when all four sets of three different values of (μ, ν, λ) are chosen:

$$F_{01,2} + F_{20,1} + F_{12,0} = 0,$$

$$F_{01,3} + F_{30,1} + F_{13,0} = 0,$$

$$F_{02,3} + F_{30,2} + F_{23,0} = 0,$$

$$F_{12,3} + F_{31,2} + F_{23,1} = 0.$$

(5.13)

It is readily verified by direct substitution that the first three of these equations lead to

$$\nabla \times \boldsymbol{E} = -\dot{\boldsymbol{B}},$$

whereas the fourth is

$$\nabla \cdot \boldsymbol{B} = 0.$$

These are the sourceless field equations. The set of four permutations formed in eqn. (5.13) is sometimes indicated by the compact symbolism

$$\{F_{\mu\nu,\lambda}\} = 0. \tag{5.13'}$$

The current- and charge-containing field equations [eqn. (5.14)] may be written in terms of tensor densities $\mathfrak{F}^{\mu\nu}$ and $\mathfrak{J}^{\mu}$, in the light of the definition of the tensor density [eqn. (2.83)], as

$$\mathfrak{F}^{\mu\nu}{}_{,\nu} = \mu_0\mathfrak{J}^{\mu}. \tag{5.14'}$$

In rectangular Cartesian coordinates $\sqrt{-g}$ is a constant. This factor therefore cancels from eqn. (5.14), and in rectangular coordinates this equation becomes

$$F^{\mu\nu}{}_{,\nu} = \mu_0 J^{\mu}. \tag{5.14a}$$

Both indices of $F_{\mu\nu}$ must of course be raised, to form this equation. With μ equal to zero for the time-like coordinate element, this equation yields

$$\nabla \cdot \boldsymbol{E} = \varrho/\varepsilon_0,$$

in which the identity $\mu_0 \varepsilon_0 c^2 = 1$, in the mks coordinate system, has been used. The remaining three equations of (5.14) correspond to the fourth Maxwell equation:

$$\nabla \times \boldsymbol{B} = \mu_0 \boldsymbol{J} + \frac{1}{c^2} \dot{\boldsymbol{E}}.$$

When curvilinear space coordinate components are employed, the electromagnetic field tensor must be written in suitable form. These may be found by coordinate transformation. In *cylindrical space coordinates* ($x^\mu = t, r, \theta, z$), the electromagnetic field tensor and contravariant current density vector take the form

$$F_{\mu\nu} = \begin{pmatrix} 0 & -E_r & -rE_\theta & -E_z \\ E_r & 0 & rB_z & -B_\theta \\ rE_\theta & -rB_z & 0 & rB_r \\ E_z & B_\theta & -rB_r & 0 \end{pmatrix}, \tag{5.15}$$

$$J^\mu = (J^0, J^1, J^2, J^3) = (\varrho, J_r, 1/r\, J_\theta, J_z) \tag{5.16}$$

where J_r, J_θ and J_z are the conventional physical components of current density in cylindrical coordinates, and ϱ is the conventional volume charge density. The field and current density tensors in *spherical coordinates* ($x^\mu = t, r, \theta, \phi$) are

$$F_{\mu\nu} = \begin{pmatrix} 0 & -E_r & -rE_\theta & -r\sin\theta E_\phi \\ E_r & 0 & rB_\varphi & -r\sin\theta B_\theta \\ rE_\theta & -rB_\phi & 0 & r^2\sin\theta B_r \\ r\sin\theta E_\phi & r\sin\theta B_\theta & -r^2\sin\theta B_r & 0 \end{pmatrix}, \tag{5.17}$$

$$J^\mu = (J^0, J^1, J^2, J^3) = \left(\varrho, J_r, \frac{1}{r} J_\theta, \frac{1}{r\sin\theta} J_\phi \right). \tag{5.18}$$

It may be verified that the forms of $F_{\mu\nu}$ and J^μ given above satisfy eqns. (5.13) and (5.14) in the respective coordinate systems.

5.3. The Electromagnetic Energy Tensor

It was stated in Section 3.4 that the mass-energy tensor $T^{\mu\nu}$ could be complemented by terms representing the energy and momentum contributions of the electromagnetic field:

$$T^{\mu\nu} = \varrho_0 \frac{dx^\mu}{ds} \frac{dx^\nu}{ds} + S^{\mu\nu} \tag{5.19}$$

where

$$S^{\mu\nu} = \varepsilon_0(F^{\mu\sigma}F_\sigma{}^\nu + \tfrac{1}{4}g^{\mu\nu}F^{\varkappa\lambda}F_{\varkappa\lambda}). \tag{5.20}$$

It will be instructive to evaluate $S^{\mu\nu}$ in terms of the physical components of the electromagnetic field. Selecting rectangular coordinates in an inertial frame, $F_{\mu\nu}$ has the form of eqn. (5.12). The mixed tensor components are given by

$$F_\sigma{}^\nu = g^{\mu\nu}F_{\sigma\mu} = g^{\nu\nu}F_{\sigma\nu}. \tag{5.21}$$

(No sum on ν in form at right.)

The metric tensors for the inertial frame we now employ are

$$g_{\mu\nu} = \begin{pmatrix} c^2 & 0 & 0 & 0 \\ 0 & -1 & 0 & 0 \\ 0 & 0 & -1 & 0 \\ 0 & 0 & 0 & -1 \end{pmatrix}, \quad g^{\mu\nu} = \begin{pmatrix} 1/c^2 & 0 & 0 & 0 \\ 0 & -1 & 0 & 0 \\ 0 & 0 & -1 & 0 \\ 0 & 0 & 0 & -1 \end{pmatrix}. \tag{5.22}$$

Therefore, eqn. (5.21) becomes

$$F_\sigma{}^\nu = \begin{pmatrix} 0 & E_1 & E_2 & E_3 \\ E_1/c^2 & 0 & -B_3 & B_2 \\ E_2/c^2 & B_3 & 0 & -B_1 \\ E_3/c^2 & -B_2 & B_1 & 0 \end{pmatrix}. \tag{5.23}$$

The contravariant electromagnetic field tensor is

$$F^{\alpha\beta} = g^{\mu\alpha}g^{\nu\beta}F_{\mu\nu} = g^{\alpha\alpha}g^{\beta\beta}F_{\alpha\beta}. \tag{5.24}$$

(No sum on α, β in form at right.)

With use of eqns. (5.12) and (5.22) this becomes

$$F^{\mu\nu} = \begin{pmatrix} 0 & E_1/c^2 & E_2/c^2 & E_3/c^2 \\ -E_1/c^2 & 0 & B_3 & -B_2 \\ -E_2/c^2 & -B_3 & 0 & B_1 \\ -E_3/c^2 & B_2 & -B_1 & 0 \end{pmatrix}. \tag{5.25}$$

With eqns. (5.25) and (5.23) the first term of eqn. (5.20) is

$$\varepsilon_0 F^{\mu\sigma} F_\sigma{}^\nu = \varepsilon_0$$

$$\begin{bmatrix} E^2/c^4 & (E_2 B_3 - E_3 B_2)/c^2 & (E_3 B_1 - E_1 B_3)/c^2 & (E_1 B_2 - E_2 B_1)/c^2 \\[2mm] \cdot & \left(B^2 - B_1{}^2 - \dfrac{E_1{}^2}{c^2}\right) & \left(-\dfrac{E_1 E_2}{c^2} - B_1 B_2\right) & \left(-\dfrac{E_1 E_3}{c^2} - B_1 B_3\right) \\[4mm] \cdot & \cdot & \left(B^2 - B_2{}^2 - \dfrac{E_2{}^2}{c^2}\right) & \left(-\dfrac{E_2 E_3}{c^2} - B_2 B_3\right) \\[4mm] \cdot & \cdot & \cdot & \left(B^2 - B_3{}^2 - \dfrac{E_3{}^2}{c^2}\right) \end{bmatrix}$$

$$\tag{5.26}$$

where the terms below the diagonal have been omitted because the tensor is symmetric. The quantity $F^{\varkappa\lambda} F_{\varkappa\lambda}$ is readily evaluated from eqns. (5.12) and (5.25). The sum contains sixteen terms and is found to be $-2E^2/c^2 + 2B^2$, where $E^2 = (E_x{}^2 + E_y{}^2 + E_z{}^2)$ and B^2 is similarly defined. With this result and eqn. (5.26), the electromagnetic energy tensor $S^{\mu\nu}$ in this coordinate frame is found to have the form

$$S^{\mu\nu} = \varepsilon_0 \begin{pmatrix} S_{00} & S_{01} & S_{02} & S_{03} \\ S_{10} & S_{11} & S_{12} & S_{13} \\ S_{20} & S_{21} & S_{22} & S_{23} \\ S_{30} & S_{31} & S_{32} & S_{33} \end{pmatrix} \tag{5.27}$$

where

$$S_{00} = \frac{1}{2c^4}(E^2 + c^2 B^2),$$

$$S_{11} = \frac{1}{c^2} \tfrac{1}{2}(E^2 + c^2 B^2) - (E_1{}^2 + c^2 B_1{}^2),$$

$$S_{22} = \frac{1}{c^2} \tfrac{1}{2}(E^2 + c^2 B^2) - (E_2{}^2 + c^2 B_2{}^2),$$

$$S_{33} = \frac{1}{c^2} \tfrac{1}{2}(E^2 + c^2 B^2) - (E_3{}^2 + c^2 B_3{}^2)$$

and S_{0i}, S_{j0} and S_{ij} ($i, j = 1, 2, 3$) are identical with the corresponding off-diagonal terms inside the tensor brackets in eqn. (5.26).

Equations (5.26) and (5.27) indicate that the mass energy tensor $T^{\mu\nu}$ containing contributions from the electromagnetic field can have lengthy form, even for relatively simple field distributions. Therefore, the solution of the equation

$$R^{\mu\nu} - \tfrac{1}{2} g^{\mu\nu} R = - \frac{8\pi G}{c^2} T^{\mu\nu}$$

for the metric tensor of a region containing electromagnetic fields may be a tedious task. Fortunately this is rarely necessary in practical instances, since the effect of the gravitational fields of electromagnetic energy distributions is usually negligible. A space region of one cubic meter filled with the enormous electric field of 10^{10} V/m would have an equivalent mass of the order of 10^{-8} kg, and therefore would have an unmeasurable gravitational effect. Strong electric fields tend also to be rapidly neutralized in nature, and their effects on the metric of a region is normally negligible.

The influence of electromagnetic fields on the motion of charged particles is of course very great, however. These forces may be incorporated into the equations of motion by adding to the geodesic equation [eqn. (5.1)] an electromagnetic force term

$$f^\mu = q \frac{dx^\alpha}{ds} g^{\mu\beta} F_{\alpha\beta} \tag{5.28}$$

where q is the charge of the particle and $F_{\alpha\beta}$ is the field tensor. This covariant force term introduces the physical Lorentz force $qE + qV \times B$ into the geodesic equations of motion.

5.4. Transformation of Fields: Inertial Frames

The transformation of the covariant field tensor $F_{\mu\nu}$ from one coordinate manifold to another yields concurrently the transformation relations for E and B, the physical components of the electromagnetic fields, corresponding to the given change of coordinates. The procedure for obtaining these may be illustrated by its use on the familiar case of inertial frames in uniform relative motion. The latter is of course the situation in which the Lorentz coordinate transformation is applicable. We utilize the real Lorentz transformation [eqn. (1.28)] appropriate to the real field tensor $F_{\mu\nu}$ that we have discussed in this section. The matrix of transformation coefficients is

$$\frac{\partial x^{\alpha}}{\partial \bar{x}^{\mu}} = \begin{pmatrix} \gamma & \beta\gamma/c & 0 & 0 \\ c\beta\gamma & \gamma & 0 & 0 \\ 0 & 0 & 1 & 0 \\ 0 & 0 & 0 & 1 \end{pmatrix}.$$

The Lorentz transformation coefficients are to be used in the transformation

$$F_{\mu\nu} = \frac{\partial x^{\alpha}}{\partial \bar{x}^{\mu}} \frac{\partial x^{\beta}}{\partial \bar{x}^{\nu}} F_{\alpha\beta}. \tag{5.29}$$

In the matrix of transformation coefficients $\partial x^{\alpha}/\partial \bar{x}^{\mu}$, the upper index α is associated with rows, the lower index μ with columns of the matrix. The coordinate transformation can be facilitated by the use of the procedure for matrix multiplication (Section 2.5), with attention to correct configuration of the matrices since neither $F_{\mu\nu}$ nor $\partial x^{\alpha}/\partial \bar{x}^{\mu}$ is symmetric. The first intermediate stage in this calculation may be written

$$F_{\alpha\bar{\nu}} = [F_{\alpha\beta}] \left[\frac{\partial x^{\beta}}{\partial \bar{x}^{\nu}} \right] \tag{5.30}$$

where the small square brackets indicate the matrix of the enclosed quantity. Using eqns. (5.12) and (1.28) we find by matrix multiplication:

$$
F_{\alpha\bar{v}} = \begin{pmatrix}
-c\beta\gamma E_1 & -\gamma E_1 & -E_2 & -E_3 \\
\gamma E_1 & E_1\beta\gamma/c & B_3 & -B_2 \\
(E_2 - c\beta B_3)\gamma & (E_2\beta/c - B_3)\gamma & 0 & B_1 \\
(E_3 + c\beta B_2)\gamma & (E_3\beta/c + B_2)\gamma & -B_1 & 0
\end{pmatrix}. \tag{5.31}
$$

Inspection of the form of $F_{\alpha\bar{v}}$ shows us that the intermediate product does not possess the symmetry of the final tensor $F_{\mu v}$, as it is of course not necessary that it possess any specific symmetry.

Completion of the tensor transformation can be accomplished by means of the matrix product:

$$
F_{\mu v} = \left[\widetilde{\frac{\partial x^\alpha}{\partial \bar{x}^\mu}}\right][F_{\alpha\bar{v}}]
$$

where the transposition sign ($\sim$) designates that the transposed matrix of $\partial x^\alpha/\partial\bar{x}^\mu$ is to be used. Completion of the product yields:

$$
F_{\mu v} = \begin{bmatrix}
0 & -E_1 & -(E_2 - VB_3)\gamma & -(E_3 + VB_2)\gamma \\
E_1 & 0 & \left(B_3 - \dfrac{V}{c^2}E_2\right)\gamma & -\left(B_2 + \dfrac{V}{c^2}E_3\right)\gamma \\
(E_2 - VB_3)\gamma & -\left(B_3 - \dfrac{V}{c^2}E_2\right)\gamma & 0 & B_1 \\
(E_3 + VB_2)\gamma & \left(B_2 + \dfrac{V}{c^2}E_3\right)\gamma & -B_1 & 0
\end{bmatrix}.
$$

$$\tag{5.32}$$

The components of the tensor $F_{\mu v}$ are here written in terms of the electromagnetic field components of the "unbarred" frame. Identification of these components allows us to write down the transformation law for the electromagnetic field appropriate to inertial frames:

$$\bar{E}_1 = E_1, \qquad\qquad \bar{B}_1 = B_1,$$

$$\bar{E}_2 = \gamma(E + V \times B)_2, \quad \bar{B}_2 = \gamma\left(B - \frac{1}{c^2} V \times E\right)_2, \qquad (5.33)$$

$$\bar{E}_3 = \gamma(E + V \times B)_3, \quad \bar{B}_3 = \gamma\left(B - \frac{1}{c^2} V \times E\right)_3$$

where the vector of relative velocity V has an x-component only.

5.5. Transformation of the Field Equations: Non-inertial Frame

The equations of the classical electromagnetic field constitute a proto-type illustration of the formulation of physical equations in a covariant manner, i.e. in a form that is independent of specific coordinate frames. The covariant field equations

$$\{F_{\mu\nu,\lambda}\} = 0, \qquad \mathfrak{F}^{\mu\nu}{}_{,\nu} = \mu_0 \mathfrak{F}^{\mu} \qquad (5.34)$$

are true in all Riemannian coordinate manifolds. Although when the operations indicated in eqn. (5.34) are carried out in terms of the coordinates of different systems, the results may differ in appearance, it is the tensor equations (5.34) that are regarded as having covariant character.

The aggregate of all possible inertial frames form a distinctive set, in that in these frames the equations of the electromagnetic field (Maxwell's equations) always assume the same form, whatever the magnitude or orientation of their relative velocities. It was the experimental consequences of this fact that gave rise to the special theory of relativity.

We observed in the preceding section that the individual members of the transformed tensor $\bar{F}_{\mu\nu}$ may present a complex appearance when expressed in terms of the "old" field components, but that whatever quantity occupies, for example, the positions F_{10} and F_{23} of the transformed tensor are the $\bar{E}_1$ component of electric field and the $\bar{B}_1$ component of magnetic field in the new system, respectively. It is necessary to properly take account of this characteristic feature of the operation of coordinate transformation in order to interpret the character of the electromagnetic equations predicted for the new coordinate frame by any given transformation.

Let us illustrate the transformation of electromagnetic field equations by investigating the physical laws predicted by the Galilean transformation:

$$t = \bar{t},$$

$$x = V\bar{t} + \bar{x},$$

$$y = \bar{y},$$

$$z = \bar{z}$$

(5.35)

where the unbarred coordinates are assumed to be the coordinates of an inertial frame. The matrix of the transformation is

$$\frac{\partial x^\alpha}{\partial \bar{x}^\mu} = \begin{pmatrix} 1 & 0 & 0 & 0 \\ V & 1 & 0 & 0 \\ 0 & 0 & 1 & 0 \\ 0 & 0 & 0 & 1 \end{pmatrix}.$$

(5.35a)

By use of a procedure like that employed in the preceding section, the transformed covariant field tensor in the Galilean frame is found to be

$$F_{\mu\nu} = \begin{pmatrix} 0 & -E_1 & -(E_2 - VB_3) & -(E_3 + VB_2) \\ E_1 & 0 & B_3 & -B_2 \\ (E_2 - VB_3) & -B_3 & 0 & B_1 \\ (E_3 + VB_2) & B_2 & -B_1 & 0 \end{pmatrix}.$$

(5.36)

The transformation laws for the physical components of electromagnetic field may be read from eqn. (5.36) and are seen to be

$$\bar{E}_1 = E_1, \qquad\qquad \bar{B}_1 = B_1,$$

$$\bar{E}_2 = (E + V \times B)_2, \qquad \bar{B}_2 = B_2,$$

$$\bar{E}_3 = (E + V \times B)_3, \qquad \bar{B}_3 = B_3.$$

(5.37)

Equations (5.37) show that at low velocity ($V \ll c$) the Galilean transformation of fields is in agreement with the Lorentz transformation [eqns. (5.33)].

The source-free Maxwell equations (containing no charge or current terms) are based upon the covariant tensor $F_{\mu\nu}$:

$$\{F_{\mu\nu,\lambda}\} = 0.$$

In the light of the remarks made above, the source-free equations will always have the same appearance when written in terms of the $\bar{E}$ and $\bar{B}$ fields observed within any coordinate frame.

In terms of our present example of the Galilean frame, we identify the members of the Galilean field tensor [eqn. (5.36)] as

$$F_{\mu\nu} = \begin{pmatrix} 0 & -\bar{E}_1 & -\bar{E}_2 & -\bar{E}_3 \\ \bar{E}_1 & 0 & \bar{B}_3 & -\bar{B}_2 \\ \bar{E}_2 & -\bar{B}_3 & 0 & \bar{B}_1 \\ \bar{E}_3 & \bar{B}_2 & -\bar{B}_1 & 0 \end{pmatrix} \tag{5.38}$$

where the barred quantities are the physically observable fields *within* the Galilean frame, their values in terms of the unbarred fields being given by eqn. (5.36).

The metric tensor of individual coordinate manifolds are used, however, in raising indices to obtain $F^{\mu\nu}$, upon which the remaining field equations are based:

$$F^{\mu\nu} = \bar{g}^{\mu\alpha}\bar{g}^{\nu\beta}F_{\alpha\beta}, \tag{5.39}$$

$$(\sqrt{-g}.F^{\mu\nu})_{,\nu} = \mu_0 \sqrt{-g}.\bar{J}^{\mu}. \tag{5.40}$$

Therefore we may expect the charge- and current-containing electromagnetic field equations to exhibit differences peculiar to individual coordinate spaces.

Let us consider the form assumed by eqns. (5.40) when transformed to the Galilean coordinate space (which we know is not a true inertial frame). From eqn. (5.35) the Galilean metric is

$$ds^2 = (c^2 - V^2)\,dt^2 - 2V\,dx\,dt - dx^2 - dy^2 - dz^2 \tag{5.41}$$

for which the metric tensor forms are

$$\bar{g}_{\mu\nu} = \begin{bmatrix} (c^2 - V^2) & -V & 0 & 0 \\ -V & -1 & 0 & 0 \\ 0 & 0 & -1 & 0 \\ 0 & 0 & 0 & -1 \end{bmatrix}, \quad \bar{g}^{\mu\nu} = \begin{bmatrix} \dfrac{1}{c^2} & -\dfrac{V}{c^2} & 0 & 0 \\ -\dfrac{V}{c^2} & -K^2 & 0 & 0 \\ 0 & 0 & -1 & 0 \\ 0 & 0 & 0 & -1 \end{bmatrix}, \quad (5.42)$$

$$\bar{g} = -c^2$$

where we have put $K^2 = (1 - V^2/c^2)$ in $\bar{g}^{\mu\nu}$.

Calculation of the contravariant field tensor by the use of the Galilean metric in eqn. (5.40) with eqn. (5.42) yields the result

$$\bar{F}^{\mu\nu} = \frac{1}{c^2}$$

$$\begin{pmatrix} 0 & \bar{E}_1 & (\bar{E}_2 + V\bar{B}_3) & (\bar{E}_3 - V\bar{B}_2) \\ -\bar{E}_1 & 0 & -(V\bar{E}_2 - c^2 K^2 \bar{B}_3) & -(V\bar{E}_3 + c^2 K^2 \bar{B}_2) \\ -(\bar{E}_2 + V\bar{B}_3) & (V\bar{E}_2 - K^2 c^2 \bar{B}_3) & 0 & c^2 \bar{B}_1 \\ -(E_3 - VB_2) & (V\bar{E}_3 + c^2 K^2 \bar{B}_2) & -c^2 \bar{B}_1 & 0 \end{pmatrix}.$$

$$(5.43)$$

The source-containing field equations [eqns. (5.40)] valid within the Galilean frame may then be written, after grouping of terms,

$$\nabla \cdot \bar{E} = \frac{1}{\varepsilon_0} \bar{\varrho} - V(\nabla \times \bar{B})_1, \quad (5.44)$$

$$\left(1 - \frac{V^2}{c^2}\right)(\nabla \times \bar{B})_1 = \mu_0 \bar{J}_1 + \frac{1}{c^2} \dot{\bar{E}}_1 + \frac{V}{c^2} (\nabla \cdot \bar{E} - \bar{E}_{1,1}), \quad (5.45)$$

$$\left(1 - \frac{V^2}{c^2}\right)(\nabla \times \bar{B})_2 = \mu_0 \bar{J}_2 + \frac{1}{c_2} \dot{\bar{E}}_2 + \frac{V}{c^2} \dot{\bar{B}}_3 + \frac{V}{c^2} \bar{E}_{2,1} - \frac{V^2}{c^2} \bar{E}_{3,1},$$

$$(5.46)$$

$$\left(1 - \frac{V^2}{c^2}\right)(\nabla \times \bar{B})_3 = \mu_0 \bar{J}_3 + \frac{1}{c^2} \dot{\bar{E}}_3 + \frac{V}{c^2} \dot{\bar{B}}_2 - \frac{V}{c^2} \bar{E}_{3,1} + \frac{V^2}{c^2} \bar{B}_{1,2}.$$

$$(5.47)$$

Equations (5.44) to (5.47) show that the equations of the electromagnetic field in the Galilean frame are distinctly unlike the Maxwell equations of inertial frames, which have the form

$$\nabla \cdot \bar{E} = \frac{1}{\varepsilon_0} \varrho,$$

$$(\nabla \times \bar{B})_i = \mu_0 J_i + \frac{1}{c^2} \dot{\bar{E}}_i \quad (i = 1, 2, 3).$$

The field components appearing in eqns. (5.44–47) are not the result of transformation from another coordinate frame, but are the actual observable components of $\bar{E}$ and $\bar{B}$ within the Galilean manifold. The equations were obtained, as we have seen, by raising indices in the "standard" form of $F_{\mu\nu}$ given in eqn. (5.38), and use of field equation (5.40).

The characteristic that the form of the equations of the electromagnetic field is determined by the metric of a given space furnishes us with a valuable tool for obtaining information concerning the metric by means of experiment. If solutions can be found for the electromagnetic field equations predicted by the covariant formalism we have discussed above, then experimental verification of these solutions can, in principle, provide validation of the metric. The importance of electromagnetism to general relativity is indicated by the fact that many of the experimental tests of general relativity have involved electromagnetic signals: e.g. the bending of light rays from the stars in the gravitational field of the sun, the red shift of radiation emitted by atoms or nuclei in a gravitational potential, that were discussed in Chapter 4.

Problems

5.1. Verify that eqn. (5.11) in Cartesian-coordinate form $F_{\mu\nu} = A_{\nu,\mu} - A_{\mu,\nu}$, leads to the electromagnetic field tensor as given in eqn. (5.12).

5.2. Prove by direct calculation that terms containing Christoffel symbols cancel in eqn. (5.13), leaving only partial derivative terms.

5.3. Calculate $F^{\mu\nu}$ from $F_{\mu\nu}$ [eqn. (5.12)] in the metric

$$ds^2 = (1 + h)(c^2 dt^2 - dx^2 - dy^2 - dz^2).$$

Then show that in this metric, eqn. (5.14) leads to the electromagnetic field equations:

$$\varepsilon_0 \, \nabla \cdot \mathfrak{E} = \varrho(1 + h)^2,$$

$$\nabla \times \mathfrak{H} = \mathfrak{J}(1 + h)^2 + \varepsilon_0 \dot{\mathfrak{E}}.$$

5.4. With use of eqns. (5.12) and (5.25), calculate $F^{\alpha\beta}F_{\alpha\beta}$, showing that the result has the form specified below eqn. (5.26).

5.5. Construct $g^{\alpha\beta}$ for an inertial frame with spherical space coordinates, and with use of eqn. (5.17), find the spherical-coordinate form of the Lorentz forces f^μ, eqn. (5.28). Show that the component f^0 represents the rate at which work is done on the charge q, and therefore depends on the components of E field only. Verify that the remaining components $f^i(i = 1, 2, 3)$ correspond to the conventional Lorentz force in spherical coordinates.

Chapter 6

Gravitational Fields and Waves

WE HAVE thus far made extensive use of the typically relativistic technique of the coordinatization of physical laws in terms of the 1 + 3 coordinates of event-space, without any explicit examination of the intrinsic nature of time and space coordinates, or of the specific means to be used in their measurement. In so far as we restrict our consideration to inertial frames, no difficulties arise, and we can take over the concepts of distance and time and their measurement from classical non-relativistic physics without change. An inertial observer can establish a uniform time scale throughout his coordinate domain by transmitting flashing light signals, which travel at a constant known velocity, and for which transit-time corrections can be readily made at any point. Distance measurements may be made from the origin of coordinates to any point by means of a standard meter bar. No concern is felt for the reliability or meaning of length measurements made at any point in the inertial frame, since there are no stresses in the meter bar produced by gravitational or inertial forces. The inertial-frame observer knows, moreover, how to account for measurements made on objects or clocks in uniform motion with respect to himself by use of the Lorentz transformation, and the meaning of the time and space coordinates and their measurement is well defined. In non-inertial coordinate frames, this simple situation does not prevail, however, and some conventions concerning the meaning of the time and space coordinates (t, x, y, z) or (t, r, ϱ, ϕ) must be established.

6.1. Space and Time Measurements in Non-inertial Frames

In a non-inertial coordinate system having a metric which is equivalent to a weakly perturbed inertial metric, of the form discussed in Section 3.3,

$g_{\mu\nu} = g^0_{\ \mu\nu}(1 + f_{\mu\nu})$, where $f_{\mu\nu} \ll 1$, the concepts of distance and time measurement can be carried over from inertial frames with slight modification. It is assumed that correction will be made for the elastic deformation of meter sticks employed in an inertial or gravitational field. Measuring rods used to measure radial distances in a point-mass gravitational field will suffer elongation under their own weight by a predictable amount, which may be corrected for. Alternatively, such measurement may be made with meter sticks of progressively higher elastic stiffness constants, the limiting value of these distance readings being taken as the "true" distance measured. By these means, the concept of the ideal measuring rod may be approached. Coordinate intervals of distance dx^j ($j = 1, 2, 3$) between a pair of events in a non-inertial frame are defined by meter-stick measurements (where dx^j has the dimensions of length). The contribution of dx^j to the invariant interval ds^2 between events is given by $g_{jj}(dx^j)^2$, if the metric has no off-diagonal components. The concept of a coordinate distance increment dx, or dr, is analogous to the conventional concept of measured distance. Likewise, angular coordinate intervals in non-inertial frames are defined as the result of conventional goniometer measurements.

The time coordinate variable, t, of the event space of general relativity is, however, not in general measured as the rate of a physical clock, in the same way that the coordinate time of special relativity is measured. The basic invariant of general relativity is the infinitesimal increment of world line:

$$ds = (g_{\mu\nu} \, dx^\mu \, dx^\nu)^{1/2} = \text{invariant}. \tag{6.1}$$

In coordinates ($\bar{x}^\nu = \bar{t}, \bar{x}, \bar{y}, \bar{z}$) of the rest frame of a clock that moves so as to be present successively at the initial and final events bounding the interval ds, this is

$$d\bar{s} = \bar{g}_{00}^{1/2}(\bar{x}^j = 0) \, d\bar{t} \tag{6.2}$$

where $\bar{g}_{00}(\bar{x}^j = 0)$ is the value of $\bar{g}_{00}$ evaluated at the origin in the rest frame of the clock. The *proper time* of the clock is defined to be

$$d\bar{\tau} = \frac{1}{c} \, d\bar{s},$$

$$d\bar{\tau} = \frac{1}{c} \, [\bar{g}_{00}(\bar{x}^j = 0)]^{1/2} \, d\bar{t}. \tag{6.3}$$

Because of eqn. (6.1) the increment of proper time $d\tau$ is an invariant, i.e. it has the same magnitude, when evaluated between a pair of infinitesimally separated events in the coordinates of any frame of reference

$$d\bar{\tau} = \frac{1}{c} \left(g_{\mu\nu}(x^\lambda) \, dx^\mu \, dx^\nu \right)^{1/2}, \tag{6.4}$$

where the space-like components dx^μ of $d\tau$ do not vanish if the proper frame is in motion relative to the frame of the coordinates x^μ.

Because of the coordinate dependence of the metric tensor $g_{\mu\nu}$, the value of the integral of $d\tau$ between two events with finite separation is not unique, being dependent upon the path of integration in coordinate space. The coordinate–time difference $(t_2 - t_1)$ between two finitely separated events is, however, uniquely determined by the coordinates (t_1, x_1, y_1, z_1) and (t_2, x_2, y_2, z_2) of the two events. To summarize the foregoing:

$$d\tau_{12} = \text{invariant,}$$

$$(\Delta\tau)_{12} = \int_1^2 d\tau : \text{non-unique (path-dependent),}$$

$$(\Delta t)_{12} = \int_1^2 dt = (t_2 - t_1): \text{unique, within given coordinate frame.}$$

In the light of its definition, eqn. (6.3), the proper time interval $d\tau$ is taken to be definable as the period of oscillation of a natural clock, such as a maser or vibrating molecule. The coordinate–time scale of t may be established by adopting a specific natural clock in the coordinate system as the standard clock. Light pulses sent out by the standard clock and received in all parts of the coordinate frame establish the coordinate-time rate everywhere. The rate of local natural clocks can then in principle be regulated to coincide with the rate of the standard clock.

The coordinate–time difference between pulses of the standard clock remains constant during propagation of the light. This may be seen as follows: in the propagation of light, $ds^2 = 0$. Assuming, for example, the radial propagation of light in spherical coordinates from $r = 0$ to r_f,

$$0 = g_{00} \, dt^2 - g_{11} \, dr^2, \tag{6.5}$$

$$\int_0^T dt = \int_0^{r_f} (g_{11}/g_{00})^{1/2} \, dr \tag{6.6}$$

$$= F(r_f).$$

Changing limits of integration on the left in eqn. (6.6),

$$\int_{n\Delta T}^{T_n} dt = \int_{(n+1)\Delta T}^{T_{n+1}} dt = F(r_f) \tag{6.7}$$

where T_j and $j \Delta T$ are the arrival time and departure time of the jth pulse, respectively. At any location r_f, the difference in arrival times of pulses that start at time intervals ΔT is

$$\{T_{n+1} - (n + 1) \Delta T\} - \{T_n - n \Delta T\} = F(r_f) - F(r_f), \tag{6.8}$$

$$T_{n+1} - T_n = \Delta T. \tag{6.9}$$

Thus, on the coordinate–time scale, the period of arrival of pulses at any point is constant and independent of location.

Thus, by use of the characteristic that light propagates on null geodesics, we have deduced the constancy of the coordinate–time interval Δx^0 between two successive light signals, in all parts of the coordinate manifold during propagation of the light.

Our discussion has centered around the contravariant component, Δx^0, of the time interval. It will be of interest to inquire at this point concerning the significance of the covariant component Δx_0, and the absolute magnitude of "physical" component, $(\Delta x^0 \Delta x_0)^{1/2}$, of a time interval. For events separated by a purely timelike interval in the coordinate frame of interest, the covariant component is

$$\Delta x_0 = g_{00} \, \Delta x^0 \tag{6.10}$$

and the scalar magnitude of the interval is

$$(\Delta x^0 \Delta x_0)^{1/2} = \sqrt{g_{00}} \cdot \Delta x^0. \tag{6.11}$$

The "physical" component of time interval [eqn. (6.11)] is identical therefore with the quantity we have defined as the proper time interval, $\Delta\tau = \sqrt{g_{00}} \cdot \Delta t$.

6.1a. Spatial Line Element of a General Metric

We frequently wish to know the spatial line element $d\sigma^2$ in the three-dimensional subspace of a general $(3 + 1)$-dimensional region described by a metric:

$$ds^2 = g_{\mu\nu}\, dx^\mu\, dx^\nu.$$

When the metric contains no off-diagonal elements, $(g_{\mu 0} = 0)$, the spatial interval separates from the time-like component of the interval, in the form

$$ds^2 = g_{00}(dx^0)^2 - d\sigma^2.$$

The interval $d\sigma$ has the physical significance that it is a length measured by a free (unconstrained) meter stick in the given coordinate manifold. In a similar way, the proper time $d\tau$, measured by a free but stationary clock, is given when $g_{\mu 0} = 0$ by

$$d\tau^2 = (1/c^2)\, g_{00}\, dt^2 \qquad (d\sigma^2 = 0)$$

where dt is the coordinate–time interval corresponding to proper time interval $d\tau$. If the world-line element ds^2 has undergone coordinate transformation to the coordinates of the rest frame or proper frame of the clock, the restriction of stationarity may be lifted and the clock may move with respect to the spatial coordinates of the enveloping manifold.

In the event that the metric tensor of a given manifold has off-diagonal elements, the metric is not time-orthogonal, having a line element of the form

$$ds^2 = g_{00}(dx^0)^2 + g_{j0}\, dx^j\, dx^0 + g_{ij}\, dx^i\, dx^j$$

where $i, j = i, 2, 3$. The correct spatial part of the line element is here not obtained by setting $dx^0 = 0$ in the metric $d\sigma^2 \neq g_{ij}\, dx^i\, dx^j$. The correct spatial line element for a non-time-orthogonal metric is given by†

$$-d\sigma^2 = \left(g_{ij} - \frac{g_{i0}g_{j0}}{g_{00}}\right) dx^i\, dx^j.$$

6.2. The Schwarzschild Gravitational Field

It has been seen in Section 3.4 that the differential equation to be satisfied by the metric tensor $g_{\mu\nu}$ in matter-free space is obtained from the requirement that the contracted Riemann tensor vanish:

$$R_{\alpha\beta} = 0.$$

It was shown that the resulting set of four differential equations [eqns. (4.26a–d)] can be satisfied by the metric

$$ds^2 = (1 + f)\, c^2\, dt^2 - \frac{dr^2}{(1 + f)} - r^2(d\theta^2 + \sin\theta\, d\phi^2). \qquad (6.12)$$

Schwarzschild's solution arises when the function f takes the form

$$f = -\frac{2MG}{c^2 r}. \qquad (6.13)$$

Extensive use is made of this metric, as has been shown by the discussion of the experimental tests of general relativity in Sections 4.3 to 4.5. The applications which were made of the metric in those sections were confined to spatial regions of weak gravitational field, where

$$|f| = \frac{2MG}{c^2 r} \ll 1. \qquad (6.14)$$

Our considerations have thus far remained away from the apparent singularity in the metric that occurs at the gravitational radius, or "Schwarzschild radius", $r_c = 2MG/c^2$:

$$ds^2 = \left(1 - \frac{2MG}{c^2 r}\right) c^2\, dt^2 - \frac{dr^2}{\left(1 - \frac{2MG}{c^2 r}\right)} - r^2(d\theta^2 + \sin^2\theta\, d\phi^2).$$

$$(6.15)$$

† C. Møller, *The Theory of Relativity*, p. 238, Oxford University Press, 1962.

The weak-field limitation of eqn. (6.14) is a characteristic one, since the magnitude of f is small nearly everywhere in the universe. Table 6.1 lists the value of f at the extremal surface of various objects.

TABLE 6.1. SCHWARZSCHILD'S $f = 2MG/c^2 r_{surf}$.

Proton	$1 \cdot 75 \times 10^{-39}$
Iron sphere (1 kg)	$2 \cdot 2 \times 10^{-26}$
Earth	$1 \cdot 4 \times 10^{-9}$
Neutron star†	$0 \cdot 57$
Universe‡	$\simeq 1$

Clearly, no objects accessible to immediate observation will exhibit a Schwarzschild singularity, but there is reason to be interested in the properties of this metric in its singular region. Neutron stars having densities of the order of 10^{15} g/cm^3 and radii of a few kilometers have been hypothesized to explain astronomical observations.

We may investigate the motion of free mass points in a Schwarzschild field by use of the geodesic equations of motion

$$\ddot{x}^\mu + \left\{ \begin{matrix} \mu \\ \nu\lambda \end{matrix} \right\} \dot{x}^\nu \dot{x}^\lambda = 0$$

where a dot implies d/dk. Using the Christoffel symbols of this metric [eqns. (4.22)] we find

$$\ddot{t} + \frac{f'}{1+f} \dot{t}\dot{r} = 0, \tag{6.16}$$

$$\ddot{r} + \frac{c^2}{2}f'(1+f)\dot{t}^2 - \tfrac{1}{2}\frac{f'}{1+f}\dot{r}^2 - r(1+f)\dot{\theta}^2 - r(1+f)\sin^2\theta\,\dot{\phi}^2 = 0, \tag{6.17}$$

$$\ddot{\theta} + \frac{2}{r}\dot{r}\dot{\theta} - \sin\theta\cos\theta\dot{\phi}^2 = 0, \tag{6.18}$$

$$\ddot{\phi} + \frac{2}{r}\dot{r}\dot{\phi} + 2\cot\theta\dot{\theta}\dot{\phi} = 0. \tag{6.19}$$

† Ya. B. Zeldovich and I. D. Novikov, *Stars and Relativity*, p. 285, University of Chicago Press, Chicago, 1971.
‡ W. Rindler, *Essential Relativity*, p. 195, Van Nostrand Reinhold Co., New York, 1969. This somewhat fanciful value is based on a "radius" of the universe of 10^{10} light years and a mean mass density of 10^{-29} g/cm^3.

Equation (6.16) may be integrated to yield

$$\dot{t} = \frac{K}{1 + f} \qquad (6.20)$$

where K is a constant of integration. We may first investigate the case of purely radial motion, with $\theta = 0 = \dot{\phi}$. With this condition, and using eqn. (6.20), eqn. (6.17) becomes

$$\ddot{r} = -\frac{c^2}{2} \frac{f'}{1 + f} \left(K^2 - \frac{\dot{r}^2}{c^2} \right). \qquad (6.21)$$

This equation for coordinate r in radial motion may be integrated directly by the procedure shown in some detail below:

$$\frac{d\dot{r}}{dk} = -\frac{c^2}{2} \left(K^2 - \frac{\dot{r}^2}{c^2} \right) \frac{d \ln (1 + f)}{dr}.$$

Using $dr/dk = \dot{r}$, this becomes

$$\frac{2\dot{r} \, d\dot{r}}{c^2 \left(K^2 - \dfrac{\dot{r}^2}{c^2} \right)} = -d \ln (1 + f),$$

$$\ln \left(K^2 - \frac{\dot{r}^2}{c^2} \right) = \ln (1 + f) + \ln A$$

where $\ln A$ is a constant of integration.

$$\dot{r}^2 = c^2 [K^2 - A(1 + f)],$$

$$\frac{dr}{dk} = c[K^2 - A(1 + f)]^{1/2}.$$

From eqn. (6.20), $dk = (1/K)(1 + f) \, dt$. Eliminating dk from the preceding equation, we obtain

$$\frac{dr}{dt} = c(1 + f) \left[1 - \frac{A}{K^2} (1 + f) \right]^{1/2}. \qquad (6.22)$$

Equation (6.22) is the equation of coordinate velocity, defined with respect to coordinate time t, of a point mass in a Schwarzschild gravitational field. In this field, $f = -2MG/c^2 r$.

The constant A/K^2 may be evaluated in terms of the initial velocity V_i at initial radius r_i. Substitution of this limit into eqn. (6.22) yields

$$V_i = c(1 + f_i)\left[1 - \frac{A}{K^2}(1 + f_i)\right]^{1/2}, \quad \text{where} \quad f_i = -2MG/c^2 r_i.$$

We may now define

$$\chi_i{}^2 \equiv \frac{A}{K^2} = \frac{1}{1 + f_i}\left[1 - \frac{V_i{}^2}{c^2(1 + f_i)^2}\right]. \tag{6.23}$$

The velocity of an infalling point mass with an initial velocity of V_i at $r = r_i$ is, therefore, from eqns. (6.22) and (6.23),

$$v_r = \frac{dr}{dt} = c(1 + f)[1 - \chi_i{}^2(1 + f)]^{1/2}. \tag{6.24}$$

Equation (6.24) indicates that the coordinate velocity of the falling particle vanishes at the Schwarzschild singularity, where $f = -1$. In the region between $2MG/c^2 < r < \infty$, the velocity of the particle undergoes variations markedly unlike the monotonic increase predicted by Newtonian gravitational theory. At a radius r_e, the velocity $dr/dt = v_r$ reaches an extremal value, which we may calculate in the following way:

$$\frac{dv_r}{dr} = 0,$$

$$0 = cf'[1 - \chi_i{}^2(1 + f)]^{1/2} - \frac{c}{2}\chi_i{}^2(1 + f)f'[1 - \chi_i{}^2(1 + f)]^{-1/2}$$

where $f = f(r_e)$. This expression reduces to

$$1 = \tfrac{3}{2}\chi_i{}^2(1 + f).$$

Using $f = -2MG/c^2 r_e$, evaluated at the radius at which maximum velocity occurs, we find for this radius

$$r_e = \frac{2MG/c^2}{1 - (2/3)\chi_i{}^2}.$$

In terms of the radius of Schwarzschild singularity $r_s = 2MG/c^2$, the radius of maximum v_r is

$$r_e = \frac{r_s}{1 - (2/3)\chi_i^2}. \tag{6.25}$$

Equations (6.25) and (6.23) show that if the particle begins accelerating at large r ($r \to \infty$) with zero initial velocity, it will attain a maximum value of coordinate velocity at a distance of three Schwarzschild radii from the mass point at the origin. From eqn. (6.24) the maximal coordinate velocity v_r attained, from $V_i = 0$, is $v_{r\max} = c(2/3)(\sqrt{1/3}) = 0.39c$. This relativistic behavior of the particle motion cannot be observed in any experiment within the solar system, for the Schwarzschild radius of all attainable masses is far inside the exterior surface of all objects, and no singularity is actually ever formed. Table 6.2 shows Schwarzschild radii r_c corresponding to the mass of various objects.

TABLE 6.2. SCHWARZSCHILD RADII r_c

Proton	2.47×10^{-52} cm
10-kg sphere	1.48×10^{-25} cm
Earth	0.89 cm
Sun	2.95 km
Neutron star ($r = 9.3$ km)[†]	4.5 km
Galaxy NGC 2403	7×10^{12} km

Equation (6.21) shows that the geodesic acceleration d^2r/dk^2 of a particle becomes infinite at the Schwarzschild radius r_c (K^2 assumed equal to unity). It is concluded that no particle reaching the Schwarzschild radius of a gravitational field can escape being pulled inside that radius. Therefore, a body around which a genuine surface of Schwarzschild singularity exists is assumed to be an infinite sink for nearby masses pulled into its gravitational field. Such an object is therefore called a black hole. Since the accumulation of infalling particles increases the total mass and critical radius, r_c, of a black hole, the growth of such an object is progressive. It is assumed to be the final state of the gravitational collapse of stars to extremely great density.

[†] Ya. B. Zeldovich and I. D. Novikov, *Stars and Relativity*, p. 285, University of Chicago Press, 1971.

The coordinate time required for an object to fall from rest to the singular radius is infinite. This may be illustrated by writing eqn. (6.24) for a particle that starts with zero initial velocity at $r = r_i$ ($V_i = 0$, $\chi_i = (1 + f_i)^{-1/2}$).

$$\int\limits_0^{t_s} dt = \int\limits_{r_i}^{r_s} \frac{dr}{c(1 + f)\,[1 - (1 + f)\,(1 + f_i)^{-1}]^{1/2}}.$$

Integration shows the coordinate time t_s to be infinite. It is assumed, however, that formation of a black hole is possible, through the gravitational collapse of an ultradense star.

The physical character of the region interior to the Schwarzschild radius r_c has been the subject of much inquiry.† Because of the reversal of sign of $(1 + f)$ at r_c, the signs of the time-like and space-like terms of the world-line element ds^2 are interchanged [eqn. (6.12)]. The correct physical interpretation of this behavior must remain speculative. Phenomena in the interior of a black hole are inaccessible to observation, since neither photons nor particles can escape through the Schwarzschild radius.

The Schwarzschild metric [eqn. (6.15)] predicts an anisotropic velocity of light:

$$ds^2 = \left(1 - \frac{2MG}{c^2 r}\right) c^2\,dt^2 - \frac{dr^2}{\left(1 - \dfrac{2MG}{c^2 r}\right)} - r^2(d\theta + \sin^2\theta\,d\phi^2). \quad (6.15')$$

Setting $ds^2 = 0$ for the propagation of light, the radial velocity is found by equating $d\theta$ and $d\phi$ to zero,

$$\frac{dr}{dt} = c\left(1 - \frac{2MG}{c^2 r}\right) \quad \text{radial.} \quad (6.26)$$

The peripheral velocity can be found similarly by setting dr and $d\phi$ equal to zero,

$$\frac{r\,d\theta}{dt} = c\left(1 - \frac{2MG}{c^2 r}\right)^{1/2} \quad \text{peripheral.} \quad (6.27)$$

† B. K. Harrison, K. S. Thorne, M. Wakano and J. A. Wheeler, *Gravitational Theory and Gravitational Collapse*, University of Chicago Press (1965); Ya. B. Zeldovich and I. D. Novikov, *op. cit.*, pp. 144ff.; R. Ruffini and J. A. Wheeler, *Physics Today* **24**, 30 (Jan. 1971).

At the surface of the earth (cf. Table 6.1) the velocities in the two perpendicular directions differ by approximately

$$c(2MG/c^2 r_E) \left(\tfrac{1}{2}\right) = 21 \text{ cm/sec.}$$

The Schwarzschild metric may be converted to "isotropic" form by introduction of a new coordinate of radial measure, $\bar{r}$, defined by

$$r = \frac{r_s}{2} + \bar{r} + \frac{r_s^2}{16\bar{r}}$$

or

$$\bar{r} = \tfrac{1}{2}\left(r - \frac{r_s}{2}\right)[1 \pm \{1 - r_s^2(2r - r_s)^{-2}\}^{1/2}] \qquad (6.28)$$

where $r_s = 2MG/c^2$.

When the change of variable is introduced into the Schwarzschild metric, it assumes the form

$$ds^2 = \frac{\left(1 - \dfrac{MG}{2c^2\bar{r}}\right)^2}{\left(1 + \dfrac{MG}{2c^2\bar{r}}\right)^2} c^2\, dt^2 - \left(1 + \frac{MG}{2c^2\bar{r}}\right)^4 (d\bar{r}^2 + \bar{r}^2\, d\theta^2 + \bar{r}^2 \sin^2\theta\, d\phi^2).$$

$$(6.29)$$

From the standpoint of practical applicability the isotropic form of the metric, eqn. (6.29), is of academic interest only. The variable $\bar{r}$ cannot be interpreted as the conventional radial distance. In eqn. (6.29) such an assumption would predict an isotropic velocity of light, unlike the characteristic of the centrosymmetric gravitational field metric we have seen above.

We have investigated the precession of the perihelion of an elliptical orbit in a Schwarzschild metric in Section 4.3. We may now investigate the conditions for the existence of stable orbits in this metric. Starting with eqn. (6.15) the geodesic line element ds itself may be used as a path parameter. Dividing this equation by ds^2 gives the result:

$$1 = c^2(1 + f)\,\dot{t}^2 - \frac{\dot{r}^2}{(1 + f)} - r^2\dot{\theta}^2 - r^2 \sin^2\theta\dot{\phi}^2 \qquad (6.30)$$

where $f = -2MG/c^2r$. Considering the planar orbits which remain in the plane $\theta = \pi/2$, we may set $\theta = 0$ and $\sin \theta = 1$ in eqn. (6.30), to yield

$$1 = (1 + f)\, \dot{t}^2 - \frac{\dot{r}^2}{(1 + f)} - r^2\dot{\phi}^2. \qquad (6.30\text{a})$$

From eqns. (4.21) and (4.22) we may obtain $\dot{t} = a/(1 + f)$ and $r^2\dot{\phi} = b$ where b is the angular momentum constant. Then, eqn. (6.30) becomes

$$\dot{r}^2 = (c^2a^2 - 1) + \frac{2MG}{c^2r} - \frac{b^2}{r^2} + \frac{2MGb^2}{c^2r^3}. \qquad (6.31)$$

If angular momentum b is zero, eqn. (6.31) is recognized as the classical energy equation

$$\frac{1}{2}\left(\frac{dr}{d\tau}\right)^2 - \frac{MG}{r} = E. \qquad (6.32)$$

In eqn. (6.32) $ds = c\, d\tau$ has been used, and $d\tau \simeq dt$ at low velocities. The energy $E = c^2(c^2a^2 - 1)/2$ has also been defined. Hence, the relativistic orbital equation may be written

$$E = \frac{1}{2}\left(\frac{dr}{dt}\right)^2 - \left[\frac{MG}{r} - \frac{c^2b^2}{2r^2} + \frac{MGb^2}{r^3}\right]. \qquad (6.33)$$

The terms in the square brackets on the right in eqn. (6.33) may be regarded as an effective potential energy for the orbital motion:

$$V(r) = -\frac{MG}{r} + \frac{c^2b^2}{2r^2} - \frac{MGb^2}{r^3}. \qquad (6.34)$$

Without the final term in $1/r^3$ eqn. (6.34) would be the classical Newtonian expression for the effective potential, consisting of the gravitational potential proportional to $1/r$ and the "centrifugal potential" proportional to $1/r^2$. The inverse third power term in eqn. (6.34) is a characteristic of the general-relativistic solution and is the cause of the precession of the perihelion of an elliptical orbit, as has been seen in Section 4.3.

From eqn. (6.34) there may be derived some characteristic features of the relativistic orbital motion of a particle. To simplify this equation we may assume the motion to occur in the field of a mass M having a Schwarzschild radius of 1 meter: i.e. $2MG/c^2 = 1$, therefore of approximately 110 earth masses. Equation (6.34) then becomes

$$(2/c^2)V(r) = -\frac{1}{r} + \frac{b^2}{r^2} - \frac{b^2}{r^3}. \tag{6.35}$$

In the classical Newtonian equation of motion, the potential consists of the first two terms only. Thus it has the form $(2/c^2) V(r) = -1/r + b^2/r^2$. The Newtonian potential is plotted in Fig. 6.1. For positive or

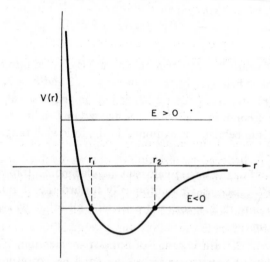

FIG. 6.1. Classical Newtonian potential.

zero particle energy E, the orbit is an open orbit (hyperbolic or parabolic, respectively). The distance of closest approach to the origin is given by the intersection of the ordinate of energy E with the potential curve, $V(r)$. For negative energy ($E < 0$), the Newtonian orbit is an ellipse. The radii of perihelion and apihelion are determined by the two intersections of the energy ordinate with $V(r)$ at r_1 and r_2, respectively.

In the relativistic case, the potential curve $V(r)$ given by eqn. (6.35) is negatively infinite at the origin. The shape of the curve and the extremal values of orbital radius depend upon the magnitude of the angular momentum b. The maxima and minima of the relativistic $V(r)$ can be found by setting dV/dr in eqn. (6.35) to zero:

$$0 = \frac{dV}{dr},$$

$$0 = \frac{1}{r^2} - \frac{2b^2}{r^3} + \frac{3b^2}{r^4}. \tag{6.36}$$

The solution of eqn. (6.36) is

$$\frac{1}{r} = \tfrac{1}{3}[1 \pm \sqrt{(1 - 3/b^2)}]. \tag{6.37}$$

The range of values of angular momentum b is divided into three regions of characteristic behavior by the values $b = \sqrt{3}$ and $b = 2$. The radii of extremal $V(r)$ are, from eqn. (6.37), $r = 3$ in the first case, and $r = 2$ and 6 in the second, in units of the Schwarzschild radius r_c.

Characteristic behavior is exhibited in the following ranges of angular momentum:

1. $b < \sqrt{3}$. For the lowest values of angular momentum, the potential curve $V(r)$ decreases monotonically toward the origin. A distance of minimum radius does not exist, and all orbits will pass through the origin.

2. $\sqrt{3} < b < 2$. In this range of angular momentum, $V(r)$ is always negative and has two extrema, at r_1 and r_2, corresponding to the selection of the negative or positive sign in eqn. (6.37), respectively. Bound elliptical orbits exist for particles having energies E between $V(r_1)$ and $V(r_2)$.

3. $b > 2$. The potential curve exhibits a positive maximum of $V(r)$, as indicated in Fig. 6.2. Particles with angular momentum $b > 2$ and positive energy E less than the maximum of $V(r)$ will not reach the origin, although for $E > V(r)_{\max}$ they will do so. The distinguishing feature of the relativistic orbits of particles in a Schwarzschild field is that particles with non-zero angular momentum, and which have energies in excess of the values at which a stable orbit can be formed, will have orbits that pass through the origin. This is

markedly unlike the behavior of Newtonian orbits, in which a particle with any non-zero angular momentum can never reach the origin.†

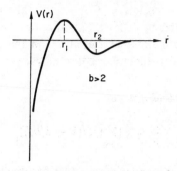

FIG. 6.2. Schwarzschild potential with $b > 2$.

6.3. Gravitational Waves

The gravitational fields investigated thus far have been assumed to be described by metric tensor functions $g_{\mu\nu}$ which are independent of the time coordinate. The only parameter available for introducing a time variation into the centrally symmetric Schwarzschild gravitational metric is the magnitude of the source mass M. Few practical schemes short of the conversion of mass to radiation are available for creating a reasonably rapid time dependence of M. Most of the conceivable methods for varying the gravitational field in time involve the spatial rearrangement of components of the source mass M. In view of the energy cost of moving large masses, it can be anticipated that if time-dependent gravitational fields appear, these will consist of only relatively weak fluctuations.

In the course of early efforts to prove that the components of the metric tensor played the role of gravitational potentials and therefore satisfied an equation of the form of Laplace's equation, it became apparent, in the $(1 + 3)$-dimensional coordinate manifolds of relativity,

† For an extensive discussion of particle orbits in Schwarzschild fields see H. P. Robertson and T. W. Noonan, *Relativity and Cosmology*, chap. 9, W. B. Saunders Co., Philadelphia, 1968.

that the metric satisfied a Helmholtz equation. This finding implied that perturbations of the metric should therefore propagate as waves with the velocity of light.

The basis for the expectation of gravitational waves is most readily demonstrated by utilizing again the assumption of weak gravitational fields that constitute a slight perturbation on the Lorentz metric. For simplicity we assume rectangular coordinates: (ct, x, y, z). The metric is therefore

$$g_{\mu\nu} = \begin{pmatrix} (1 + f_{00}) & f_{01} & f_{02} & f_{03} \\ f_{10} & -(1 + f_{11}) & f_{12} & f_{13} \\ f_{20} & f_{21} & -(1 + f_{22}) & f_{23} \\ f_{30} & f_{31} & f_{32} & -(1 + f_{33}) \end{pmatrix}. \quad (6.38)$$

In eqn. (6.38) the $f_{\mu\nu}$ are small quantities which are retained to first order only in the analysis.

The metric tensor is required to satisfy the field equation

$$R_{\alpha\beta} = 0.$$

The contracted Riemann tensor is given by eqn. (2.98):

$$R_{\alpha\beta} = -\begin{Bmatrix} \varrho \\ \alpha\beta \end{Bmatrix} [\ln \sqrt{-g}]_{,\varrho} + [\ln \sqrt{-g}]_{,\alpha,\beta} - \begin{Bmatrix} \varrho \\ \alpha\beta \end{Bmatrix}_{,\varrho} + \begin{Bmatrix} \sigma \\ \varrho\beta \end{Bmatrix} \begin{Bmatrix} \varrho \\ \sigma\alpha \end{Bmatrix}.$$

$$(6.39)$$

In evaluating $R_{\alpha\beta}$ to first order in the small quantities $f_{\mu\nu}$ we note that each term of the Christoffel symbols contains a derivative of a metric tensor element:

$$\begin{Bmatrix} \varrho \\ \alpha\beta \end{Bmatrix} = \tfrac{1}{2} g^{\varrho\nu}(g_{\alpha\nu,\beta} + g_{\beta\nu,\alpha} - g_{\alpha\beta,\nu}).$$

The derivative removes the unit elements on the diagonal which are the dominant members of $g_{\mu\nu}$ [eqn. (6.38)]. Therefore, the Christoffel symbols are at most of first order in the $f_{\mu\nu}$ and their derivatives. Consequently, the products of Christoffel symbols in $R_{\alpha\beta}$ are of second order of smallness and are hence neglected. With this assumption, the equation $R_{\alpha\beta} = 0$

becomes

$$\left\{ \begin{array}{c} \varepsilon \\ \alpha\beta \end{array} \right\}_{,\varepsilon} = [\ln \sqrt{-g}]_{,\alpha,\beta}. \tag{6.40}$$

The determinant g of eqn. (6.38) is, to first order in the $f_{\mu\nu}$,

$$g = -(1 + f_{00})(1 + f_{11})(1 + f_{22})(1 + f_{33}),$$

$$g = -1 - \sum_\mu f_{\mu\mu}. \tag{6.41}$$

When this value of g is inserted into eqn. (6.40) and the logarithm expanded to first order in the $f_{\mu\mu}$, the result may be used in eqn. (6.39) to yield

$$\tfrac{1}{2} [g^{\varepsilon\nu}(f_{\alpha\nu,\beta} + f_{\beta\nu,\alpha} - f_{\alpha\beta,\nu})]_{,\varepsilon} = \tfrac{1}{2} \sum_\mu f_{\mu\mu,\alpha,\beta} \tag{6.42}$$

where the full expression for the Christoffel symbol has been used on the left. The dominant terms in $g^{\varepsilon\nu}$ are terms of unit magnitude on the diagonal. That is, $g^{\varepsilon\nu} \simeq (\pm\delta_{\varepsilon\nu} + \text{terms of order of } f_{\mu\nu})$. In this expression the $(+)$ sign is used when $\varepsilon = \nu = 0$, and the $(-)$ sign with $\varepsilon = \nu = 1, 2, 3$. Using this property of $g^{\varepsilon\nu}$ in eqn. (6.42) and neglecting higher order terms, the equation becomes

$$g^{\varepsilon\varepsilon}(f_{\alpha\varepsilon,\beta,\varepsilon} + f_{\beta\varepsilon,\alpha,\varepsilon} - f_{\alpha\beta,\varepsilon,\varepsilon}) = \sum_\mu f_{\mu\mu,\alpha,\beta} \tag{6.43}$$

where, because of eqn. (6.42), summation is carried out over ε. The order of partial differentiation may be inverted in the first two terms of eqn. (6.43). Doing this, and regrouping terms, the equation may be written

$$\left[g^{\varepsilon\varepsilon} f_{\alpha\varepsilon,\varepsilon} - \tfrac{1}{2} \sum_\mu f_{\mu\mu,\alpha} \right]_{,\beta} + \left[g^{\varepsilon\varepsilon} f_{\beta\varepsilon,\varepsilon} - \tfrac{1}{2} \sum_\mu f_{\mu\mu,\beta} \right]_{,\alpha} - g^{\varepsilon\varepsilon} f_{\alpha\beta,\varepsilon,\varepsilon} = 0 \tag{6.44}$$

where the sum over μ has been divided into the two equal terms shown.

The functions $f_{\mu\nu}$ are still arbitrary, and we are free to specify their properties. Therefore we impose the following condition:

$$g^{\varepsilon\varepsilon} f_{\alpha\varepsilon,\varepsilon} - \tfrac{1}{2} \sum_\mu f_{\mu\mu,\alpha} = 0. \tag{6.45}$$

Since the first two terms of eqn. (6.44) are equivalent they both vanish with eqn. (6.45), and there remains

$$g^{\varepsilon\varepsilon} f_{\alpha\beta,\varepsilon,\varepsilon} = 0. \qquad (6.46)$$

As the index ε assumes its four values, eqn. (6.46) represents the Helmholtz equation,† which may also be written

$$\square^2 f_{\alpha\beta} = \frac{\partial^2 f_{\alpha\beta}}{\partial x^2} + \frac{\partial^2 f_{\alpha\beta}}{\partial y^2} + \frac{\partial^2 f_{\alpha\beta}}{\partial z^2} - \frac{1}{c^2} \frac{\partial^2 f_{\alpha\beta}}{\partial t^2} = 0. \qquad (6.47)$$

Equation (6.47) shows that the gravitational potentials $f_{\alpha\beta}$ propagate as waves with the velocity of light.

The gravitational forces acting on test particles in the path of the waves are in planes transverse to the direction of propagation of the waves. The forces have quadrupole symmetry, because of the conditions placed on the gravitational potentials by eqn. (6.45). Test particles in a plane normal to the direction of wave propagation will undergo relative displacements as indicated in Fig. 6.3. Over an expanding wave front of

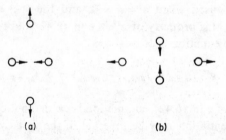

(a)   (b)

FIG. 6.3. Displacement of test particles by a gravitational wave.

a gravitational wave the displacements of a distribution of test particles will be analogous to the displacements of coordinate lines painted on a hollow rubber ball near its equator, as it undergoes elongation and compression along its axis (Fig. 6.4).

† The preceding calculation, which has made plausible the existence of gravitational waves, is confirmed by more rigorous treatment. See R. Adler, M. Bazin and M. Schiffer, *op. cit.*, p. 250; J. Weber, *General Relativity and Gravitational Waves*, Interscience Publishers, N.Y., 1961.

Weber† has shown that the motion of test particles resulting from the passage of gravitational waves can be expressed by the equation of

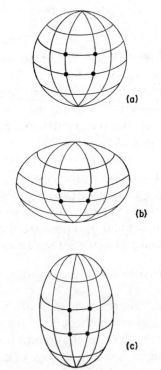

FIG. 6.4. Representation of particle displacements on a spreading gravitational wave front, near equator of ellipsoidal figure.

geodesic deviation [eqn. (3.68)],

$$\frac{D^2 y^\mu}{Dk^2} + R^\mu_{\alpha\beta\gamma}\dot{x}^\alpha y^\beta \dot{x}^\gamma = \frac{1}{mc^2}\frac{DF^\mu}{Dh}\,dh, \qquad (6.48)$$

where y^μ is the transverse separation between the geodesic lines of two test particles, such that $y^\mu = r^\mu + \xi^\mu$ where r^μ is their mean separation, and F^μ is the physical force acting between particles (Fig. 6.5).

† J. Weber, *Phys. Rev.* **117**, 306 (1960).

For time-like geodesic lines cD/Dk may be replaced by d/dt in eqn. (6.48). The equation of motion of test particles of mass m then becomes

$$\frac{d^2\xi^\mu}{dt^2} + \frac{\lambda^{\mu\alpha}}{m}\frac{d\xi^\alpha}{dt} + \frac{k^\mu{}_\alpha\xi^\alpha}{m} = -c^2 R^\mu{}_{0\alpha0}r^\alpha \qquad (6.49)$$

where $k^\mu{}_\alpha$ is a spring force or elastic constant of the medium, and $\lambda^\mu{}_\alpha$ a damping constant. The time-dependent Riemann curvature tensor component acts as the driving force of the gravitational disturbance. The solution of eqn. (6.49) is an oscillation of the form

$$\xi^\mu = \frac{-mc^2 R^\mu{}_{0\alpha0}r^\alpha}{(k - \omega^2 m) + i\omega\lambda} e^{i\omega t} \qquad (6.50)$$

where the deflection is assumed to be unidirectional, and the damping and elastic constants reduce to the scalars λ and k, respectively.

FIG. 6.5. Schematic representation of gravitational wave detector.

Figure 6.5 is a schematic representation of the essential features of the deformation of any elastic body under gravitational forces. The deformation may be made to drive electromechanical transducers which provide an electrical signal upon the passage of a gravitational wave. In order to attain maximum signal, the deformation [eqn. (6.50)] is maximized by choosing a resonant mechanical configuration ($m\omega^2 = k$) and by minimizing inelastic forces, represented by the loss constant λ. In the terminology of oscillatory systems, a high-Q resonator is required. A detector designed in keeping with these principles has been built and operated by Weber.† The detector consists of an aluminum cylinder of 1400 kg mass, having a lowest normal mode of oscillation at 1660 Hz. Piezoelectric strain gauges bonded to the surface of the cylinder detect its deformations under fluctuating gravitational forces. This detector, operated in coincidence with a similar unit at large distance to discriminate

† J. Weber, *Phys. Rev. Letters* 17, 1228 (12 Dec. 1966); 18, 498 (27 Mar. 1967); 20, 1307 (8 June 1968); 22, 1320 (16 June 1969).

against local perturbations, shows occasional pulses of response above thermal noise background. The magnitude of the responses observed is interpreted to indicate that during the pulse a gravitational energy flux of the order of 20 watts per square meter passes the detector. This large energy flux, observed within the narrow detector bandwidth of about 0·16 Hz, implies very energetic sources of gravitational radiation, if these are located at distances of the order of the dimensions of the galaxy.

The choice of the frequency of resonance of a resonant detector is a somewhat arbitrary matter, since the frequencies of principal gravitational wave intensity necessarily depend upon the character of the sources. A calculation of the frequencies and intensities of the gravitational radiation to be expected from various astronomical phenomena known or presumed to exist has been made by Ezawa.†

The emission of gravitational radiation is to be expected from the non-uniform motions of massive objects. The most massive objects, the galaxies and clusters of galaxies, typically have extremely slow periodic motions, with periods of the order of 10^6 years. The rate of radiation of energy from a rotating asymmetrical object is proportional to the sixth power of the angular velocity. The power radiated by a spinning rod is‡

$$P = 1.73 \times 10^{-59} I^2 \omega^6 \text{ ergs/sec}$$

where I is the moment of inertia of the rod. (The frequency of the gravitational radiation emitted is twice the angular frequency of rotation due to the quadrupole character of the source.) Therefore the rotating galaxies, or even multiple-star groups with periods of order 10^3–10^5 sec, will not be looked to as sources of gravitational radiation, in spite of their great masses. In order to account for gravitational waves with periods of the order of 10^{-3} sec, it is necessary to look for other phenomena. Among the sources which have been suggested are collision events involving massive stars or possibly black holes, or events involving matter in the ultradense form of neutron stars.

It has been shown, however, that binary stellar systems in the last stages of their existence can emit large amounts of gravitational radiation

† Z. F. Ezawa, *J. Phys. Soc. Japan* **28**, 1576 (1970).
‡ A. S. Eddington, *Proc. Roy. Soc. (Lond.)* A **102**, 268 (1923).

at high frequency.† A binary stellar system is defined as a pair of bodies rotating under their mutual gravitational attraction. These may range in size from objects having 10^6 to 10^8 solar masses to collapsed neutron stars having masses of the order of one solar mass. Neutron stars, the existence of which has been hypothesized but not verified, may have small radii, of the order of 5–10 km.

The rotational energy of a binary pair of stars of masses m and M respectively, separated by distance l, decays through gravitational radiation. The rate of emission of energy and the frequency of the radiation increase rapidly with decreased l during the final stages of decay, until the two objects come into contact. The emitted power and the frequency of the gravitational waves are given by:

$$P(t) = \frac{GmM}{8}\, \gamma^{-1/4} t^{-5/4} \text{ ergs/sec,}$$

$$f = (1/\pi)\,[G(m + M)]^{1/2}\, \gamma^{-3/8} t^{-3/8} \text{ Hz}$$

where t is the time remaining until final collapse of the system, and

$$\gamma = 2^8 G^3 mM(m + M)/5c^5.$$

For a pair of stars, each having one solar mass, the rate of emission rises to 10^{49} watts at the end of the lifetime of the system, while the angular speed of rotation increases to 10^3 to 10^4 rad/sec. Hence a binary star could account for a flux of gravitational radiation of 20 W/m² in the range of 1–2 kHz at a distance of 10^{20} km.

The maximum range R at which an optimally constructed detector can detect a decaying binary star source is calculated to be‡

$$R^2{}_{\max} = \frac{25c^2\mu l^2}{1536\pi kTQ^2}$$

where μ is the mass of the detecting block of matter, l its length, and Q the resonator quality factor. It is assumed that the signal power in the antenna is just equal to the thermal noise power level of kT, where T is the temperature of the antenna. From this relation, if collapsing neutron–

† R. L. Forward and D. Berman, *Phys. Rev. Letters* **18**, 1070 (1967).
‡ R. Forward and D. Berman, *op. cit.*

binary star systems exist, they could just be detected at a distance of 3000 light years.

Problems

6.1. In the gravitational metric,

$$ds^2 = c^2(1 - b/r)\,dt^2 - (1 + b/r)\,dr^2 - r^2\,d\theta^2 - r^2 \sin^2\theta\,d\phi^2,$$

calculate the proper time difference between points 1 and 2 in the diagram, when $\int_1^2 d\tau$ is evaluated (a) along the circular arc connecting points 1 and 2, and (b) along the path 1, 3, 4, 2. Assume in each case that the path is traversed at a coordinate velocity such that $r\,d\theta = V\,dt$, or $dr = V\,dt$, for travel along an arc or radius, respectively. Assume that $(V/c)^2 \ll 1$, and $(b/r) \ll 1$.

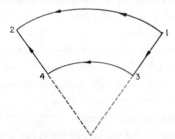

6.2. Discuss the gravitational red shift. (a) Does a molecule (or atom) on the surface of the sun vibrate more slowly than a molecule or atom of similar kind on the earth? Define clearly all terms used in answer. (b) Does the period of oscillation of a photon change during transit of the photon from sun to earth? (c) Can any significance be attached to the concept of proper time of a moving photon? Explain.

6.3. Compare the radial velocity of fall, v_r, of an object in a Schwarzschild field [eqn. (6.24)] with the velocity of a falling particle predicted by Newtonian theory: $(m/2) (v_n^2 - V_i^2) = mMG(1/r - 1/r_n)$. Assuming that an object starts at $r \to \infty$ from rest ($V_i = 0$), would the deviation of Newtonian velocity v_n from the relativistic value v_r be measurable?

6.4. Construct the spatial line element $d\sigma^2$ for the metric of the rotating disc found in eqn. (3.11b): $ds^2 = (c^2 - r^2\omega^2)\,dt^2 - dr^2 - r^2d\theta^2 - 2r^2\omega\,d\theta\,dt - dz^2$. Show that the spatial interval on the disc is†

$$d\sigma^2 = dr^2 + r^2\,d\theta^2/(1 - r^2\omega^2/c^2) + dz^2.$$

6.5. In the propagation of a gravitational wave in the (x^1) direction, assume the plane-wave condition $\partial/\partial x^2 = 0 = \partial/\partial x^3$ (i.e. no dependence of metric on coordinates in transverse planes). Calculate the Riemann tensor component $R^2{}_{020}$, under the weak-field assumptions employed: products of $f_{\mu\nu}$ negligible, $g^{\mu\nu} = \delta_{\mu\nu}$. Show that $R^2{}_{020} = -(1/2)\,g_{22,\,0,\,0}$.

† Cf. C. W. Berenda, *Phys. Rev.* **62**, 280 (1942).

Chapter 7

Relativity in Cosmology

GENERAL relativity was initially constructed as a theory of the gravitational field that would provide a rational basis for the equivalence of gravitational and inertial masses. The theory showed that all free mass points, as well as photons, move along geodesic trajectories in the (1 + 3)-coordinate manifold of event-space. General relativity further showed that the mass content of the universe has a part in determining the curvature of space and, consequently, of governing the mechanics of free mass points and the propagation of light. General relativity thus has a fundamental significance for cosmology, the science of the structure of the universe.

A basic task of cosmology is to establish the correct relationship between the geometrical structure of the universe and its matter and energy content. This relationship is embodied in Einstein's equation, in its most general form:

$$R_{\alpha\beta} - \tfrac{1}{2} g_{\alpha\beta} R + \Lambda g_{\alpha\beta} = -\frac{8\pi G}{c^2} T_{\alpha\beta}. \qquad (7.1)$$

Knowledge of, or a hypothesis for, the metric tensor $g_{\alpha\beta}$ of the universe is necessary for the construction of the left side of eqn. (7.1). Knowledge of the distribution of matter and energy in space in the form of galaxies, dust clouds, gas and radiation is necessary for the construction of the right side of the equation. In this sense Einstein's equation may be said to provide the link between theory and observation in astrophysics.

The overall appearance of the universe, as presented to observation at the maximum distances visible to the largest telescope, is that of a roughly uniform distribution of matter in the form of stars collected into the gravitationally bound associations called galaxies, or nebulae. The sun is one of possibly 10^{11} stars in the local galaxy, or the Milky Way. The total number of galaxies visible approaches the order of 10^8.[†] Although galaxies are observed to occur in large clusters, containing up to 10^3 to 10^4 galaxies in loose association, the general distribution of matter as seen throughout the visible universe appears to be broadly uniform. In addition to the matter visible by its luminosity, the universe contains an unknown amount of matter within and between the galaxies. This invisible matter includes dust, gas, and particulate and electromagnetic radiation. Its mass may equal or exceed that of the visible matter in some parts of the universe.[‡]

The radius of the visible universe is generally assumed to be of the order of 10^{10} light years, or $9 \cdot 5 \times 10^{22}$ km. This radius is the estimated distance to the most remote nebulae visible with the 200-in.-diameter Hale reflecting telescope. Distances to less-remote galaxies can be estimated with some confidence by identifying in the galaxy a stellar object similar to well-known objects in our local galaxy. The distance to the stellar object in the distant galaxy is then calculated on the basis of its apparent magnitude, by use of the inverse square law for radiation intensities. Objects useful for distance measurements in this manner are the Cepheid variable stars and the red giants, whose properties are well known and studied.

In estimating the distance l to a distant star of a well-known type, the intensity of radiation $I(10)$ which would be received from a star of that type located at a standard distance of 10 parsecs is used[§] in the inverse square law formula:

$$l = 10 \sqrt{\{I(10)/I(l)\}} \text{ parsecs}$$

where $I(l)$ is the intensity of light actually received from the star situated at distance l. In terms of the astronomical measure of stellar magnitudes

† G. Abell, *Exploration of the Universe*, Holt, Rinehart & Winston, New York, 1964.

‡ *Ibid.*, p. 574; B. Pontecorvo and J. Smorodinsky, *J. Exp. Theor. Phys.* (trans.) **14**, 173 (1962).

§ The parsec is a distance of $3 \cdot 08 \times 10^{16}$ m.

m, this distance may be calculated from

$$l = 10^{\frac{5+m-M}{5}} \text{ parsecs}$$

where m is the apparent magnitude of the distant star, and M is its absolute magnitude, assumed known.

The distance to a remote galaxy in which individual stars cannot be resolved may be estimated on the basis of the apparent magnitude of the galaxy, if it is of a normal type. Since galaxies vary greatly in luminosity, distance estimates made in this way are not known to be correct within a factor of possibly 2 to 5.

For the most distant objects in the universe, the concept of a meter-stick-measured distance from the earth cannot have any operational significance. Distance values estimated from apparent magnitudes have the character of defined quantities, and must be regarded as such. Thus, whereas in the treatment of the gravitational field of the solar system it was conceptually meaningful to speak of a measure of coordinate distance based on physical measurements which could perhaps be carried out, at least in principle, this concept of distance measurement is no longer conceivable on the cosmological scale. Our concept of physical distances on the scale of the cosmic universe will therefore tend necessarily to assume the character of quantities defined by their mode of estimate.

It was discovered by V. M. Slipher in 1912 to 1925, and confirmed by E. M. Hubble in 1929, that spectral lines in the light from stars in the distant galaxies predominantly exhibit a shift in wavelength toward the red end of the spectrum. The magnitude of the fractional wavelength shift is proportional to the distance l to the galaxy according to

$$\frac{\Delta\lambda}{\lambda} = \frac{Hl}{c} \tag{7.2}$$

where H is Hubble's constant, equal to $3 \cdot 2 \times 10^{-18}$ sec^{-1}. The fractional red shift $\Delta\lambda/\lambda$ is apparently proportional to the distance l, to the most remote galaxies observed. Because of this consistent behavior, eqn. (7.2) may be inverted, and the distance to a remote galaxy estimated on the basis of its observed red shift, when a spectral line can be recorded in the light received from the galaxy.

The characteristics of structural uniformity in the visible appearance of the cosmic universe have led to the adoption of the following list of criteria which any cosmological theory is expected to fulfill:

1. It must predict an isotropic universe with uniform characteristics everywhere, to conform to the picture of the actual universe uniformly filled with a nearly constant matter density.
2. The universe should present the same aspect to all observers, situated in any region of the universe at a given time. This requirement is known as the cosmological principle, and expresses the belief that the part of the universe in which our galaxy is located is not unique in any way.
3. A theory of the universe must provide an explanation of the linearly increasing red shift of light from matter at increasing distances from any observer.

Due to the nature of astronomical observations, no means is available whereby a hypothesis for the physical mechanism causing the red shift of spectral lines from the distant galaxies can be directly verified. The cosmological red shift might be assumed to be gravitational in origin (Section 4.5), and a metric tensor of the universe constructed to predict this property. The consequences of such an assumption would violate the first two requirements in the foregoing list, if a non-uniform gravitational field were predicated to exist in the universe, however. The viewpoint adopted in cosmological theory has not assumed a gravitational explanation for the red shift, but has instead preferred to consider the cosmological red shift to be a Doppler shift caused by motion of the distant galaxies away from observers on earth.

7.1. Metric Tensor of the Universe: the Robertson–Walker Metric

The hypothesis of a high-velocity recession of distant matter in the universe is tenable in the light of the cosmological principle, if the mass points are assumed to be situated on the axes of a coordinate framework that is assumed to be undergoing a uniform expansion everywhere. The concept of an expanding scale of the universe which is envisioned in this model is illustrated in Fig. 7.1. The galaxies (the mass "particles" of the model) are located at points of constant coordinate value,† while the coordinate framework, shown as a rectangular mesh in the diagram,

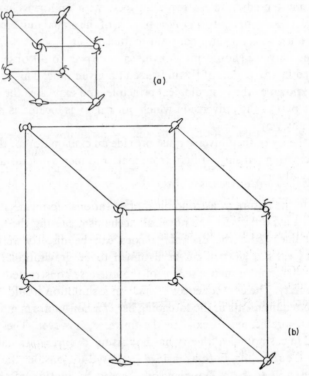

(a)

(b)

FIG. 7.1. Expanding Robertson–Walker coordinate network. Galaxies remain associated with fixed coordinate points.

expands at a uniform rate everywhere. In an extended network of such galaxies, the galaxy at every coordinate point will see all the other galaxies receding from itself, the relative velocity of recession being greater, the greater is the *coordinate* separation between the pair of galaxies considered.

† The "peculiar" motions of the galaxies, or their individual velocities relative to the center of mass of the surrounding galaxies, are ignored in this model.

The fact that one may speak of a relative velocity of galaxies due to the expansion of the coordinate axes implies that there is an underlying coordinate space which is not expanding, and in which rigid measuring rods exist† that may be used to define the velocity of expansion of the cosmic frame. This underlying frame is a local frame of inertia [eqn. (4.12)] and, because of the manner in which the coordinates are defined, may be taken to be the proper coordinate frame of any one of the galaxies.

To the cosmological model of a mechanically expanding universe is added the classical Newtonian assumption of the existence of a universal time, t, which progresses at a constant rate uniformly everywhere in the universe. This assumption is effected by assigning to g_{00} the Lorentz value: $g_{00} = c^2$. The assumption that the intersections of the space-coordinate network are occupied by free mass particles has the effect of making the coordinate lines of the time coordinate $x^0 = t$ identical with geodesic lines. The three-dimensional network of the spatial coordinates, identified by the lattice of free mass points at its nodes, is called *comoving*. At any instant of time, in this picture, the matter of the world is at rest with respect to the space coordinates (again neglecting peculiar motions of the particles).

The metric tensor of the universe which embodies the preceding assumptions is the Robertson–Walker (RW) metric:

$$ds^2 = c^2 \, dt^2 - R^2(t) \frac{d\bar{r}^2 + \bar{r}^2 \, d\theta^2 + \bar{r}^2 \sin^2 \theta \, d\phi^2}{(1 + k\bar{r}^2/4)^2}. \qquad (7.3)$$

In eqn. (7.3), $R(t)$ is a function of time, which has the dimensions of a length, and which has the role of the "radius" of the universe.‡ The coordinate $\bar{r}$ is a dimensionless variable normalized to a constant length r_0,

$$\bar{r} = r/r_0, \qquad (7.3a)$$

---

† R. S. Tolman, *op. cit.*, p. 384.
‡ The symbol $R(t)$, which has been adopted by conventional usage, should not be confused with the Riemann curvature scalar, R. The latter will be denoted by $R^\alpha{}_\alpha$, to avoid confusion.

where r is the conventional radial distance. The constant k in eqn. (7.3) may assume the values $+1$, 0, or -1. The RW metric did not originally arise as a postulate, but was obtained historically as the most general isotropic metric satisfying the three postulates of cosmology and the field equations [eqn. (7.1)]. The metric satisfies the requirement of spatial isotropy, since it contains the Euclidean spacelike line element $dr^2 + r^2\,d\theta^2 + r^2\sin^2\theta\,d\phi^2$, normalized to the length r_0. The spatial isotropy of eqn. (7.3) is made more evident by writing it in terms of Cartesian space coordinates,

$$ds^2 = c^2\,dt^2 - R^2(t)\frac{d\bar{x}^2 + d\bar{y}^2 + d\bar{z}^2}{[1 + (k/4)(\bar{x}^2 + \bar{y}^2 + \bar{z}^2)]^2}, \qquad (7.4)$$

where $\bar{x}, \bar{y}, \bar{z}$ are the usual space coordinates x, y, z, divided by the normalizing constant r_0:

$$\bar{x}, \bar{y}, \bar{z} = x/r_0,\ y/r_0,\ z/r_0. \qquad (7.4a)$$

The line element ds^2 of eqn. (7.4) is unchanged by rotation of coordinates $\bar{x}, \bar{y}, \bar{z}$. Thus it is spatially isotropic.

The spacelike part of eqn. (7.4),

$$dl^2 = R^2(t)\frac{d\bar{x}^2 + d\bar{y}^2 + d\bar{z}^2}{[1 + (k/4)(\bar{x}^2 + \bar{y}^2 + \bar{z}^2)]^2}, \qquad (7.5)$$

was investigated in Section 2.7, and was there found to be the metric of a three-space of constant curvature. Its Riemann curvature invariant $R^\alpha{}_\alpha$ was found to have the value

$$R^\alpha{}_\alpha = -\frac{6k}{R^2(t)} \quad \text{(3-space).} \qquad (7.6)$$

When the spacelike element [eqn. (7.5)] is incorporated into the RW metric, the curvature invariant of the resulting $(3 + 1)$-dimensional manifold is found to be†

$$R^\alpha{}_\alpha = \frac{6R_{tt}}{c^2 R} + \frac{6R_t{}^2}{c^2 R^2} + \frac{6k}{R^2} \quad \text{(RW metric)} \qquad (7.7)$$

† Cf. eqn. (7.35).

where R_{tt} denotes $\partial^2 R/\partial t^2$. The four-dimensional Riemann curvature scalar of the RW metric is uniform throughout coordinate space, but the time derivative terms in R_α^α have appeared in addition to the curvature of the spatial manifold. (The sign change of the latter term is due to the difference in overall sign assumed for the metric in the respective cases.)

The form of the time-dependent function $R(t)$ is governed by the requirement that the RW metric must be a solution of the field equations for matter-filled space [eqn. (7.1)].

Before proceeding to investigate the extent to which the form of $R(t)$ is determined by our knowledge of the matter–energy tensor of the universe $T_{\alpha\beta}$, it will be of interest to verify that the RW metric does indeed predict a red shift of galactic spectral lines in keeping with Hubble's law [eqn. (7.2)]. For the propagation of light, eqn. (7.4) is a null geodesic, and without loss of generality we may consider propagation of light along the x-axis, between two nebulae situated at x_1 and x_2 ($y = 0 = z$). Equation (7.4) then becomes

$$0 = c^2\, dt^2 - R^2(t)\frac{dx^2}{\left[1 + \dfrac{kx^2}{4}\right]^2}. \tag{7.8}$$

Therefore,

$$\int_{t_1}^{t_2} \frac{c\, dt}{R(t)} = \int_{x_1}^{x_2} \frac{dx}{\left[1 + \dfrac{kx^2}{4}\right]}. \tag{7.9}$$

We may regard successive crests of a light wave as separate signals. Therefore eqn. (7.9) represents the departure of a crest from point x_1 at time t_1 and its arrival at x_2 at time t_2. We then consider that the next succeeding crest leaves x_1 at time $t_1 + \Delta t_1$, and arrives at x_2 at time $t_2 + \Delta t_2$. For the transit of this second "signal", eqn. (7.9) then takes the form

$$\int_{t_1+\Delta t_1}^{t_2+\Delta t_2} \frac{c\, dt}{R(t)} = \int_{x_1}^{x_2} \frac{dx}{\left[1 + \dfrac{kx^2}{4}\right]}. \tag{7.10}$$

The right sides of eqn. (7.9) and eqn. (7.10) have the same value for both of these signal transits, since the limits x_1 and x_2 are the same in both cases. It is a result of the definition of the concept of comoving coordinates that fixed coordinate numbers always remain associated with each free mass point. Thus we may combine the two equations to yield

$$\int_{t_1}^{t_2} \frac{c\, dt}{R(t)} = \int_{t_1 + \Delta t_1}^{t_2 + \Delta t_2} \frac{c\, dt}{R(t)}. \tag{7.11}$$

The two integrals may be broken up into separate segments in the following way:

$$\int_{t_1}^{t_1 + \Delta t_1} + \int_{t_1 + \Delta t_1}^{t_2} = \int_{t_1 + \Delta t_1}^{t_2} + \int_{t_2}^{t_2 + \Delta t_2}. \tag{7.12}$$

Cancellation of equal terms yields

$$\int_{t_1}^{t_1 + \Delta t_1} \frac{dt}{R(t)} = \int_{t_2}^{t_2 + \Delta t_2} \frac{dt}{R(t)}. \tag{7.13}$$

If the intervals Δt_1 and Δt_2 are short enough so that $R(t)$ may be considered to have the constant values $R(t_1)$ and $R(t_2)$ through the intervals, respectively, eqn. (7.13) may be written

$$\frac{\Delta t_1}{\Delta t_2} = \frac{R(t_1)}{R(t_2)}. \tag{7.14}$$

In our example, Δt_1 and Δt_2 are the periods of the light wave as observed at points x_1 and x_2 respectively, at the coordinate times t_1 and t_2. Each galaxy has been assumed to be in geodesic motion under no force, and the velocity of light as observed in each local frame is thus assumed to have the standard value c. Therefore the observed wavelengths of the light wave in the present example will be $\lambda_1 = c\,\Delta t_1$ and $\lambda_2 = c\,\Delta t_2$, respectively. Therefore, eqn. (7.14) becomes

$$\frac{\lambda_1}{\lambda_2} = \frac{R(t_1)}{R(t_2)}. \tag{7.15}$$

Defining the shift in the wavelength of the light as received at x_2 to be $\Delta\lambda = \lambda_2 - \lambda_1$, eqn. (7.15) may be written

$$\frac{\lambda_1 + \Delta\lambda}{\lambda_1} = \frac{R(t_2)}{R(t_1)}. \tag{7.16}$$

A relative shift in wavelength z is defined

$$z = \frac{\Delta\lambda}{\lambda} = \frac{R(t_2)}{R(t_1)} - 1. \tag{7.17}$$

Equation (7.17) shows that if $R(t)$ increases with time, $R(t_2) > R(t_1)$, the shift in the received wavelength will be positive, or toward the red end of the spectrum. In this way the RW metric accounts for the red shift of the light from the galaxies.

The quantity $R(t_2)$ in eqn. (7.17) may be expanded in terms of $(t_2 - t_1)$:

$$R(t_2) = R(t_1) + \dot{R}_1(t_2 - t_1) + \ddot{R}_1 \frac{(t_2 - t_1)^2}{2} + \cdots \tag{7.18}$$

where the dot indicates time differentiation, and $\dot{R}_1$ is the value of $\dot{R}$ at t_1. When eqn. (7.18) is substituted into eqn. (7.17), the result, to first order in $(t_2 - t_1)$, is

$$z = \frac{\dot{R}(t_1)}{R(t_1)}(t_2 - t_1). \tag{7.19}$$

If the classical value l/c is substituted for $(t_2 - t_1)$, where l is the astronomical distance between galaxies, the red shift parameter z becomes

$$z = \frac{\Delta\lambda}{\lambda} = \frac{\dot{R}}{R}\frac{l}{c}. \tag{7.20}$$

Comparison with eqn. (7.2) shows that this is Hubble's law, with Hubble's constant given by $H = \dot{R}/R$.

In order to make a more specific test of the suitability of the RW metric as a description of the cosmic universe, it is necessary to determine its properties as a solution of the Einstein field equations:

$$R_{\alpha\beta} - \tfrac{1}{2}g_{\alpha\beta}R + \Lambda g_{\alpha\beta} = -\frac{8\pi G}{c^2}T_{\alpha\beta}. \tag{7.21}$$

The cosmological constant Λ is included in this equation although, as has been seen in the discussion following eqn. (4.68), the arguments for its retention are inconclusive. Einstein originally included this term in the field equation while attempting to construct a static (non-time-dependent) metric of the universe in the form of eqn. (4.56). He found the Λ term necessary to permit the presence of a non-zero mass density ϱ, without the assumption of an unrealistic-seeming negative pressure in the universe. It will be seen below, however, that the admission of a non-static metric of the universe, in the form of the factor $R(t)$ of the RW metric, allows a model of the universe in which ϱ is present without the necessity for negative pressure.

In carrying out the test of the RW metric in the field equations [eqn. (7.21)], it will be convenient to exploit the fact that working with tensor quantities in Cartesian coordinate form can often facilitate lengthy algebraic calculations through use of the similarity of tensor components that differ only in the rotation of coordinate indices. This property may be used at will to obtain internal checks on calculation, or to eliminate duplication of labor in the calculation of tensor components. Let us therefore begin with the Cartesian-coordinate metric of eqn. (7.4), writing this in the abbreviated form†

$$ds^2 = c^2\, dt^2 - f(dx^2 + dy^2 + dz^2) \tag{7.22}$$

where we have defined:

$$f = f(t, x, y, z) \equiv \frac{R^2(t)}{[1 + (k/4)(x^2 + y^2 + z^2)]^2}. \tag{7.23}$$

In order to calculate the Riemann curvature variables in eqn. (7.21) it will be necessary to find the Christoffel symbols belonging to this metric. To do this we proceed in standard fashion, dividing eqn. (7.22) by the squared geodesic path parameter dk,

$$\left(\frac{ds}{dk}\right)^2 = c^2\dot{t}^2 - f\dot{x}^2 - f\dot{y}^2 - f\dot{z}^2 \tag{7.24}$$

where a dot over the coordinate symbol indicates differentiation with

† The barred coordinate notation is dropped for simplicity, although we retain coordinates normalized to r_0 as before.

respect to k, as in previous usage. We now form the Euler–Lagrange equations:

$$\frac{d}{dk}\left[\frac{\partial}{\partial \dot{x}^{\mu}}\left(\frac{ds}{dk}\right)^2\right] = \frac{\partial}{\partial x^{\mu}}\left(\frac{ds}{dk}\right)^2.$$

The set of four geodesic equations for the t, x, y and z coordinates are found to be

$$\ddot{t} + \frac{f_t}{2c^2}\dot{x}^2 + \frac{f_t}{2c^2}\dot{y}^2 + \frac{f_t}{2c^2}\dot{z}^2 = 0,$$

$$\ddot{x} + \frac{f_t}{f}\dot{x}\dot{t} + \frac{f_x}{2f}\dot{x}^2 + \frac{f_y}{f}\dot{x}\dot{y} + \frac{f_z}{f}\dot{x}\dot{z} - \frac{f_x}{2f}\dot{y}^2 - \frac{f_x}{2f}\dot{z}^2 = 0, \tag{7.25}$$

$$\ddot{y} + \frac{f_t}{f}\dot{y}\dot{t} + \frac{f_x}{f}\dot{x}\dot{y} + \frac{f_y}{2f}\dot{y}^2 + \frac{f_z}{f}\dot{y}\dot{z} - \frac{f_y}{2f}\dot{x}^2 - \frac{f_y}{2f}\dot{z}^2 = 0,$$

$$\ddot{z} + \frac{f_t}{f}\dot{z}\dot{t} + \frac{f_x}{f}\dot{x}\dot{z} + \frac{f_y}{f}\dot{y}\dot{z} + \frac{f_z}{2f}\dot{z}^2 - \frac{f_z}{2f}\dot{x}^2 - \frac{f_z}{2f}\dot{y}^2 = 0,$$

where the subscripts on f denote differentiation with respect to the corresponding variables. The Christoffel symbols may be obtained from eqns. (7.25) by inspection. Letting index 0 represent coordinate t, and i or j represent x, y, z, the symbols are:

$$\begin{Bmatrix} 0 \\ ii \end{Bmatrix} = \frac{f_t}{2c^2}, \qquad \begin{Bmatrix} i \\ 0i \end{Bmatrix} = \frac{f_t}{2f},$$

$$\begin{Bmatrix} i \\ ii \end{Bmatrix} = \frac{f_i}{2f}, \tag{7.26}$$

$$\begin{Bmatrix} i \\ jj \end{Bmatrix} = -\frac{f_i}{2f},$$

$$\begin{Bmatrix} i \\ ij \end{Bmatrix} = \frac{f_j}{2f}.$$

The components of $R_{\alpha\beta}$ may be obtained by use of eqn. (2.98)

$$R_{\alpha\beta} = p_{,\alpha,\beta} - \left\{ \begin{matrix} \sigma \\ \alpha\beta \end{matrix} \right\}_{,\sigma} - \left\{ \begin{matrix} \sigma \\ \alpha\beta \end{matrix} \right\} p_{,\sigma} + \left\{ \begin{matrix} \sigma \\ \alpha\varrho \end{matrix} \right\} \left\{ \begin{matrix} \varrho \\ \sigma\beta \end{matrix} \right\}$$

where $p = \ln \sqrt{-g} = \ln c + (3/2) \ln f$. Evaluation of $R_{\alpha\beta}$ in terms of the function f yields

$$R_{00} = \frac{3}{2} \frac{f_{tt}}{f} - \frac{3}{4} \left(\frac{f_t}{f} \right)^2, \tag{7.27}$$

$$R_{ii} = \frac{f_{ii}}{2f} - \frac{3}{4} \left(\frac{f_i}{f} \right)^2 + \frac{1}{2} \frac{\nabla^2 f}{f} - \frac{1}{4} \left(\frac{\nabla f}{f} \right)^2 - \frac{f_{tt}}{2c^2} - \frac{1}{4c^2} \frac{f_t^2}{f}, \tag{7.28}$$

$$R_{ij} = \frac{f_{ij}}{2f} - \frac{3}{4} \frac{f_i f_j}{f^2} \qquad (i \neq j). \tag{7.29}$$

Substitution of the function $f = R(t)^2 [1 - kr^2/4]^{-2}$ into eqns. (7.27), (7.28) and (7.29) leads to the Riemann tensor components

$$R_{ii} = - \frac{[2k + (2/c^2) R_t^2 + (1/c^2) RR_{tt}]}{(1 + kr^2/4)^2}, \tag{7.30}$$

$$R_{00} = 3 \frac{R_{tt}}{R}, \tag{7.31}$$

$$R_{ij} = 0 \quad (i = j). \tag{7.32}$$

The Riemann curvature invariant is given by

$$R^{\alpha}_{\ \alpha} = g^{\alpha\alpha} R_{\alpha\alpha},$$

$$= g^{00} R_{00} + g^{11} R_{11} + g^{22} R_{22} + g^{33} R_{33}. \tag{7.33}$$

The contravariant RW metric tensor, used for raising indices in eqn. (7.33), has the form

$$g^{\alpha\beta} = \begin{pmatrix} 1/c^2 & 0 & 0 & 0 \\ 0 & -(1/f) & 0 & 0 \\ 0 & 0 & -(1/f) & 0 \\ 0 & 0 & 0 & -(1/f) \end{pmatrix}. \tag{7.34}$$

Combining eqns. (7.30) through (7.34), $R^{\alpha}{}_{\alpha}$ is found to be

$$R^{\alpha}{}_{\alpha} = \frac{6}{c^2 R^2} [RR_{tt} + R_t{}^2 + kc^2]. \tag{7.35}$$

The necessary quantities are now at hand for the construction of Einstein's equations [eqn. (7.1)]. These equations take the form

$$3 \frac{R_t{}^2}{R^2} - c^2 \left(\Lambda - \frac{3k}{R^2} \right) = \frac{8\pi G}{c^2} T_{00}, \tag{7.36}$$

$$\frac{kc^2 + R_t{}^2 + 2RR_{tt} - c^2 \Lambda R^2}{c^2 (1 + kr^2/4)^2} = -\frac{8\pi G}{c^2} T_{ii}. \tag{7.37}$$

Equations (7.36) and (7.37) are explicit formulations of the field equations in the presence of matter,

$$G_{\alpha\alpha} + \Lambda g_{\alpha\alpha} = (8\pi G/c^2) T_{\alpha\alpha},$$

evaluated in the Robertson–Walker metric [eqn. (7.23)]. The equations can be put into more compact form by raising an index to obtain the mixed-tensor equations. Thus, multiplying by $g^{\alpha\alpha}$ [eqn. (7.34)], these become

$$\frac{3R_t{}^2}{c^2 R^2} + \frac{3k}{R^2} - \Lambda = \frac{8\pi G}{c^2} T^0{}_0, \tag{7.38}$$

$$-\frac{2R_{tt}}{c^2 R} - \frac{R_t{}^2}{c^2 R^2} - \frac{k}{R^2} + \Lambda = \frac{8\pi G}{c^2} T^i{}_i. \tag{7.39}$$

The components of the mass-energy tensor, given by eqn. (3.60), are now needed for the completion of eqns. (7.38) and (7.39). Because of the assumed configuration of the Robertson–Walker universe, in which all of the mass appears in the form of a smoothed-out distribution of dust particles all of which are stationary in coordinate space, the tensor $T^{\alpha}{}_{\beta}$ has the particularly simple form:

$$T^{\alpha}{}_{\beta} = \begin{pmatrix} \varrho & 0 & 0 & 0 \\ 0 & -(p/c^2) & 0 & 0 \\ 0 & 0 & -(p/c^2) & 0 \\ 0 & 0 & 0 & -(p/c^2) \end{pmatrix}. \tag{7.40}$$

The appearance of the pressure terms in this tensor may seen anomalous in view of the fact that it should be impossible for a "gas" of stationary dust particles to sustain a pressure. The pressure term is customarily included in $T^\alpha{}_\beta$, however, in order to provide an additional parameter for use in constructing world models. At the present epoch of the universe the pressure must be very small ($p \ll c^2\varrho$), but in non-static models of the universe there is reason to assume that a pressure may exist due to the secular motions of particles, in a highly contracted epoch of the universe.

After substitution from eqn. (7.40), eqns. (7.38) and (7.39) take the form

$$\frac{3R_t{}^2}{c^2R^2} + \frac{3k}{R^2} - \Lambda = \frac{8\pi G}{c^2}\varrho, \tag{7.41}$$

$$\frac{2R_{tt}}{c^2R} + \frac{R_t{}^2}{c^2R^2} + \frac{k}{R^2} - \Lambda = -\frac{8\pi G}{c^2}\frac{p}{c^2}. \tag{7.42}$$

The field equations are independent of coordinates, and determine the time-dependent amplitude factor $R(t)$ of the RW metric. If R is assumed to be a constant, independent of time, then $R_{tt} = 0 = R_t$. With this condition the character of the earlier static-universe models is easily deduced from eqns. (7.41) and (7.42). These become, for the static case,

$$\frac{3k}{R^2} - \Lambda = \frac{8\pi G}{c^2}\varrho, \tag{7.43}$$

$$\frac{k}{R^2} - \Lambda = -\frac{8\pi G}{c^2}\frac{p}{c^2}. \tag{7.44}$$

Combining eqns. (7.44) and (7.43), we obtain

$$\Lambda = \frac{4\pi G}{c^2}(3p + \varrho). \tag{7.45}$$

We now see from eqn. (7.45) why the term containing the cosmological constant was originally introduced into the field equations for the static universe: if $\Lambda = 0$, it is necessary to assume either that $p = 0 = \varrho$, or that a negative pressure exists in the universe, in order to satisfy eqn. (7.45).

Neither of these assumptions was considered to be physically realistic. Therefore the introduction of the cosmological constant provided a reasonable solution for the dilemma.

In a zero-pressure, static universe, eqn. (7.44) shows that $\Lambda = k/R^2$. Substitution of this result into eqn. (7.43) indicates that k must be a positive number. The parameter k has been restricted to the values $k = +1, 0, -1$ by the assumption of the RW metric, hence $k = +1$. This value of k corresponds to a geometrical space of finite extent. A finite universe has astrophysical advantages over an infinite universe, since in the latter, a uniform distribution of galaxies would make the sky appear infinitely bright.

The assumption $k = 1$ in a static universe would lead to a radius R equal to $R = c^2[4\pi G(\rho c^2 + p)]^{-\frac{1}{2}}$, from eqns. (7.43) and (7.45). With zero pressure, and an assumed matter density of 10^{-27} kg/m^3, we find R to be approximately 10^{10} light years, which is of the order of the maximum distance at which nebulae are now visible.

Speculation concerning the static models of the universe is now regarded as being of historical interest only. The time-dependent RW metric of the universe with positive dR/dt is considered to provide a theoretical picture in satisfactory agreement with observations.

7.2. The Time-dependent Scale of the Universe

The time-dependent scale factor $R(t)$ multiplies the space-like part of the Robertson–Walker metric:

$$ds^2 = c^2\,dt^2 - R^2(t)\frac{(dx^2 + dy^2 + dz^2)}{[1 + kr^2/4]^2}.$$

This scale factor $R(t)$ is determined in principle by eqns. (7.41) and (7.42). These equations may be solved in accordance with arbitrarily assumed conditions:

$$k = +1, 0, -1,$$

$$\Lambda = 0, \quad \Lambda \neq 0,$$

$$p = 0, \quad p \neq 0.$$

It is necessary to assign values to the foregoing parameters in order to proceed with the calculation of $R(t)$. In addition, an estimate of ϱ, the mean mass density of the universe, must be employed. A value of $R(t)$ at a given time t is required, in principle, to provide an initial condition for the problem. Rather than proceeding to discuss all twelve possible cases resulting from arbitrary assignment of values to k, Λ and p, let us consider a selected set of conditions. This will suffice to illustrate the nature of the problem confronting astrophysics, in the utilization of the time-dependent RW metric.

On the basis of observation of the visible universe, the mean mass density ϱ is thought to be in the range[†] 10^{-28} to 10^{-24} kg/m^3. Values of $(dR/dt)/R$ can be deduced from red shift measurements of light from the galaxies. Such observations may be used in principle to calculate $1/R$ from a series expansion, of the form[‡]

$$\frac{1}{R(t)} = \frac{1}{R_0} - \frac{R_0'}{(R_0)^2}(t - t_0) + \left[\frac{(R_0')^2}{R_0{}^3} - \frac{R_0''}{2(R_0)^2}\right](t - t_0)^2 \quad (7.46)$$

where $R_0'' = d^2R/dt^2$ and $R_0' = dR/dt$, evaluated at t_0, the time of emission of the light. This procedure is useful for red shifts z smaller than $0\cdot2$, but for larger z becomes excessively tedious.

The admission of the possibility of time variation of the metric of the universe removes the condition that forced the introduction of the cosmological constant Λ into the field equations for the metric tensor. Let us therefore now investigate solutions of eqns. (7.41) and (7.42) subject to the condition $\Lambda = 0$. These equations then become

$$\frac{R_t{}^2}{c^2R^2} = \frac{8\pi G\varrho}{3c^2} - \frac{k}{R^2}, \quad (7.47)$$

$$\frac{2R_{tt}}{c^2R} = -\frac{8\pi Gp}{c^4} - \frac{k}{R^2} - \frac{R_t{}^2}{c^2R^2}. \quad (7.48)$$

† P. J. E. Peebles, *Physical Cosmology*, Princeton University Press, 1971.
‡ G. C. McVittie, *General Relativity and Cosmology*, p. 150, The University of Illinois Press, Urbana, 1965.

Substitution from eqn. (7.47) into eqn. (7.48) yields

$$R_{tt} = -\frac{4\pi G}{3}\left(\rho + 3\frac{p}{c^2}\right)R. \qquad (7.49)$$

In the comoving coordinate model of the RW metric, the mass particles remain at fixed coordinate points. If the masses were subdivided in such a way that a particle having a mass of μ kg remained associated with each unit cell of coordinate space, the density of mass would remain constant at a value of μ kg/m³ *in coordinate measure* in the RW universe, during the expansion of the coordinate space. The matter–energy tensor was defined, however, by eqn. (4.71) in such a way that $T^{00} = \varrho_0(dt/ds)^2$, where ϱ_0 is the density of mass as measured in the rest frame of the mass particles, i.e. in proper coordinates. This density does not remain constant in time in the RW metric. Therefore the quantity ϱ in eqns. (7.47) and (7.49) is a function of time. We can simplify the solution for $R(t)$ by eliminating ϱ between these equations. Therefore, combining eqns. (7.47) and (7.49), we obtain

$$R_t^2 + 2RR_{tt} + kc^2 = 0. \qquad (7.50)$$

In writing eqn. (7.50) the pressure p has been assumed to be equal to zero. In the notation we are using, $R_{tt} = d^2R/dt^2$, $R_t = dR/dt$. Equation (7.50) can be simplified by use of the identity $d(R_t^2R)/dt = R_t(2RR_{tt} + R_t^2)$. With substitution of this expression, eqn. (7.50) becomes

$$\frac{d(R_t^2R)}{dt} = -kc^2\frac{dR}{dt}. \qquad (7.51)$$

This equation may be integrated and written in the form:

$$R_tR^{1/2} = \pm\sqrt{(\alpha^2 - kc^2R)} \qquad (7.52)$$

where α^2 is a constant of integration. Let us now investigate the solution of eqn. (7.52) in which k is given the value $k = +1$.

Equation (7.52) can be simplified by introduction of the change of variable: $\beta^2R = \sin^2\theta$, where $\beta^2 = c^2/\alpha^2$. The equation then takes the form

$$\sin^2\theta\,d\theta = \pm\frac{\alpha\beta^3}{2}dt. \qquad (7.53)$$

The integral of eqn. (7.53) is

$$\theta - \sin\theta\cos\theta = \pm\alpha\beta^3(t - t_0) \tag{7.54}$$

where t_0 is a constant of integration. After restoring the variable R, the solution takes the form

$$\sin^{-1}(\beta^2 R)^{1/2} - \beta R^{1/2}\sqrt{(1 - \beta^2 R)} = \pm\alpha\beta^3(t - t_0). \tag{7.54a}$$

Equation (7.54a) describes a cyclic variation of R with time, in which R is restricted to the range of values $0 \le R \le \beta^{-2}$. The fact that the model allows R, the "radius" of the universe, to reach zero is physically unrealistic, but is assumed to be a consequence of the neglect of pressure in the model.

We may now proceed to investigate the case $k = 0$, retaining the assumption that $\Lambda = 0$. For this case, eqn. (7.52) assumes the simple form

$$R^{1/2}\,dR = \pm\alpha\,dt. \tag{7.55}$$

The solution for $R(t)$ in this case is

$$R^{3/2} = R_0^{3/2} + \tfrac{3}{2}\alpha(t - t_0). \tag{7.56}$$

If t_0 is allowed to have the value $t_0 = (2/3\alpha)\,R_0^{3/2}$, $R(t)$ starts from zero and increases monotonically with time. This behavior is characteristic of the so-called exploding, or "Big Bang", models of the universe. The matter-filled closed universe with zero pressure having a radius $R(t)$ that increases monotonically in time was first proposed by Lemaître.† Time-dependent metrics for the universe had earlier been investigated by Friedmann.‡

We consider finally the world model with $\Lambda = 0$ and $k = -1$. For this case, eqn. (7.52) becomes

$$R^{1/2}\,dR = \pm\alpha\sqrt{(1 + \beta^2 R)}\,dt \tag{7.57}$$

† G. Lemaître, *Ann. Soc. Sci. Bruxelles* **47 A**, 49 (1927).
‡ A. Friedmann, *Z. Physik* **10**, 377 (1922).

where, again, $\beta^2 = kc^2/\alpha^2$. Now, with use of the change of variable, $\beta^2 R = \sinh^2 \theta$, eqn. (7.57) is converted to

$$\sinh^2 \theta \, d\theta = \pm \frac{\alpha\beta^3}{2} \, dt. \tag{7.58}$$

This equation is easily integrated to yield:

$$\sinh \theta \cosh \theta - \theta = \pm\alpha\beta^3(t - t_0). \tag{7.59}$$

Reinserting the variable R, we find the solution to be

$$\beta R^{1/2} \sqrt{(1 + \beta^2 R)} + \sinh^{-1}(\beta R^{1/2}) = \alpha\beta^3(t - t_0). \tag{7.60}$$

Equation (7.60) describes a monotonically increasing $R(t)$. This is most easily seen from eqn. (7.59). At large θ, the left side of this equation is dominated by the term $(\sinh 2\theta)/2 \simeq (1/2) \exp(2\theta)$. Therefore, for very large R, $R(t)$ increases logarithmically with t. Thus this is another model of an "exploding" universe.

It would be desirable to test the three models of the universe we have just discussed for agreement of their predictions with the observed properties of the universe. Astronomical observation furnishes estimates of ϱ, the density of matter in the universe, and the Hubble parameter $(dR/dt)/R$ from galactic red shift data. Due to the complexity of eqns. (7.54) and (7.60), a direct analytical expression for the Hubble parameter of either of the models with non-zero k is not available for comparison with observed red shift data, although of course numerical evaluations of the parameter may be made. All three equations for $R(t)$, for cases $k = +1, 0$ and -1, contain the unknown constant of integration α, however.

We may obtain an heuristic indication of the physical significance of the constant α by means of the following calculation. From eqn. (7.52) we obtain

$$R_t^2 = \frac{\alpha^2 - kc^2 R}{R}. \tag{7.61}$$

Substitution of R_t^2 into eqn. (7.50) yields the result

$$R_{tt} = -\frac{\alpha^2}{2R^2}. \tag{7.62}$$

Placing R_{tt} from eqn. (7.62) into eqn. (7.49), we find

$$\alpha^2 = 2\left(\frac{4\pi R^3}{3}\varrho\right)G. \tag{7.63}$$

The quantity in parentheses in eqn. (7.63) has the formal structure of the calculation of the mass of a sphere of radius R and density ϱ. Therefore, α^2 has the character of the product: $2G$ times the "mass" of the universe. This quantity cannot be given a literal significance, but since α is a constant, the result implies the conservation of the total mass of the universe, which is expected in the comoving coordinate system of the RW model.

An avenue of approach to the experimental verification of the cosmological models investigated here is available, however, through the use of eqn. (7.47):

$$\left(\frac{R_t}{R}\right)^2 = \frac{8\pi G\varrho}{3} - \frac{kc^2}{R^2}. \tag{7.47'}$$

Since the left side of this equation is positive, the correct sign of k can in principle be deduced by insertion of observed values of density ϱ and of the Hubble parameter (R_t/R). The values of ϱ and (R_t/R) employed should correspond to the same time t, or epoch of the universe. The time of emission of the red-shifted light from a galaxy can be estimated from the assumed distance to the galaxy, but a value of the time t at which the observed ϱ of the universe exists is not easily assigned. The Hubble parameter (R_t/R) is approximately 3×10^{-18} sec^{-1}, and if an estimated density of $\varrho = 10^{-26}$ to 10^{-27} kg/m^3 is inserted in eqn. (7.47), the sign of k cannot be conclusively deduced. It is apparent that more precise observational data are needed before a selection can be made among models of the expanding universe.

The concept of an expanding universe has gained wide acceptance as a mechanism suitable for the explanation of the red shift of the distant galaxies through the elementary Doppler shift resulting from the recessional motion of the distant matter. The RW metric has been regarded as a most suitable time-dependent metric of the cosmos because of its spatial homogeneity, in agreement with the requirements of the cosmological principle. The temporal inhomogeneity of exploding models which require a cataclysmic event of birth of the universe has been regarded as an objectionable feature in some viewpoints, however. Expanding models of the universe which lack a distinct initial event have been postulated, which avoid the latter objection. Lemaître[†] and Robertson[‡] made early proposals of metrics in which the scale factor of the universe follows an exponential growth:

$$R(t) = R_0 e^{t/T}. \tag{7.64}$$

For philosophical reasons the view may be adopted that the universe should present the same appearance to observers at all times. This viewpoint extends the cosmological principle in effect to the time axis, requiring uniformity of aspect of the universe to observers at all points in the four-dimensional manifold of coordinates.[§]

7.3. The Steady State Universe

A cosmological model that requires the universe to maintain constant properties throughout all times is the steady state model proposed by Bondi and Gold.[††]

The Bondi–Gold steady state cosmological model postulates an expanding universe with a Robertson–Walker metric having $k = 0$. The coordinates of the steady state metric are comoving, and the three-dimensional space is flat. The metric hence has the form

$$ds^2 = c^2 \, dt^2 - \frac{R(t)^2}{R_0{}^2} (dx^2 + dy^2 + dz^2). \tag{7.65}$$

The cosmological constant of the steady state universe is assumed to be zero.

The distinction between the steady state model and the RW metric with $k = 0$ and $\Lambda = 0$ we have previously studied is that, in the latter model, the total mass of the universe was conserved, while the proper mass density ϱ decreased as $1/R^3$. In the steady state model, however,

---

† G. Lemaître, *J. Math. and Phys.* (*MIT*) **4**, 188 (1925).
‡ H. Robertson, *Phil. Mag.* **5**, 835 (1928).
§ The principle requiring temporal as well as spatial uniformity of the universe is called the perfect cosmological principle.
†† H. Bondi and T. Gold, *M. N. Roy. Astron. Soc.* **108**, 252 (1948).

the proper mass density is held constant in time. This constancy of ϱ is maintained by an assumed steady rate of creation of matter uniformly throughout the universe. The process of matter creation may be represented in the formalism of the field equations by replacing the term containing the matter tensor with a term containing the tensor $U^{\mu\nu}$,

$$R^{\mu\nu} - \tfrac{1}{2} g^{\mu\nu} R^{\alpha}_{\alpha} = \frac{3H^2}{c^2} \frac{R_0{}^2}{R(t)^2} U^{\mu\nu} \tag{7.66}$$

where H is Hubble's parameter, $H = R_t/R$, defined by eqns. (7.2) and (7.20), and $U^{\mu\nu}$ is the tensor

$$U^{\mu\nu} = \begin{pmatrix} -R(t)^2/R_0{}^2 & 0 & 0 & 0 \\ 0 & 1 & 0 & 0 \\ 0 & 0 & 1 & 0 \\ 0 & 0 & 0 & 1 \end{pmatrix}. \tag{7.67}$$

The time-dependent scale factor of the universe $R(t)$ can be calculated by use of a procedure similar to that employed in the preceding section. We construct the field equations [eqn. (7.66)] and solve the resulting differential equations for $R(t)$. The tensor components necessary for this procedure have already been found, in eqns. (7.30), (7.31) and (7.35). The equation $G^{00} = (3H^2/c^2)(R_0{}^2/R^2) U^{00}$ leads to an identity. To construct the equation in G_{ii}, we must calculate

$$R^{ii} - \tfrac{1}{2} g^{ii} R^{\alpha}_{\alpha} = \frac{3H^2}{c^2} \frac{R_0{}^2}{R(t)^2} U^{ii}. \tag{7.68}$$

Since we have calculated covariant components R_{ii} in eqn. (7.30), we must form: $R^{ii} = g^{ii} g^{ii} R_{ii}$. The contravariant metric tensor for the steady state model is

$$g^{\mu\nu} = \begin{pmatrix} 1/c^2 & 0 & 0 & 0 \\ 0 & -R_0{}^2/R^2 & 0 & 0 \\ 0 & 0 & -R_0{}^2/R^2 & 0 \\ 0 & 0 & 0 & -R_0{}^2/R^2 \end{pmatrix}. \tag{7.69}$$

Substituting into eqn. (7.68) from eqn. (7.69) and eqn. (7.30) with $k = 0$, we obtain

$$-\frac{1}{c^2}(RR_{tt} + 2R_t{}^2)\left(\frac{R_0{}^2}{R^2}\right)^2 + \frac{3}{c^3}\left(\frac{R_0{}^2}{R^2}\right)(RR_{tt} + R_t{}^2) = \frac{3H^2}{c^2}\frac{R_0{}^2}{R^2}$$

(7.70)

where, as before, subscript t indicates differentiation with respect to time. With use of eqn. (7.20) we substitute $H = R_t/R$ on the right, and obtain finally

$$RR_{tt} - R_t{}^2 = 0.$$

(7.71)

Equation (7.71) is equivalent to

$$\frac{d}{dt}\left(\frac{R_t}{R}\right) = 0.$$

(7.72)

Integrating,

$$\frac{R_t}{R} = \text{constant}.$$

(7.73)

We set the constant of integration in eqn. (7.73) equal to $1/T$, and $R(t)$ therefore has the form

$$R(t) = R_0 e^{t/T}.$$

(7.74)

Thus the scale factor $R(t)$ of the spatial region of the steady state universe increases monotonically with a constant red shift parameter, $H = 1/T$.

On the basis of present knowledge, an unequivocal choice cannot be made between the steady state model of the universe, or models that imply an explosive initial event at a time in the past. In addition to purely cosmological criteria based on red shift vs. distance observations, other evidence has been adduced in favor of the hypothesis of an origin of the universe at a time of the order of 10^{10} years ago. Measurement of the relative abundances of naturally radioactive elements with respect to their decay products, in the cases of U^{235} and U^{238} on earth and K^{40} and Rb^{87} in meteorites, tends to indicate an interval of $4\cdot5 \times 10^9$ years since the formation of the elements.[†] This period is in reasonable corre-

† P. J. Peebles, *op. cit.*, chap. 3.

spondence with the reciprocal of the Hubble parameter: $H^{-1} = (3 \cdot 08 \times 10^{-18} \text{ sec})^{-1} = 1 \cdot 03 \times 10^{10}$ years.

A theory advanced by Gamow† hypothesized that, during a period of explosive origin of the universe at temperature T_0 and time t_0, much of the energy of the universe must have existed as electromagnetic radiation. After the rapid expansion and cooling of the universe and condensation of energy as matter, a residual background of black-body radiation in equilibrium at a lower temperature $T(t)$ given by

$$T(t) = T_0[R(t_0)/R(t)] \tag{7.75}$$

should still exist. A search for this radiation, initiated by Penzias and Wilson,‡ indicates the presence of a background radiation of extragalactic origin, having a black-body spectrum corresponding to $T = 2 \cdot 7$K. These radiation measurements are generally thought to lend support to the theory of an explosive origin of the universe, although the question of possible contribution to this radiation from non-thermal discrete sources in the universe has been raised.§

7.4. Non-expanding Model of the Universe: the Goedel Metric

Although the Doppler effect due to the motion of receding galaxies constitutes a satisfactory explanation of the red shift of light from distant galaxies, this explanation remains essentially a most plausible hypothesis. There has been discovered since 1963 a large class of objects, called quasars, which show red shift parameters, $z = \Delta\lambda/\lambda$, distributed over the range $0 < z < 2 \cdot 4$.†† The quasar red shifts exhibit a strong tendency to cluster in particular ranges, there being a large excess over random oc-

---

† G. Gamow, *Rev. Mod. Phys.* **21**, 367 (1949).

‡ A. A. Penzias and R. W. Wilson, *Astrophys. J.* **142**, 419 (1965).

§ A. M. Wolfe and G. R. Burbridge, *Astrophys. J.* **156**, 345 (1969).

†† For light-source velocities greater than $(v/c) = 0 \cdot 1$, the relativistic Doppler shift formula must be used. In comoving coordinates for free particles, the special relativistic expression applicable is

$$1 + z = (\lambda + \Delta\lambda)/\lambda = (1 + v/c)(1 - v^2/c^2)^{-1/2}.$$

This may be inverted to yield the velocity formula:

$$v/c = [(1 + z)^2 - 1][(1 + z)^2 + 1]^{-1}.$$

currences for $2 \cdot 2 > Z > 1 \cdot 95$, and $0 \cdot 5 > z > 0$. The nature of the quasars and their distances are at present unknown. The existence of these objects underlines the fact that various mechanisms causing red shift of spectral lines may exist, and that red shift may not be a uniformly varying function of distance. Therefore it is of some interest to consider a model of the universe not involving the concept of an expanding scale of distance. We consider one such model, proposed by Goedel in 1949.† The metric of this model may be written in the form

$$ds^2 = (c \, dt + h \, d\theta)^2 - dr^2 - (1/2) \, (h \, d\theta)^2 - dz^2 \qquad (7.76)$$

where cylindrical space coordinates have been used, and $h = h(r)$ is a function of r only. This function was specified by Goedel to have the form: $h(r) = e^{ar}$.

The Goedel metric has properties which we summarize below:

1. It is a solution of Einstein's field equations [eqn. (7.1)] with non-zero cosmological constant, but does not produce any red shift of spectral lines.
2. It does not specify an absolute time, in the sense of the Gaussian time coordinate of the RW metric.
3. It assumes comoving coordinates: the mass of the universe, assumed distributed as dust particles with uniform density ϱ kg/m³, is stationary with respect to the coordinate lines.
4. The coordinate frame (and the matter) are in rotation with respect to a local frame of inertia, at angular velocity $\omega = \sqrt{(4\pi\varrho G)}$, where G is the gravitational constant.

The proof that Goedel's metric is a solution of Einstein's equations with constant proper density of mass ϱ is readily verified by use of the standard procedure we have employed with the RW metric. We shall indicate below the outlines of this calculation. Expanding eqn. (7.76) and dividing by dk^2, we obtain

$$\left(\frac{ds}{dk} \right)^2 = c^2 \dot{t}^2 + 2ch\dot{\theta}\dot{t} + \frac{h^2}{2} \dot{\theta}^2 - \dot{r}^2 - \dot{z}^2 . \qquad (7.77)$$

† K. Goedel, *Rev. Mod. Phys.* **21**, 447 (1949).

When the Lagrange equations are calculated, the Christoffel symbols of his metric are found to be

$$\left\{ \begin{matrix} 0 \\ 01 \end{matrix} \right\} = \frac{h'}{h} = a, \qquad \left\{ \begin{matrix} 0 \\ 12 \end{matrix} \right\} = \frac{2c}{h'} = \frac{ah}{2c},$$

$$\left\{ \begin{matrix} 1 \\ 02 \end{matrix} \right\} = \frac{ch'}{2} = \frac{cah}{2}, \qquad \left\{ \begin{matrix} 1 \\ 22 \end{matrix} \right\} = \frac{hh'}{2} = \frac{ah^2}{2},$$

$$\left\{ \begin{matrix} 2 \\ 01 \end{matrix} \right\} = -\frac{ch'}{h^2} = -\frac{ca}{h}$$

where a prime indicates differentiation with respect to r.

Calculation of the components of the curvature tensor $R_{\alpha\beta}$ and the scalar $R^\alpha{}_\alpha$ with use of eqns. (2.98) and (2.99) shows the non-zero components to be

$$R_{00} = -c^2 a^2,$$

$$R_{02} = -ca^2 h,$$

$$R_{22} = -\frac{a^2 h^2}{2},$$

$$R^\alpha{}_\alpha = -a^2.$$

Use of the curvature components in the field equations

$$R_{\alpha\beta} - \tfrac{1}{2} g_{\alpha\beta} R^\alpha{}_\alpha + \Lambda g_{\alpha\beta} = -\frac{8\pi G}{c^2} T_{\alpha\beta}$$

shows that a solution is provided if the cosmological constant has the value:

$$\Lambda = -\frac{a^2}{2}, \quad a^2 = \frac{8\pi G}{c^4} \varrho$$

and the matter tensor has the form

$$T_{\alpha\beta} = \varrho \begin{pmatrix} 1 & 0 & h & 0 \\ 0 & 0 & 0 & 0 \\ h & 0 & h^2 & 0 \\ 0 & 0 & 0 & 0 \end{pmatrix}.$$

The principal interest relating to Goedel's cosmological model is that it demonstrates the existence of a second solution for Einstein's field equations, alternate to the RW metric. Since it does not provide any mechanism for the origin of the red shift of the distant nebulae, which is one of the principal observational properties of the universe, it has found little application in cosmology.

The property that the Goedel metric implies a rotation of the entire matter content of the universe may be shown by means of a somewhat lengthy calculation which will not be presented here. The fact that the entire matter of the universe rotates may be said to be in violation of Mach's principle, since there remains no reference body, with respect to which the matter is rotating. The answer to the latter question for Goedel's universe is that it rotates with respect to the line of travel of a free test particle moving in a local frame of inertia.

Problems

7.1. In eqn. (7.9) for the propagation of light in the RW universe, assume $R(t)$ $= R =$ constant, and $k = 0$. (a) Evaluate the integrals in this equation between the limits: $0 \leqq t \leqq R/c$, and $0 \leqq x \leqq x_{max}$, respectively. What does the result imply concerning the normalizing factor r_0 defined in eqn. (7.3a)? [Note also eqn. (2.111).] (b) Repeat using the assumption $k = 1$.

7.2. Derive eqns. (7.25), starting with eqn. (7.24).

7.3. Consider a model of the universe in which the cosmological constant Λ is assigned in first approximation the value for the zero-pressure static universe deduced in the discussion following eqn. (7.45): $\Lambda = k/R^2$. Using this Λ in eqn. (7.42) and assuming zero pressure, calculate the function $R(t)$.

7.4. Demonstrate that eqn. (7.54) represents a cycloidal variation of $R(t)$ with time. [*Suggestion*: Using $\beta^2 = 1/R_{max}$, convert eqn. (7.54) and the definition $\beta^2 R = \sin^2 \theta$ into the parametric equations for a cycloidal curve in the $(t - t_0)$, R-plane in terms of the parameter 2θ.

7.5. Compare the Goedel metric with the form taken by the rotating-coordinate metric of eqn. (3.11b) when the new time-like interval $dt = (1 - \omega^2 r^2/c^2)^{1/2} dt$ is substituted into eqn. (3.11b). What assumed function $h(r)$ would bring the two metrics into approximate correspondence?

7.6. Using eqns. (7.30) and (7.31) with $k = 0$, construct the field equations of the steady state universe. Show that $G^{00} = (3H^2/c^2) (R_0^2/R^2) U^{00}$ is satisfied, and complete the calculations to obtain eqn. (7.71) from the G^{ii} equation ($i = 1, 2, 3$).

7.7. The null-geodesic equation for the RW universe $dx/dt = cR^{-1}(1 + kr^2/4)$ apparently implies that the coordinate velocity of light can approach infinity for sufficiently large r, or can approach zero at large t, if $R(t)$ increases indefinitely. Discuss the experimental significance of these statements.

Chapter 8

Unified Theories and Quantized Theories of General Relativity

8.1. Unified Field Theories

Upon the appearance in 1916 of Einstein's general theory of relativity, it was recognized as being capable of uniting the laws of mechanics of free mass points and the motion of particles in gravitational fields in one comprehensive theory based on the geometry of the 1 + 3-dimensional space–time coordinate manifold. Many workers then felt that it should be possible to expand the relativity theory to include the forces of the electromagnetic field, thus to create a unified field theory, comprising all of the important fields known at that time. In one instance it might be said that this effort even preceded the development of the general theory itself, for, as early as 1909, Bateman had proposed that the propagation of light in a gravitational field should be characterized by null values of the quadratic form expressing the interval in 1 + 3-dimensions:†

$$ds^2 = g_{\mu\nu}\, dx^\mu\, dx^\nu. \tag{8.1}$$

It was observed in Section 3.4 that the ten independent metric coefficients $g_{\mu\nu}$, which serve as the gravitational potentials for Einstein's theory, are completely accounted for by the field equations $G^{\alpha\beta} = CT^{\alpha\beta}$ and $G^{\alpha\beta}_{\ ;\beta} = 0$. The $g_{\mu\nu}$, in turn, completely determine the equations of motion of free particles, via the Christoffel symbols. Therefore, the first

† H. Bateman, *Proc. Lond. Math. Soc.* **8**, 223 (1910).

task in constructing a unified theory is to enlarge the Einstein system to accommodate the electromagnetic field variables. The efforts to enlarge the analytical structure of relativity theory may be represented by two types of approach: methods such as those of Kaluza and Klein, who expanded the coordinate manifold to five dimensions in order to make room for the electromagnetic field variables, and the methods of Einstein, who worked within a four-dimensional domain, but gave the theory additional flexibility by allowing the coefficients of the affine connection, $\Gamma^{\alpha}_{\beta\lambda}$, to have antisymmetric as well as symmetric components.

In the five-dimensional theory of Kaluza[†] and Klein[‡] a metric tensor $\bar{g}_{\mu\nu}$ is defined, where barred metric components belong to the five-dimensional space. All components of $\bar{g}_{\mu\nu}$ are independent of the fifth coordinate, x^5. Kaluza defined functions $h_{\mu\nu}$ and ϕ_{ν}:

$$h_{\mu\nu} = \bar{g}_{\mu\nu} - \bar{g}_{\mu 5}\bar{g}_{\nu 5}/\bar{g}_{55}, \tag{8.2}$$

$$g_{\mu\nu} = h_{\mu\nu} \quad (\mu, \nu, = 1, \dots 4), \tag{8.3}$$

$$\phi_{\nu} = \bar{g}_{\nu 5}/(\sqrt{2}.\bar{g}_{55}) \quad (\nu = 1, \dots 4), \tag{8.4}$$

$$\bar{g}_{55} = -1. \tag{8.5}$$

The definition of eqn. (8.5) reduces the number of independent $g_{\mu\nu}$ from fifteen to fourteen, the latter being equal to the total number of field variables: the ten gravitational potentials $g_{\mu\nu}$ of the original Einstein theory, plus the four components of the electromagnetic four-potential ϕ_{ν}. The Lagrangian density of the five-space is given in terms of quantities from the four-dimensional theory

$$\sqrt{\bar{g}}.\bar{R} = \sqrt{g}.(R - \tfrac{1}{2}F_{\alpha\beta}F^{\alpha\beta}) \tag{8.6}$$

where $\bar{g}$ and g are the determinants of the metrics of the five-space and the four-space, respectively, and

$$F_{\mu\nu} = \phi_{\mu,\nu} - \phi_{\nu,\mu} \tag{8.7}$$

is the electromagnetic field tensor. The gravitational equations of the Kaluza theory then are

$$\bar{G}^{\mu\nu} \equiv G^{\mu\nu} + T^{\mu\nu} = 0 \tag{8.8}$$

† T. Kaluza, *Berichte Preuss. Akad. Wiss.* 966 (1921).
‡ O. Klein, *Zeits. f. Physik* **36**, 835 (1926).

and Maxwell's equations of the electromagnetic field are

$$\bar{G}_5{}^\nu = (1/\sqrt{2})\, F^{\mu\nu}{}_{;\mu} = 0. \tag{8.9}$$

A world line of a charged particle in four-dimensional space time corresponds to a geodesic of the five-dimensional space. The fifth dimension of Kaluza's theory had only the function of increasing the number of components in the metric tensor. No physical significance was attached to this additional dimension.

An attempt to develop a unified theory of the electromagnetic and gravitational fields was made by Einstein, working within a four-dimensional coordinate space, in which he abandoned the symmetry of the coefficients of the affine connection which is typical of Riemannian geometry:

$$\delta A^\beta = -\Gamma^\beta_{\mu\nu} A^\mu\, dx^\nu = -\Gamma^\beta_{\nu\mu} A^\mu\, dx^\nu{}_{\text{(Riemannian)}}. \tag{8.10}$$

The metric tensor of this theory was also assumed to be non-symmetrical. The nonsymmetric metric tensor $g_{\alpha\beta}$ retains the property

$$g_{\alpha\beta} g^{\alpha\nu} = \delta_\beta{}^\nu.$$

A tensor density $\mathfrak{G}^{\alpha\beta}$ is also defined

$$\mathfrak{G}^{\alpha\beta} = \sqrt{g}\cdot g^{\alpha\beta}. \tag{8.11}$$

This density has symmetric and antisymmetric parts:

$$^s\mathfrak{G}^{\alpha\beta} = \tfrac{1}{2}\,(\mathfrak{G}^{\alpha\beta} + \mathfrak{G}^{\beta\alpha}), \tag{8.12}$$

$$^a\mathfrak{G}^{\alpha\beta} = \tfrac{1}{2}\,(\mathfrak{G}^{\alpha\beta} - \mathfrak{G}^{\beta\alpha}). \tag{8.13}$$

Symmetric and antisymmetric affinities $^s\Gamma^\alpha_{\beta\nu}$ and $^a\Gamma^\alpha_{\beta\nu}$ are defined in the same way as in eqns. (8.12) and (8.13), from the unsymmetrized coefficients $\Gamma^\alpha_{\beta\nu}$.

A Lagrangian density is defined for this theory as

$$\mathscr{L} = \mathfrak{G}^{\mu\nu} R_{\mu\nu}. \tag{8.14}$$

There are two sets of field equations for the metric tensor of Einstein's theory:

$$R_{\mu\nu} = 0, \tag{8.15}$$

$$\mathfrak{G}^{\mu\nu}{}_{,\beta} + \Gamma^\nu_{\sigma\beta}\mathfrak{G}^{\sigma\nu} + \Gamma^\nu_{\beta\sigma}\mathfrak{G}^{\mu\sigma} - \Gamma^\sigma_{\beta\sigma}\mathfrak{G}^{\mu\nu} + \tfrac{2}{3}\,\delta^\nu_\beta \Gamma^\alpha_{\sigma\alpha}\mathfrak{G}^{\mu\sigma} = 0. \tag{8.16}$$

Equation (8.15) is the free-space gravitational field equation, and eqn. (8.16) implies the vanishing divergence:

$$^a\mathfrak{G}^{\mu\beta}{}_{,\beta} = 0. \tag{8.17}$$

Equation (8.17) generates Maxwell's curl equations, if the field component identifications are made:

$$(E_1, E_2, E_3) = (\mathfrak{G}^{23}, \mathfrak{G}^{31}, \mathfrak{G}^{12}), \tag{8.18}$$

$$(B_1, B_2, B_3) = (\mathfrak{G}^{14}, \mathfrak{G}^{24}, \mathfrak{G}^{34}). \tag{8.19}$$

By the foregoing means, Einstein was able to build up a mathematical structure capable of handling the complete array of electromagnetic and gravitational fields. However, this structure, in common with all of the numerous attempts to construct a unified field theory, has failed to achieve the compact and satisfactory analytical character of the original Einstein gravitational theory. The large increase in the number of fields recognized by physics as being natural parts of the description of nature, meson fields, virtual photon fields and particle fields of various kinds has greatly diminished the apparent significance of the unification of the gravitational and electromagnetic fields. Therefore, efforts to attain this end have largely ceased, and the classical gravitational field is accepted as an independent field in nature which is adequately described in a classical sense by the theory of general relativity.

8.2. "Already Unified" Field Theory

The point of view has been put forward that efforts to unify the electromagnetic and gravitational fields are unnecessary, and that the electromagnetic and other fields are already adequately describable as manifestations of distortions occurring in the four-dimensional coordinate frame of event space.† The metric tensor in a region occupied by a pure electromagnetic field is a solution of Einstein's field equations, in which the energy tensor $T_{\alpha\beta}$ has the form as given in eqn. (5.20), with which the

† J. A. Wheeler, *Geometrodynamics*, Academic Press, New York, 1962.

field equations become

$$R_{\dot\alpha\beta} - \tfrac{1}{2} g_{\alpha\beta} R^{\mu}{}_{\mu} = - \frac{8\pi G}{c^2} [F_\alpha{}^\mu F_{\mu\beta} + \tfrac{1}{4} g_{\alpha\beta}(F_{\varrho\sigma}F^{\varrho\sigma})]. \qquad (8.20)$$

In eqn. (8.20) the cosmological term has been omitted, with sufficient accuracy for non-cosmical distances. Multiplying eqn. (8.20) by $g^{\alpha\beta}$ and summing, we obtain

$$R^\alpha{}_\alpha - \tfrac{4}{2} R^\mu{}_\mu = - \frac{8\pi G}{c^2} [F^{\beta\mu}F_{\mu\beta} + \tfrac{4}{4}(F_{\varrho\sigma}F^{\varrho\sigma})]. \qquad (8.21)$$

Due to the antisymmetry of $F^{\mu\nu}$, $F^{\beta\mu} = -F^{\mu\beta}$, and the square bracket in eqn. (8.21) vanishes:

$$[-F^{\mu\beta}F_{\mu\beta} + F_{\varrho\sigma}F^{\varrho\sigma}] = 0.$$

We therefore deduce from eqn. (8.21) that, in an electromagnetic field, the Riemannian curvature invariant vanishes:

$$R^\alpha{}_\alpha = 0 \quad \text{(electromagnetic field)}. \qquad (8.22)$$

Therefore, in an electromagnetic field, the field equation for the metric tensor assumes the simple form:

$$R_{\alpha\beta} = - \frac{8\pi G}{c^2} T_{\alpha\beta} \quad \text{(electromagnetic field)}. \qquad (8.23)$$

It was shown by Rainich,[†] and later by Wheeler and Misner[‡] that the Riemann curvature tensor $R_{\alpha\beta}$ in a region containing electromagnetic fields satisfies the additional relations:

$$R_\alpha{}^\mu R_{\mu\beta} - \tfrac{1}{4} g_{\alpha\beta}(R_{\varrho\sigma}R^{\varrho\sigma}) = 0, \qquad (8.24)$$

$$R_{00} \geqq 0 \quad \text{(all coordinates real)}. \qquad (8.25)$$

Since $R_{\alpha\beta}$ is symmetric, eqn. (8.24) may be written

$$R_\alpha{}^\mu R_{\mu\beta} - \tfrac{1}{4} g_{\alpha\beta}(R_{\sigma\varrho}R^{\varrho\sigma}) = 0, \qquad (8.26)$$

$$R_{00} \geqq 0. \qquad (8.26a)$$

† G. Y. Rainich, *Trans. Am. Math. Soc.* **27**, 106 (1925).
‡ J. A. Wheeler and C. W. Misner, *Ann. Phys. (USA)* **2**, 225 (1957).

Again using the antisymmetry of $F_{\mu\nu}$, eqn. (8.20) may be written

$$F_\alpha{}^\mu F_{\mu\beta} - \tfrac{1}{4} g_{\alpha\beta} F_{\sigma\varrho} F^{\varrho\sigma} = - \frac{c^2}{8\pi G} R_{\alpha\beta} \qquad (8.27)$$

and, from eqn. (5.27), for the electromagnetic field

$$T_{00} = \frac{\varepsilon_0}{2c^4} (E^2 + c^2 B^2) \geqq 0. \qquad (8.27\text{a})$$

No physical significance is attached to the similarities (and dissimilarities) existing between the sets of eqns. (8.26) and (8.27). The electromagnetic field tensor $F_{\mu\nu}$ is to be regarded as a convenient intermediary that allows us to calculate curvatures from eqn. (8.20) when the physical components of field are known, rather than as a counterpart of curvature. Equations (8.23) and (8.26), and additional relationships between the electromagnetic field tensor and the curvature tensor, have been interpreted by J. A. Wheeler and his coworkers to indicate that the curvature of the four-dimensional coordinate manifold reflects the presence of electromagnetic field, in an "already unified" way.[†]

8.3. Quantization of the Gravitational Field

Quantum theory developed in close relationship with the special theory of relativity. In de Broglie's original wave postulate, free particles travel with a plane-wave function $\exp(i\phi)$ in which the phase function ϕ is equal to $(1/\hbar)$ times the inner product of the momentum four vector with the position four vector of the particle (cf. Chapter 9):

$$e^{i\varphi} = e^{i(p_j x^j)\hbar}. \qquad (8.28)$$

General relativity and the theory of gravitation developed essentially without relation to quantum theory. After techniques for the quantization of classical fields were devised, however, numerous efforts were made to apply to the gravitational field methods of quantization that have been successful, for example, with the electromagnetic field.

No experimentally observable effects of the quantum nature of the gravitational field are known. This situation is in sharp contrast to the

[†] J. A. Wheeler, *Geometrodynamics*, Academic Press, New York, 1962.

case of the electromagnetic field, wherein the quantized interaction of the field with matter is easily observable in simple laboratory experiments. One reason given for the lack of observed quantum phenomena in gravitation is that the gravitational quanta are so large as to escape the normal range of observation.[†] This situation is explained by the assumption that the gravitational interaction between a pair of particles of mass m does not become significant until the de Broglie wavelength of the particles is of the order of their Schwarzschild radius.

For a Schwarzschild radius of $r_s = 2mG/c^2$, the interaction energy for highly relativistic particles ($E \simeq pc \gg m_0 c^2$, where m_0 is rest energy) may be written

$$E_{\text{grav.}} \simeq \frac{hc}{\lambda} = mc^2. \tag{8.29}$$

The energy is thus found to be[‡]

$$E = \sqrt{\left(\frac{hG}{2c^3}\right)} \frac{c^4}{G} = 10^{28} \text{ eV}. \tag{8.30}$$

An interaction energy of 10^{28} eV would escape detection in experimental observations of normal type.

Because of its interest as a problem in theoretical physics, numerous attempts have been made to formulate the quantum theory of the gravitational field. These efforts may be classified generally into two principal categories. The first of these is the canonical approach, in which a Hamiltonian function is constructed in terms of a suitable set of variables, and canonical commutation relations leading to quantum conditions are sought. The second approach is through the use of manifestly covariant formalism, which, unlike the canonical method, preserves formal covariance of the expressions throughout the analysis.

The principal obstacle to both of the foregoing procedures is that Einstein's equations are nonlinear in the metric functions $g_{\mu\nu}$, thus greatly complicating the calculations. The canonical method is hampered by the fact that when the $g_{\mu\nu}$ are taken as the field variables, not all of them possess conjugate momenta, and of the $g_{\mu\nu}$ that possess canonical con-

---

[†] B. S. DeWitt, *Phys. Rev.* **160**, 1113 (1967).

[‡] This energy is found by the calculation: $E = hc/\lambda$, with $\lambda = r_s = 2mG/c^2$, and substitute $m = E/c^2$.

jugates, not all of the latter are independent. This lack leads to the so-called problem of constraints.

In addition to the foregoing, further difficulty stems from the fact that in conventional field theories, the initial conditions are fixed by specifying values of the commuting field variables throughout a spacelike hypersurface. In general relativity, however, when the metric $g_{\mu\nu}$ is a dynamical variable, an unambiguous significance cannot be attached to the specification of a spacelike hypersurface.[†] Finally, the "graviton", or quantum emitted in gravitational radiation, cannot be assigned a definite spin. It can be shown that this particle must involve a super-position of spin 0, spin 1, and spin 2 contributions.[‡] In spite of much work on the quantization problem and many advances in overcoming the difficulties involved, no completed quantum theory of gravitation can be summarized at the level of this text. For further details, the literature should be consulted.[§]

† J. R. Klauder, *Nuovo Cimento* **25**, 242 (1962).

‡ V. Ogievetsky and I. Polubarinov, *Ann. Phys. (USA)* **35**, 167 (1965).

§ P. G. Bergmann, *Helv. Phys. Acta*, Suppl. **4**, 79 (1956). P. A. M. Dirac, *Proc. Roy Soc. (London)* A **246**, 326 (1958); *Phys. Rev.* **114**, 924 (1959). F. A. E. Pirani and A. Schild, *Phys. Rev.* **79**, 986 (1950). P. G. Bergmann and A. B. Komar, in *Recent Developments in General Relativity*, Pergamon Press, Oxford, 1962. R. P. Feynman, *Acta Phys. Polon.* **24**, 697 (1963). T. W. B. Kibble, in *High Energy Physics and Elementary Particles*, IAEA, Vienna, 1965. B. S. DeWitt, *Phys. Rev.* **160**, 1113 (1967); **162**, 1195 (1967); **162**, 1239 (1967). A. B. Komar, in *Relativity* (Carmali, Fickler and Witten, Eds.), Plenum Press, New York, 1970. B. S. DeWitt, *General Relativity and Gravitation* (Journal), **1**, 181 (1970).

Chapter 9

Minkowski's Coordinates and Orthogonal Transformations

We have seen in Chapter 1 that the theory of relativity had its origin in the process of accommodation into physics of the experimentally observed fact that light propagates isotropically in all inertial frames with the standard speed c. This property is summarized in the expression which was later called a null world-line interval:

$$0 = c^2 \, dt^2 - dx^2 - dy^2 - dz^2. \tag{9.1}$$

The world-line interval ds^2 between two neighboring events occurring at points (t, x, y, z) and $(t + dt, x + dx, y + dy, z + dz)$ in $(1 + 3)$-coordinate event space was then defined,

$$ds^2 = c^2 \, dt^2 - dx^2 - dy^2 - dz^2. \tag{9.2}$$

The interval ds^2 thus defined has the characteristic that it assumes the same numerical value upon Lorentz transformation of the components (dt, dx, dy, dz) to the coordinates of any other inertial frame. Thus, the world-line element ds^2 is an invariant under Lorentz transformation. The invariance of ds^2 is also preserved, as we have seen, under general coordinate transformations among Riemannian coordinate frames.

9.1. Orthogonal Lorentz Transformations

We have seen that the analogy of the invariance of ds^2 under Lorentz transformation, to the similar invariance of the geometrical distance element $dr^2 = dx^2 + dy^2 + dz^2$ under orthogonal coordinate transfor-

196

mation in three-dimensional space, led Minkowski to define the new coordinates

$$(x_0, x_1, x_2, x_3) = (ict, x, y, z). \tag{9.3}$$

In Minkowski's coordinates, the interval ds^2 of eqn. (9.2) is now interpreted as the squared absolute value of a four-component vector, defined as

$$d\mathbf{s} = (ic\,dt, dx, dy, dz). \tag{9.4}$$

The Lorentz transformation for this four-vector is now an orthogonal transformation, for which the transformation matrix is

$$\eta_{\mu\nu} = \begin{pmatrix} \gamma & i\beta\gamma & 0 & 0 \\ -i\beta\gamma & \gamma & 0 & 0 \\ 0 & 0 & 1 & 0 \\ 0 & 0 & 0 & 1 \end{pmatrix} \tag{9.5}$$

where $\beta = V/c$, $\gamma = (1 - \beta^2)^{-1/2}$, in which V is the relative velocity of the two inertial coordinate frames along their (parallel) x-axes. The transformation [eqn. (9.5)] is seen to satisfy the orthogonality conditions

$$\sum_\nu \eta_{\mu\nu}\eta_{\nu\lambda} = \delta_{\mu\lambda} \tag{9.6}$$

where $\delta_{\mu\lambda}$ is the Kronecker delta function.

In carrying out orthogonal transformations between Minkowski frames, the rules for matrix multiplication may be used. The transformation

$$x'_\mu = \eta_{\mu\nu}x_\nu \tag{9.7}$$

is written in matrix form as

$$\begin{pmatrix} ict' \\ x' \\ y' \\ z' \end{pmatrix} = \begin{pmatrix} \gamma_1 & i\beta_1\gamma_1 & 0 & 0 \\ -i\beta_1\gamma_1 & \gamma_1 & 0 & 0 \\ 0 & 0 & 1 & 0 \\ 0 & 0 & 0 & 1 \end{pmatrix} \begin{pmatrix} ict \\ x \\ y \\ z \end{pmatrix} \tag{9.8}$$

where $\beta_1 = V_1/c$ and $\gamma_1 = (1 - \beta_1^2)^{-1/2}$. The result of this calculation is

$$\begin{pmatrix} ict' \\ x' \\ y' \\ z' \end{pmatrix} = \begin{pmatrix} i\gamma_1(ct + \beta_1 x) \\ \gamma_1(\beta_1 ct + x) \\ y \\ z \end{pmatrix}. \tag{9.9}$$

Transformations between inertial frames having relative motions along the y- or z-coordinate axial directions may be written with obvious rearrangements of terms in eqn. (9.5). For relative motion with velocity V_2 along the (parallel) y-axes, the transformation matrix takes the form

$$\eta_{\mu\nu} = \begin{pmatrix} \gamma_2 & 0 & i\beta_2\gamma_2 & 0 \\ 0 & 1 & 0 & 0 \\ -i\beta_2\gamma_2 & 0 & \gamma_2 & 0 \\ 0 & 0 & 0 & 1 \end{pmatrix} \tag{9.10}$$

and for relative motion in the z-direction with velocity V_3

$$\zeta_{\mu\nu} = \begin{pmatrix} \gamma_3 & 0 & 0 & i\beta_3\gamma_3 \\ 0 & 1 & 0 & 0 \\ 0 & 0 & 1 & 0 \\ -i\beta_3\gamma_3 & 0 & 0 & \gamma_3 \end{pmatrix}. \tag{9.11}$$

In eqns. (9.10) and (9.11), with obvious notation, $\beta_2 = V_2/c$, $\gamma_2 = (1 - \beta_2^2)^{-1/2}$; $\beta_3 = V_3/c$, $\gamma_3 = (1 - \beta_3^2)^{-1/2}$.

If two or more successive coordinate transformations are to be carried out among Minkowski frames, the overall transformation matrix may be obtained as the matrix product of the component matrices. We assume, for example, that the coordinate transformations to be carried out are

$$x'_\mu = \xi_{\mu\nu}x_\nu, \quad \text{with} \quad \beta_1 = V_1/c, \quad \gamma_1 = (1 - \beta_1^2)^{-1/2},$$

$$x''_\mu = \eta_{\mu\nu}x'_\nu, \quad \text{with} \quad \beta_2 = V_2/c, \quad \gamma_2 = (1 - \beta_2^2)^{-1/2},$$

$$x'''_\mu = \xi_{\mu\nu}x''_\nu, \quad \text{with} \quad \beta_3 = V_3/c, \quad \gamma_3 = (1 - \beta_3^2)^{-1/2}.$$

If the successive transformations are to be carried out in the sequence: $x \to x' \to x'' \to x'''$, the overall transformation may then be calculated in the matrix form

$$x'''_\mu = \chi_{\mu\nu}x_\nu \tag{9.12}$$

where $\chi_{\mu\nu}$ is the product matrix

$$\chi_{\mu\nu} = \zeta_{\mu\varrho}\eta_{\varrho\sigma}\xi_{\sigma\nu}. \tag{9.13}$$

The transformation that is to be carried out first is placed to the right in the product of eqn. (9.13), and hence it operates first on the operand x_ν.

As an example of successive transformations, let us consider the combined transformation consisting of a Lorentz transformation in the x-direction with velocity V_1, followed by a transformation in the y-direction with velocity V_2. We represent this transformation as

$$x''_\mu = \eta_{\mu\nu}\xi_{\nu\lambda}x_\lambda \tag{9.14}$$

where

$$\eta_{\mu\nu}\varepsilon_{\nu\lambda} = \begin{pmatrix} \gamma_2 & 0 & i\beta_2\gamma_2 & 0 \\ 0 & 1 & 0 & 0 \\ -i\beta_2\gamma_2 & 0 & \gamma_2 & 0 \\ 0 & 0 & 0 & 1 \end{pmatrix} \begin{pmatrix} \gamma_1 & i\beta_1\gamma_1 & 0 & 0 \\ -i\beta_1\gamma_1 & \gamma_1 & 0 & 0 \\ 0 & 0 & 1 & 0 \\ 0 & 0 & 0 & 1 \end{pmatrix} \tag{9.15}$$

$$= \begin{pmatrix} \gamma_1\gamma_2 & i\beta_1\gamma_1\gamma_2 & i\beta_2\gamma_2 & 0 \\ -i\beta_1\gamma_1 & \gamma_1 & 0 & 0 \\ -i\beta_2\gamma_1\gamma_2 & \beta_1\beta_2\gamma_1\gamma_2 & \gamma_2 & 0 \\ 0 & 0 & 0 & 1 \end{pmatrix}. \tag{9.16}$$

We note that the combined transformation matrix no longer has the antisymmetry of the simple uniaxial translation matrix. It may be verified, however, that the combined matrix [eqn. (9.16)] satisfies the orthogonality condition, eqn. (9.6). The result of application of the combined matrix to the four-vector $d\mathbf{s}$ is found by matrix multiplication to be:

$$\begin{pmatrix} ict'' \\ x'' \\ y'' \\ z'' \end{pmatrix} = \eta_{\mu\nu}\varepsilon_{\nu\lambda} \begin{pmatrix} ict \\ x \\ y \\ z \end{pmatrix} = \begin{pmatrix} i\gamma_2 \ (\gamma_1 ct + \beta_1\gamma_1 x + \beta_2 y) \\ \gamma_1 \ (\beta_1 ct + x) \\ \gamma_2 \ (\beta_2\gamma_1 ct + \beta_1\gamma_1 x + y) \\ z \end{pmatrix}. \quad (9.17)$$

In forming product transformations, the transformation matrices cannot be commuted. In general, the transformation $\chi_{\alpha\delta} = \xi_{\alpha\beta}\eta_{\beta\gamma}\zeta_{\gamma\delta}$ is not the same as the transformation $\chi_{\alpha\delta} = \zeta_{\alpha\beta}\eta_{\beta\gamma}\xi_{\gamma\delta}$, etc. In the example given above [eqn. (9.17)], the product matrix $\xi_{\mu\nu}\eta_{\mu\lambda}$ is the complex conjugate of the matrix we have found, but in the general case, no simple relationship exists between permuted matrix products.

9.2. World-line Four-vectors

The transformation law for the four-vector $d\mathbf{s}$ of eqn. (9.4) is

$$d\mathbf{s}'_\mu = \eta_{\mu\nu}\,d\mathbf{s}_\nu. \quad (9.18)$$

The validity of this transformation is not altered if we divide both sides of eqn. (9.18) by an invariant, since an invariant has the same numerical value in all coordinate frames. We select the invariant $d\tau$, derived from the world-line interval ds:

$$d\tau = ds/c = \frac{1}{c}\sqrt{(c^2\,dt^2 - dx^2 - dy^2 - dz^2)}, \quad (9.19)$$

$$d\tau = dt\sqrt{\{1 - (u_x^2 + u_y^2 + u_z^2)/c^2\}}, \quad (9.20)$$

$$= dt\sqrt{(1 - V_s^2/c^2)} \quad (9.21)$$

where $d\tau$ is an interval of proper time, which would be measured by a clock moving at constant speed through the coordinate space interval $\sqrt{(dx^2 + dy^2 + dz^2)}$, in a coordinate time interval dt. The time $d\tau$ will always be less than dt, which is measured by a clock held stationary with respect to the coordinate axes (x, y, z), whereas $d\tau$ is measured by a moving clock. By the invention of the artifice of the moving clock, we generate a convenient invariant proper time $d\tau$, which will have the same value between the pair of events terminating the interval ds, as observed from all inertial frames.†

In eqn. (9.21) we have defined

$$V_s^2 = u_x^2 + u_y^2 + u_z^2 \tag{9.22}$$

where V_s is the coordinate velocity of the moving mass point along its world line, and u_x, u_y, u_z are the components of coordinate velocity:

$$u_j = \frac{dx_j}{dt}. \tag{9.22a}$$

Then, defining

$$\gamma_s = (1 - V_s^2/c^2)^{-1/2}. \tag{9.23}$$

We may write, for the moving particle,

$$\frac{dt}{d\tau} = \gamma_s. \tag{9.24}$$

We now define the vector of four-velocity, **U**:

$$\mathbf{U}_\mu \equiv ds/d\tau. \tag{9.25}$$

Therefore, **U** has the components

$$\mathbf{U}_\mu = (ic\gamma_s, \gamma_s u_x, \gamma_s u_y, \gamma_s u_z). \tag{9.26}$$

Since **U** is a four-vector, it transforms under the Minkowski matrix [eqn. (9.5) *et al.*], and also since the transformation is length-preserving, the magnitude of **U** will have the same value in all inertial frames. Its constant squared amplitude is

$$(\mathbf{U}_\mu)^2 = \sum_\mu (\mathbf{U}_\mu)^2 = (-c^2 + V_s^2)\gamma_s^2,$$

$$(\mathbf{U}_\mu)^2 = -c^2. \tag{9.27}$$

Thus the four-velocity of a particle along its world line always has the magnitude c. The negative sign in eqn. (9.27) is an artifact resulting from the conventional choice we have made for the signature of ds^2: $(1, -1, -1, -1)$.

---

† In the world of inertial frames we may make the convenient generalization: At clocks keep (their own) proper time, and all observers agree on the *proper* time kep between a given pair of events by the clocks.

Under transformation to a Lorentz frame moving with velocity V along the x-axis, the four-velocity of a particle $\mathbf{U}_\mu^\lambda$ has transformed components which we calculate below:

$$
\mathbf{U}'_\mu = \begin{pmatrix} \gamma & i\beta\gamma & 0 & 0 \\ -i\beta\gamma & \gamma & 0 & 0 \\ 0 & 0 & 1 & 0 \\ 0 & 0 & 0 & 1 \end{pmatrix} \begin{pmatrix} i\gamma_s\, c \\ \gamma_s\, u_x \\ \gamma_s\, u_y \\ \gamma_s\, u_z \end{pmatrix} = \begin{pmatrix} i\gamma\gamma_s\,(c + \beta u_x) \\ \gamma\gamma_s(c\beta + u_x) \\ \gamma_s u_y \\ \gamma_s u_z \end{pmatrix}. \quad (9.28)
$$

It is readily verified by calculation that the transformed components of $\mathbf{U}'_\mu$ have the invariant squared amplitude $-c^2$.

We may now inquire: What is the relationship between the velocity transformation given by eqn. (9.28) and the conventional velocity transformation laws of special relativity? We may derive the transformation law for coordinate velocities from the real Lorentz transformation given by eqn. (1.21), which we write in differential form:

$$
dt' = \gamma\, dt + \gamma\, \frac{V}{c^2}\, dx,
$$

$$
dx' = \gamma V\, dt + \gamma\, dx, \quad (9.29)
$$

$$
dy' = dy,
$$

$$
dz' = dz.
$$

From eqn. (9.29), we find the transformation law for coordinate velocities:

$$
u'_x = \frac{dx'}{dt'} = \frac{(V + u_x)}{\left(1 + \dfrac{V u_x}{c^2}\right)},
$$

$$
u'_y = \frac{dy'}{dt'} = \frac{u_y}{\gamma\left(1 + \dfrac{V u_x}{c^2}\right)}, \quad (9.30)
$$

$$
u'_z = \frac{dz'}{dt'} = \frac{u_z}{\gamma\left(1 + \dfrac{V u_x}{c^2}\right)}
$$

where we have used, as before, $dx/dt = u_x$, $dy/dt = u_y$, $dz/dt = u_z$. We seemingly now have two velocity transformation laws, given by eqns. (9.30) and eqns. (9.28). With this result, the student may ask: Which is the "correct" velocity transformation law, and what is the relationship between the two laws? The answer to the first question is that the two velocities, u_j and U_μ, are differently defined quantities and therefore necessarily have different transformation laws. The coordinate velocity u_j is the ordinary physical velocity defined as the ratio of a coordinate-length increment dx_j to a coordinate-time increment dt. It is the quantity observed in ordinary physical velocity measurements. The four-velocity U_μ is a hybrid quantity defined as the ratio of a coordinate-length increment dx_j to an increment of proper time $d\tau$. Therefore its spatial components differ from the components of u_j by a factor of γ_s. Due to the hybrid character of its definition, no inertial observer measures the four-velocity U_μ by means of a conventional velocity measurement.

The value of the definition of the four-velocity U is that it is a convenient quantity which leads to further insights into the components of the energy of an inertial particle, as we shall see below.

9.3. Forces and Momenta in Three and Four Dimensions

In Newtonian physics, the concept of force is defined in terms of the accelerations which are caused, or would tend to be caused, by a given force phenomenon. The definition of force is given by Newton's second law:

$$F_j = m_0 \frac{du_j}{dt} \qquad (9.31)$$

where m_0 is the mass of the particle. With the definition of Newtonian momentum,

$$p_j = m_0 u_j, \qquad (9.32)$$

the second law is compactly given in the form

$$F_j = \frac{dp_j}{dt}. \qquad (9.33)$$

In Newtonian mechanics there have been established the familiar classes of forces: elastic, electrical and magnetic forces, Van der Waals and inertial forces, and others. We should like to establish for special relativity a relativistic form of Newton's second law, in which there appear the conventional, already defined forces of physics.

There are two forms in which a relativistic Newton's law might be expressed:

1.
$$F_j = m_0 \frac{d\mathbf{U}_j}{dt} = m_0 \frac{d}{dt}\left(\gamma_s \frac{dx_j}{dt}\right), \qquad (9.34)$$

2.
$$\mathbf{F}_\mu = m_0 \frac{d\mathbf{U}_\mu}{d\tau} = m_0\gamma_s \frac{d}{dt}\left(\gamma_s \frac{dx_\mu}{dt}\right) \qquad (9.35)$$

where m_0 is the rest mass of the particle. The first force equation [eqn. (9.34)] is a three-vector equation, and when the conventionally known forces are employed for F_j, this equation in fact yields results in agreement with experimental observation. Conventionally measured coordinate velocities and accelerations are inserted on the right in eqn. (9.34), which has the form, when the differentiation is carried out in full,

$$F_j = m_0\gamma_s \left[\frac{d^2x_j}{dt^2} + \frac{\gamma_s^2}{c^2} \frac{dx_j}{dt}(\boldsymbol{u} \cdot \dot{\boldsymbol{u}})\right] \qquad (9.36)$$

where $\boldsymbol{u}$ and $\dot{\boldsymbol{u}}$ are the three-vector coordinate velocity and acceleration, respectively.

The second force equation, eqn. (9.35), defines the four-vector called the Minkowski force, $\mathbf{F}_\mu$. It is, like other four-vectors, invariant under an orthogonal Lorentz transformation. The Minkowski force cannot be identified with the ordinary physical forces, since it differs from these by a factor of γ_s by its definition.

If the product $m_0\gamma_s$ in eqns. (9.34) and (9.36) is defined as the instantaneous mass m of the moving particle,

$$m \equiv m_0\gamma_s, \qquad (9.37)$$

the relativistic Newton's second law can then be given the simple form

$$F_j = \frac{d(mu_j)}{dt} = \frac{dp_j}{dt} \qquad (9.38)$$

where the relativistic momentum three-vector is defined

$$p_j = mu_j = (m_0\gamma_s)u_j. \tag{9.39}$$

The comparable four-vector of momentum may be defined, from eqn. (9.35),

$$\mathbf{P}_\mu = m_0\mathbf{U}_\mu. \tag{9.40}$$

From eqn. (9.26), this is equivalent to

$$\mathbf{P}_\mu = (i\gamma_s m_0 c, \gamma_s m_0 u_x, \gamma_s m_0 u_y, \gamma_s m_0 u_z). \tag{9.41}$$

The three space-like components of $\mathbf{P}_\mu$ are thus identical with the three components of p_j.

9.4. Relativistic Energy of a Free Particle in an Inertial Frame

The magnitude of the four-vector $\mathbf{P}_\mu$ is invariant under orthogonal transformation. A useful relationship can be obtained from the squared amplitude of this vector. From eqns. (9.40) and (9.27), $|\mathbf{P}_\mu|^2$ must be equal to $-m_0 c^2$. Using eqn. (9.41) we write this amplitude in terms of its component terms:

$$|\mathbf{P}|^2 = \gamma_s^2 m_0^2(-c^2 + u_x^2 + u_y^2 + u_z^2).$$

Therefore, we have

$$-m_0 c^2 = -(\gamma_s m_0 c)^2 + (\gamma_s m_0 u)^2 \tag{9.42}$$

where $u = V_s$ is the magnitude of the coordinate velocity.

Substituting from eqns. (9.37) and (9.39), and multiplying eqn. (9.42) by c^2, we obtain

$$(m_0 c^2)^2 = (mc^2)^2 - (cp)^2. \tag{9.43}$$

Each term of eqn. (9.43) has the dimensions of (energy)^2. Therefore, defining

$$E = mc^2, \tag{9.44}$$

eqn. (9.43) may be written

$$E^2 = (m_0 c^2)^2 + (cp)^2. \tag{9.45}$$

Interpreting E as the total energy of the particle, we see from eqn. (9.45) that E has contributions from the rest energy m_0c^2, and from the relativistic kinetic energy term, cp. These contributions are combined by the right-triangle rule, as shown in eqn. (9.45). The composition of energies of a moving particle can be alternatively demonstrated, in the classical limit of low velocity, by expanding the instantaneous mass m, in the total energy mc^2:

$$
\begin{aligned}
mc^2 &= m_0c^2\gamma_s, \\
&= m_0c^2(1 - V_s^2/c^2)^{-1/2}, \\
&= m_0c^2 + \frac{m_0V_s^2}{2} + \cdots
\end{aligned}
\tag{9.46}
$$

where V_s is, as before, the coordinate velocity of the particle as it moves along its world line. In eqn. (9.46), terms of order V_s^4/c^4 are neglected. This equation shows that for small V_s/c, the total energy mc^2 is composed of the rest energy m_0c^2 and the Newtonian kinetic energy $m_0V_s^2/2$.

The invariant character of the line element ds^2 [eqn. (9.2)] has led us directly to the invariant energy expression, eqn. (9.43). Thus, eqn. (9.43) is a statement of invariance, rather than of energy conservation. Equation (9.45), however, may be regarded as the trivial statement of the conservation of energy by a particle during uniform straight-line motion.

An invariant which has an informative structure is the quantity produced by forming the inner product of four-force F_μ with the interval ds_μ:

$$
\sum_\mu F_\mu \, ds_\mu = (ic \, dt)\left[m_0\gamma_s\frac{d}{dt}(ic\gamma_s)\right] + \sum_j (dx_j)\left[m_0\gamma_s\frac{d}{dt}(u_j\gamma_s)\right].
\tag{9.47}
$$

Carrying out the differentiations, and combining terms, eqn. (9.47) reduces to the form

$$
\sum_\mu F_\mu ds_\mu = -\gamma_s d(m_0\gamma_sc^2) + \gamma_s d\left(\frac{m_0\gamma u^2}{2}\right) = \gamma_s\left[-d(mc^2) + d\left(\frac{mu^2}{2}\right)\right].
\tag{9.48}
$$

Rearranging terms and using eqn. (9.44), eqn. (9.48) becomes

$$
d(E) = d\left(\frac{mu^2}{2}\right) - \frac{1}{\gamma_s}\sum F_\mu ds_\mu.
\tag{9.49}
$$

The resulting equation may be interpreted as the statement that the change in total energy of a mass particle is equal to the difference between the change in relativistic kinetic energy $(mu^2/2)$ and the final term representing the work done by external forces.

9.5. Electromagnetism in the Minkowski Frame

The necessity for finding special-relativistic forms of Maxwell's equations for the electromagnetic field does not arise, since Maxwell's equations already correctly describe the behavior of the electromagnetic field in all inertial frames. Before Einstein's presentation of the special theory of relativity, Lorentz had derived the transformation which now bears his name, as the transformation needed to preserve the covariance of Maxwell's equations in all inertial frames.†

The principal task in adapting the equations of the electromagnetic field to the Minkowski format is that of placing the electromagnetic field tensor [eqn. (5.12)] into a form which will transform correctly under the orthogonal Lorentz transformation.

For the Minkowski frame, we find it is necessary to define vector and tensor quantities which contain the characteristic imaginary factor i in the time-like components. The Minkowski formulation of electromagnetism is based upon the definition of a four-vector of potential $\mathbf{A}$, and a current four-vector $\mathbf{J}$, analogous to those defined in eqns. (5.2) and (5.3):

$$\mathbf{A} = \left(-\frac{\phi}{ic}, A_x, A_y, A_z \right), \tag{9.50}$$

$$\mathbf{J} = (ic\varrho, J_x, J_y, J_z). \tag{9.51}$$

These two vectors satisfy the Lorentz gauge condition and conservation theorem in Minkowski coordinates, respectively,

$$A_{\mu,\mu} = 0, \tag{9.52}$$

$$J_{\mu,\mu} = 0. \tag{9.53}$$

† H. A. Lorentz, *Archives Néerl.* **25**, 525 (1892). The transformation equations had already been published by W. Voigt, *Gött. Nach.* 41 (1887).

The electromagnetic field tensor is defined by

$$F_{\mu\nu} = A_{\nu,\mu} - A_{\mu,\nu}. \tag{9.54}$$

Using eqn. (9.50) in eqn. (9.54), we obtain

$$F_{\mu\nu} = \begin{pmatrix} 0 & -(E_1/ic) & -(E_2/ic) & -(E_3/ic) \\ E_1/ic & 0 & B_3 & -B_2 \\ E_2/ic & -B_3 & 0 & B_1 \\ E_3/ic & B_2 & -B_1 & 0 \end{pmatrix}. \tag{9.55}$$

The second-rank tensor $F_{\mu\nu}$ may be subjected to a Lorentz transformation which, in Minkowski's coordinates, is carried out as a matrix transformation. Denoting $F_{\mu\nu}$ by the matrix **F**, and denoting the coefficients of the Lorentz transformation [eqn. (9.5)] by the matrix **L**, the transformation of **F** to a new Minkowski coordinate frame is expressed by

$$\bar{\mathbf{F}} = \mathbf{L}^{-1}\mathbf{F}\mathbf{L}, \tag{9.56}$$

where $\mathbf{L}^{-1}$ is the matrix inverse to the matrix of coefficients **L** [eqn. (9.5)]. Matrix $\mathbf{L}^{-1}$ is obtained either by replacing β with $-\beta$, or by transposing the original matrix about its diagonal: i.e., it is the complex conjugate of **L**.

The equation of the electromagnetic field (Maxwell's equations) are obtained from the tensor $F_{\mu\nu}$ by means of relations analogous to eqns. (5.13) and (5.14):

$$F_{\lambda\nu,\nu} = \mu_0 J_\lambda, \tag{9.57}$$

$$\{F_{\mu\nu,\lambda}\} = 0. \tag{9.58}$$

The derivatives in eqns. (9.57) and (9.58) as well as in (9.52) and (9.53) are, of course, ordinary partial derivatives with respect to Minkowski's coordinates, i.e. $\partial/\partial(ict)$, $\partial/\partial x$, $\partial/\partial y$, $\partial/\partial z$. Equations (9.57) lead to the source-containing Maxwell equations:

$$\nabla \cdot E = \varrho/\varepsilon_0,$$

$$\nabla \times B = \mu_0 J + (1/c^2)\dot{E}$$

where, in mks units, $1/c^2 = \mu_0\varepsilon_0$.

Equations (9.58) are worked out by writing terms having all permutations of each set of three indices, as in eqns. (5.13). These yield the source-free equations:

$$\nabla \times E = -\dot{B},$$

$$\nabla \cdot B = 0.$$

9.6. The Wave Propagation Vector

A useful four-vector definition is that of the electromagnetic-wave propagation vector:

$$\mathbf{K} = \left(\frac{i\omega}{c}, k_x, k_y, k_z\right) \tag{9.59}$$

where $\omega = 2\pi f$ is the angular frequency of the wave, and k_x, k_y, k_z are the Cartesian components of the propagation constant k:

$$k = 2\pi/\lambda,$$

$$k^2 = k_x^2 + k_y^2 + k_z^2. \tag{9.60}$$

The wave vector is transformed as a four-vector under Lorentz transformation in the Minkowski frame:

$$\bar{\mathbf{K}} = \begin{pmatrix} \gamma & i\beta\gamma & 0 & 0 \\ -i\beta\gamma & \gamma & 0 & 0 \\ 0 & 0 & 1 & 0 \\ 0 & 0 & 0 & 1 \end{pmatrix} \cdot \begin{pmatrix} i\omega/c \\ k_x \\ k_y \\ k_z \end{pmatrix} = \begin{pmatrix} i/c(\omega + Vk_x)\gamma \\ \left(\dfrac{\omega V}{c^2} + k_x\right)\gamma \\ k_y \\ k_z \end{pmatrix}. \tag{9.61}$$

The result shows the relativistic Doppler shift of the wave observed in the barred coordinates. For example, for a wave traveling in the direction of relative motion, $k_x = k$, and, using the fact that for the wave in the unbarred frame $\omega/c = k$, the Doppler-shifted frequency and wavelength are

$$\bar{\omega} = \omega\left(1 + \frac{V}{c}\right)\gamma$$

$$\bar{\lambda} = \frac{\lambda}{\left(1 + \dfrac{V}{c}\right)}\gamma^{-1}. \tag{9.62}$$

Each four-vector in Minkowski's coordinates has an invariant amplitude, as we know. Calculating the squared amplitude $|\mathbf{K}|^2$ of the wave four-vector $\mathbf{K}$, we find

$$|\mathbf{K}|^2 = -\frac{\omega^2}{c^2} + k_x{}^2 + k_y{}^2 + k_z{}^2. \tag{9.63}$$

It is apparent from eqn. (9.63) that $\mathbf{K}$ has a null amplitude, for setting $|\mathbf{K}|^2$ equal to zero leads to the identity

$$\frac{\omega^2}{c^2} = k^2. \tag{9.64}$$

A second invariant associated with wave propagation is the invariant formed by taking the inner product of the wave four-vector $\mathbf{K}$ with the interval $d\mathbf{s}$, which has the components ($ic\, dt, dx, dy, dz$):

$$d\Phi = (-\omega\, dt + k_x\, dx + k_y\, dy + k_z\, dz). \tag{9.65}$$

The phase interval $d\Phi$ between two event points along the path of wave travel is necessarily an invariant because observers in all coordinate frames must see the same number of wavelengths of the wave between the two points.

Writing $(k_x\, dx + k_y\, dy + k_z\, dz) = k\, dr$ in eqn. (9.65), we obtain

$$d\Phi = -\omega\, dt + k\, dr. \tag{9.66}$$

If a conceptual observer moves so as to remain with a fixed phase point of the wave, for this observer, $d\Phi = 0$. His motion then must have the velocity:

$$\frac{dr}{dt} = \frac{\omega}{k}. \tag{9.67}$$

Equation (9.67) gives the phase velocity of the wave $v_p = \omega/k$.

Problems

9.1. (a) Can the Minkowski treatment of inertial frames be carried out in curvilinear spatial coordinates such as cylindrical coordinates? (b) Does the transformation to cylindrical coordinates [eqns. (2.46)] satisfy the orthogonality condition [eqn. (9.6)]? Explain. (c) Discuss limitations and changes that would be introduced by the use of curvilinear coordinates in Minkowski's frame.

9.2. Verify that the matrix of eqn. (9.16) is an orthogonal matrix.

9.3. Consider the effect of two successive Lorentz transformations such as those represented by eqns. (9.15) and (9.16), but in which $\beta_2 \ll \beta_1$, so that $\gamma_2 \simeq 1$. Assume that a particle moves in the x_l (unprimed) frame with velocity u in the x-direction $(u_x, u_y, u_z) = (u, 0, 0)$, where $u \ll c$, $(\gamma_s \simeq 1)$. (a) Transform the corresponding four-velocity to the x''_j frame. (b) Show that the transformed velocity u''_j subtends an angle with its x-axis which differs by $uV_1V_2/[c^2(u + V_1)]$ radians from the angle $V_2/(u + V_1)$ predicted by Newtonian theory. This directional change is an example of the Thomas precession.

9.4. A heavy particle traversing a nuclear apparatus is detected passing through two counting elements in succession which are spaced 10 cm apart along the path of the particle. The pulse from the second counter follows that from the first by 1 nanosecond (10^{-9} sec) of laboratory time. (a) Calculate the world-line interval Δs between the two counting events in laboratory coordinates. (b) What proper time interval $\Delta\tau$ elapses between the two events in the rest frame of the particle? (c) If the particle is one of a beam of similar particles which have a radioactive decay lifetime of $T = 10^{-10}$ sec when at rest, what fraction of the beam, calculated as $\exp(-\Delta\tau/T)$, will reach the second counter undecayed?

9.5. If the μth column or row of the electromagnetic field matrix [eqn. (9.55)], where $\mu \neq 0$, is treated as a four-vector, (a) show that this four-vector is invariant under Lorentz transformation. (b) What is the relation ship of the squared amplitude of this four-vector with the electromagnetic energy tensor $S^{\mu\nu}$? [Cf. eqn. (5.26).]

9.6. Write out in full the three spatial component equations of the relativistic equations of motion under force [eqn. (9.36)]. If the equations are solved simultaneously for the accelerations $\ddot{x}, \ddot{y}, \ddot{z}$, can they be integrated to yield the particle trajectories? Discuss methods that you might use in solving for the motion of a point mass in a given force field.

Appendix I

Numerical Data and Physical Constants

Physical constants

Velocity of light	c	$= 2 \cdot 998 \times 10^8$ m/sec
Gravitational constant	G	$= 6 \cdot 670 \times 10^{-11}$ m^3/kg sec^2
Planck's constant	h	$= 6 \cdot 626 \times 10^{-34}$ kg m^2/sec
Electron rest mass	m_e	$= 9 \cdot 107 \times 10^{-31}$ kg
Proton rest mass	m_p	$= 1 \cdot 672 \times 10^{-27}$ kg
Elementary charge	q_e	$= 1 \cdot 601 \times 10^{-19}$ coul
Proton radius	r_p	$\simeq 1 \cdot 2 \times 10^{-15}$ m

Natural data

Mass of the earth	M_E	$= 5 \cdot 996 \times 10^{24}$ kg
Mass of the sun	M_S	$= 1 \cdot 989 \times 10^{30}$ kg
Radius of the earth (av.)	r_E	$\simeq 6 \cdot 378 \times 10^6$ m
Radius of the sun	r_S	$\simeq 6 \cdot 96 \times 10^8$ m
Earth–sun distance (av.)	r_{SE}	$= 1 \cdot 495 \times 10^{11}$ m
Hubble parameter	H	$= 3 \cdot 075 \times 10^{-18}$ sec

Units and conversion factors

1 light year	1 ly $= 9 \cdot 460 \times 10^{15}$ m
1 astronomical unit	1 AU $= r_{SE}$, earth–sun distance
1 parsec†	1 pc $= 3 \cdot 083 \times 10^{16}$ m
1 megaparsec	1 Mpc $= 3 \cdot 083 \times 10^{22}$ m
1 joule	1 J $= 10^7$ ergs
1 electron volt	1 eV $= 1 \cdot 602 \times 10^{-19}$ J

† A parsec is defined as the distance from which the earth's orbital diameter would subtend an angle of 2 seconds of arc.

Appendix II

Proof of:
$$\left\{ \begin{matrix} \alpha \\ \beta\alpha \end{matrix} \right\} = \tfrac{1}{2} \frac{\partial}{\partial x^\beta} \ln(-g).$$

From the definition of the Christoffel symbol [eqn. (2.62)]:

$$\left\{ \begin{matrix} \alpha \\ \beta\alpha \end{matrix} \right\} = \tfrac{1}{2} g^{\alpha\sigma}(g_{\alpha\sigma,\beta} + g_{\beta\sigma,\alpha} - g_{\alpha\beta,\sigma}). \tag{II.1}$$

With use of the symmetry of the metric tensor, and by renaming cyclic indices,

$$g^{\alpha\sigma} g_{\beta\sigma,\alpha} = g^{\alpha\sigma} g_{\alpha\beta,\sigma}. \tag{II.2}$$

Therefore eqn. (II.1) becomes

$$\left\{ \begin{matrix} \alpha \\ \beta\alpha \end{matrix} \right\} = \tfrac{1}{2} g^{\alpha\sigma} g_{\alpha\sigma,\beta}. \tag{II.3}$$

Using eqn. (2.28), $g^{\alpha\sigma} = (1/g)\, \partial g/\partial g_{\alpha\sigma}$. Therefore eqn. (II.3) becomes

$$\left\{ \begin{matrix} \alpha \\ \beta\alpha \end{matrix} \right\} = \frac{1}{2g} \frac{\partial g}{\partial g_{\alpha\sigma}} \frac{\partial g_{\alpha\sigma}}{\partial x^\beta}$$

$$= \frac{1}{2g} \frac{\partial g}{\partial x^\beta}. \tag{II.4}$$

Therefore, finally,

$$\left\{ \begin{matrix} \alpha \\ \beta\alpha \end{matrix} \right\} = \tfrac{1}{2} \frac{\partial}{\partial x^\beta} \ln g. \tag{II.5}$$

In calculating with eqn. (II.5) we use $\ln(-g)$ instead of $\ln g$, since g is always negative for real coordinates.

213

Appendix III

Euler's Equation of the Calculus of Variations

We wish to find the extremal condition, $\delta I = 0$, for an integral of the form

$$I = \int_{x_1}^{x_2} f(y, y', x)\, dx \tag{III.1}$$

where $y = y(x)$, and $y' = \partial y/\partial x$. The variation of the integral is to be effected by allowing the functional form of the curve $y(x)$ to vary, while still requiring $y(x)$ to pass through the end points of integration at x_1 and x_2. The functional variation of y is assumed to be proportional to a parameter α:

$$y(x, \alpha) = y(x) + \alpha v(x), \tag{III.2}$$

where $v(x_1) = 0 = v(x_2)$.

The variation of the integral with α is thus given by

$$\frac{\delta I}{\delta \alpha} = \int_{x_1}^{x_2} \left[\frac{\partial f}{\partial y} \frac{\partial y}{\partial \alpha} + \frac{\partial f}{\partial y'} \frac{\partial y'}{\partial \alpha} \right] dx. \tag{III.3}$$

In eqn. (III.3), $\partial y'/\partial \alpha = \partial^2 y/\partial x\, \partial \alpha = \partial(\partial y/\partial \alpha)/\partial x$.

$$\frac{\delta I}{\delta \alpha} = \int_{x_1}^{x_2} \left[\frac{\partial f}{\partial y} \frac{\partial y}{\partial \alpha}\, dx + \frac{\partial f}{\partial y'} \frac{\partial(\partial y/\partial \alpha)}{\partial x}\, dx \right]. \tag{III.4}$$

214

Integrating by parts in the second term, eqn. (III.4) becomes

$$\frac{\delta I}{\delta \alpha} = \int_{x_1}^{x_2} \frac{\partial f}{\partial y} \frac{\partial y}{\partial \alpha} dx + \left[\frac{\partial f}{\partial y'} \frac{\partial y}{\partial \alpha} \right]_{x_1}^{x_2} - \int_{x_1}^{x_2} \frac{\partial y}{\partial \alpha} \frac{\partial}{\partial x} \left(\frac{\partial f}{\partial y'} \right) dx. \quad \text{(III.5)}$$

In the limit term, $\partial y / \partial \alpha = v(x) = 0$, at x_1 and x_2. Therefore

$$\frac{\delta I}{\delta \alpha} = \int_{x_1}^{x_2} \left[\frac{\partial f}{\partial y} - \frac{\partial}{\partial x} \left(\frac{\partial f}{\partial y'} \right) \right] \frac{\partial y}{\partial \alpha} dx. \quad \text{(III.6)}$$

The variation of I vanishes if

$$\frac{\partial f}{\partial y} = \frac{\partial}{\partial x} \left(\frac{\partial f}{\partial y'} \right) \quad \text{Euler's equation.} \quad \text{(III.7)}$$

Author Index

Page numbers in **bold type** refer to footnotes

217

Subject Index

Page numbers in **bold type** refer to more important entries

219

OTHER TITLES IN THE SERIES IN NATURAL PHILOSOPHY